INTERNATIONAL SERIES OF MONOGRAPHS IN

AERONAUTICS AND ASTRONAUTICS

DIVISION I: SOLID AND STRUCTURAL MECHANICS

EDITORS: R. L. BISPLINGHOFF AND W. S. HEMP

VOLUME 7

HEAT TRANSFER IN STRUCTURES

INTERNATIONAL SERIES OF MONOGRAPHS IN AERONAUTICS AND ASTRONAUTICS

CHAIRMAN

H. L. DRYDEN
Deputy Administrator
National Aeronautics and Space Administration
Washington, 25, D.C., U.S.A.

HONORARY ADVISORY BOARD

HEAT TRANSFER
IN
STRUCTURES

by

H. SCHUH

1963
ou
1965

PERGAMON PRESS

OXFORD · LONDON · EDINBURGH · NEW YORK
PARIS · FRANKFURT

Pergamon Press Ltd., Headington Hill Hall, Oxford
4 & 5 Fitzroy Square, London W. 1
Pergamon Press (Scotland) Ltd., 2 & 3 Teviot Place, Edinburgh 1
Pergamon Press Inc., 122 East 55th St., New York 22, N.Y.
Gauthier-Villars, 55 Quai des Grands-Augustins, Paris 6
Pergamon Press GmbH, Kaiserstrasse 75, Frankfurt–am–Main

First edition 1965

Library of Congress Catalog Card Number 63–10667

Printed in Poland
PWN—DRP

CONTENTS

LIST OF SYMBOLS — ix

PREFACE — xv

1. INTRODUCTION — 1
    1.1. General — 1
    1.2. The Thermal Environment of a Structure — 2
    1.3. Typical Examples for Aerodynamic Heating of Structures — 5

2. A SUMMARY OF EXTERNAL HEAT TRANSFER TO STRUCTURES IN HIGH SPEED FLIGHT — 9
    2.1. General — 9
    2.2. Adiabatic Wall Temperatures — 14
    2.3. Convective Heat Transfer Coefficients in Chemically Stable Air — 16
    2.4. Convective Heat Transfer in Dissociated Air at Hypersonic Speeds — 27
    2.5. The Influence of Bluntness and Angle of Attack on Heat Transfer in Supersonic Flight — 31
    2.6. Transition from Laminar to Turbulent Flow in Boundary Layers — 36
    2.7. Interaction of Boundary Layers with External Flow — 41
    2.8. Limits for the Validity of the Continuum Flow — 42
    2.9. Heat Transfer by Forced Convection and Thermal Radiation. Equilibrium Temperatures — 43
    2.10. On the Heat Transfer at the Surface of High Speed Vehicles — 45

3. FUNDAMENTAL LAWS FOR HEAT TRANSFER WITHIN STRUCTURES — 50
    3.1. Heat Conduction in Solids — 50
    3.2. Heat Flow in Shells with Uniform Temperature throughout the Thickness — 60
    3.3. Three-dimensional Heat Flow in Shells of Revolution — 64
    3.4. Ablation — 66
    3.5. Heat Transfer by Free Convection — 72
    3.6. Heat Transfer by Thermal Radiation — 77
    3.7. Thermal Conductance across Interfaces and Joints — 84

4. ON METHODS OF CALCULATING TEMPERATURE DISTRIBUTIONS IN STRUCTURES — 91

    4.1. General — 91

    4.2. Analytical and Semi-analytical Methods in Transient Heat Flow — 93

    4.3. Methods Using Finite Differences and Lumped Circuits — 94

5. STEADY HEAT FLOW I: ANALYTICAL METHODS — 97

    5.1. General — 97

    5.2. One-dimensional Heat Flow in Composite Slabs and Shells — 97

    5.3. Radial Heat Flow in Cylindrical or Spherical Layers — 100

    5.4. Radial Heat Flow in Shells — 101

    5.5. Boundary Conditions in One-dimensional Heat Flow — 102

    5.6. Variable Thermal Properties — 104

    5.7. General Remarks on Two-dimensional Heat Flow — 104

6. STEADY HEAT FLOW II: NUMERICAL METHODS — 105

    6.1. Introduction — 105

    6.2. A Finite Difference Equation for One-dimensional Heat Flow — 106

    6.3. Direct Solutions of Finite Difference Equations — 110

    6.4. A Method of Iteration for Solving Finite Difference Equations — 112

    6.5. The Method of Relaxation — 112

    6.6. The Iteration and Relaxation Method Illustrated by an Example — 114

    6.7. Accuracy of the Finite Difference Solutions — 120

    6.8. Problems with Variable and Non-linear Boundary Conditions — 122

    6.9. Two-dimensional Heat Flow. Numerical and Graphical Methods — 123

7. TRANSIENT HEAT FLOW I: ANALYTICAL METHODS — 128

    7.1. General — 128

    7.2. A Survey of Important Analytical Methods — 128

    7.3. Heating of Shells with Uniformly Distributed Temperatures — 137

    7.4. Initial Phase of Heat Penetration into Solid Bodies. Thermal Shock — 139

    7.5. One-dimensional Linear Heat Flow in Simple and Composite Bodies — 144

7.6. One-dimensional Heat Flow in Thin Shells with Heat
Transfer Conditions Varying along the Surface   156

7.7. Heat Flow with Time-dependent Boundary Conditions
of General Form (Semi-analytical Methods)   167

7.8. Heat Conduction in a Semi-infinite Solid with Melting
or Sublimation at the Surface   176

8. TRANSIENT HEAT FLOW II: NUMERICAL METHODS   182

8.1. One-dimensional Heat Flow. General Remarks on Finite
Difference Methods   182

8.2. One-dimensional Heat Flow. A Simple Explicit Finite
Difference Equation   183

8.3. One-dimensional Heat Flow. An Implicit Difference Equation   207

8.4. One-dimensional Heat Flow in Thin Shells with External
Heat Transfer. An Explicit Finite Difference Equation 211

8.5. One-dimensional Heat Flow in Composite Structures.
Method of Lumped Heat Capacities and Resistances   215

8.6. Two-dimensional and Multi-directional Heat Flow in
Composite Structures. Method of Lumped Heat Capacities
and Resistances   222

8.7. Other Approximate Methods of Solution   223

8.8. Examples   227

9. HEAT FLOW IN PARTICULAR STRUCTURAL ELEMENTS   240

9.1. A Skin Reinforced by Integral Stiffeners   240

9.2. A Skin Reinforced by a Stiffener with a Thermal Contact Resistance at the Joint   267

9.3. Examples of Aerodynamic Heating of Skins Reinforced
by Stiffeners   271

9.4. A Shell with a Discontinuity in Thickness   276

10. ANALOGUES   282

10.1. General   282

10.2. Steady Heat Flow   283

10.3. Transient Heat Flow   284

11. SIMILARITY LAWS AND MODEL-TESTING FOR HEAT FLOW IN
STRUCTURES   288

11.1. Internal Heat Flow by Conduction only. Integral Structures   289

11.2. Internal Heat Flow by Conduction, Free Convection
       and Thermal Radiation. Integral Structures   295
11.3. Temperature-dependent Thermal Properties   301
11.4. Finite Thermal Conductances across Joints   303

APPENDIX: A SURVEY OF RECENT DEVELOPMENTS   304

AUTHOR INDEX   327

SUBJECT INDEX   333

OTHER TITLES IN THE SERIES   339

LIST OF SYMBOLS

A . . . . . Area; constant

B . . . . . Constant

$\mathrm{Bi} = \dfrac{hL}{k}$ . . Biot modulus (k refers to a solid)

C . . . . . Constant

C_D . . . . . Drag coefficient

C_R . . . . . Radiation coefficient

C_σ . . . . . Constant of black-body radiation

D . . . . . Constant

D_{12} . . . . . Coefficient of diffusion for atoms in dissociated air

E . . . . . Numerical error

F . . . . . Function of one or more variables; shape factor in radiative heat transfer

F . . . . . Area of cross section in Chapter 5

$G = \mathrm{Nu}_w/\sqrt{\mathrm{Re}_w}$ in Chapter 2

G . . . . . Quantity used in Chapter 8 and defined by Eq. (8.5.11) or (8.4.12)

G_1, G_2 . . . . Quantities used in Section 3.3 and defined by Eq. (3.3.3)

Gr . . . . . Grashof number

H . . . . . Altitude

I . . . . . Function in Chapter 9

I_0 . . . . . Modified Bessel function of the first kind and zero order in Chapter 5

K . . . . . Constant; conductance, in particular between heat reservoirs

K_0 . . . . . Modified Bessel function of the second kind and zero order in Chapter 5

L . . . . . Length or characteristic length

$\mathcal{L}$ . . . . . Symbol for the Laplace transformation

Le . . . . . Lewis number (see Eq. (2.4.1))

M . . . . . Mach number (air speed divided by speed of sound)

N . . . . . Total number of finite difference sections

$\mathrm{Nu} = \dfrac{hL}{k}$ . . Nusselt number (k refers to a fluid)

O . . . . . Order of magnitude

P . . . . . Coefficient; parameter

P_c . . . . . Ratio of the local heat transfer coefficient to that of the undisturbed flow

P_D . . . . . Ratio of heat flow, with and without dissociation

$\mathrm{Pr} = \nu/\varkappa$ . . Prandtl number

Q . . . . . Rate of heat flow

R . . . . . Gas constant in Chapter 2 and 11

R . . . . . Thermal resistance in Chapter 5 and electrical resistance in Chapter 10

Ra . . . . . Rayleigh number
Re . . . . . Reynolds number
S . . . . . Heat either absorbed or developed per unit volume and per unit time.
S . . . . . Amount of heat in Section 3.4
T . . . . . Temperature
U . . . . . Circumference in the cross section of shells or bars
W . . . . . Heat capacity of a reservoir
W_g . . . . . Weight of vehicle
X . . . . . Function of x in Chapter 7
Y . . . . . Variable defined in Section 7.4
Z . . . . . Numerical solution of finite difference equation
a . . . . . Exponent in law for free convection in Section 3.5
a . . . . . Constant
a_g . . . . . Mass force in Section 3.4
b . . . . . Penetration depth for temperature profiles
c . . . . . Specific heat in solids
c_D . . . . . Coefficient of drag
c_f . . . . . Friction coefficient in compressible flow
c_{fi} . . . . . Friction coefficient in incompressible flow
c_p . . . . . Specific heat at constant pressure in fluids
c_v . . . . . Specific heat at constant volume in fluids
d . . . . . Bluntness in Chapter 2; distance between plates in Section 3.5
e . . . . . Fraction of mesh size in two-dimensional finite difference method
f . . . . . Function of one or more variables
g . . . . . Function of one or more variables
g . . . . . Particular function in Section 3.3; constant of gravity in Section 3.5
h . . . . . Heat transfer coefficient
h_i . . . . . Incompressible heat transfer coefficient
i . . . . . $\sqrt{(-1)}$
i . . . . . Enthalpy per unit mass (specific enthalpy) in Chapter 2
i . . . . . Electrical current in Chapter 10
j . . . . . Constant; summation number
k . . . . . Heat conductivity
l . . . . . Exponent in friction law
l . . . . . Number of spatial differences in y-direction in Chapter 6
l . . . . . Number of time differences in Section 7.7
m . . . . . Number of time-differences in Section 7.7 and in Chapter 8
m_P . . . . . Parameter used in Section 7.8 and defined by Eq. (7.8.7)
n . . . . . Number of spatial differences in Chapter 8
n . . . . . Exponent for time in analytical solutions
$\bar{n}$ . . . . . Distance normal to a surface
p . . . . . Pressure in Chapter 2
p . . . . . Parameter in finite difference equations in Chapters 6 and 8
p . . . . . Laplace transform variable in Chapters 7 and 9
q . . . . . Specific rate of heat flow
r . . . . . Radius
r . . . . . Distance between radiating surfaces in Section 3.6
r_0 . . . . . Radius in cross section of body of revolution; radius of a sphere

s	Coefficient in finite difference form of boundary conditions in Chapters 6 and 8
s_L	Coordinate of the surface of a liquid layer in Section 3.4
s_M	Coordinate of the surface of a solid surface in Section 3.4
t	Time
u	Velocity, air speed in Chapter 2
u	Function in Chapter 9
v	Velocity, air speed
w	Width of flange
x	Coordinate; distance
$\bar{x}$	Distance along the surface of a shell in meridian section
x_w	Coordinate on surface
y	Coordinate; distance
y_w	Coordinate on surface
z	Coordinate; distance
z	Atom mass fraction in Chapter 2
Γ	Gamma function; parameter in Section 7.8
Δ	Mesh size in finite difference method (two-dimensional)
Θ	Non-dimensional temperature
Θ_v	Temperature variable in Section 3.1.6
Λ	Yaw angle in Chapter 2; non-dimensional length in Chapter 9
Φ	Wave path length
α	Eigenvalues; constant
α	Absorptivity in Sections 2.9 and 3.6
β	Coefficient of thermal expansion; eigenvalues
γ	Ratio of specific heat $= c_p/c_v$
γ	Constant in Chapters 5 and 8
δ	Thickness of a plate or shell
δ	Boundary layer thickness in Chapter 2
ε	Thermal emissivity
ε	Small quantity in Chapter 8
ζ	Coordinate in Section 3.3, parameter in Chapter 8
ζ	Non-dimensional distance in Chapters 9 and 11 defined by Eq. (9.1.64) and (11.1.4) respectively
η	Integration variable
η	Recovery factor in Chapter 2; non-dimensional distance in Chapter 11
ϑ	Temperature difference
ϑ'	Temperature due to a step function heat input in Section 7.7
$\varkappa = k/\rho c$ . .	Thermal diffusivity
λ	Molecular mean free path in Section 2.8; wave length in Section 2.9
λ	Constant in Chapters 7, 8 and 11; parameter in Chapter 9
μ	Dynamic viscosity in Chapters 2 and 3; eigenvalues in Chapter 7
$\nu = \mu/\rho$ . . .	Kinematic viscosity
ξ	Non-dimensional distance
ξ	Variable of integration in Chapter 2; coordinate in Section 3.3
ρ	Density
σ	Ratio of $k\rho c$ in two regions of a solid
σ^*	See Eq. (9.1.16)

τ . . . . . (with subscripts) time constant; (without subscripts) non-dimensional time

φ . . . . . Latitude in spherical polar coordinates: parameter; angle

φ_i . . . . . Angle of incidence

χ . . . . . Boundary layer shock wave interaction parameter in Chapter 2

χ . . . . . Azimuth in spherical polar coordinates

χ_0 . . . . . Included angle at apex of cone or wedge

ψ . . . . . Polar angle in a circle or in a cylindrical coordinate system

ω . . . . . Solid angle

Subscripts

A . . . . . Heat exchanging surface

B . . . . . Middle of slab

C . . . . . Adiabatic surface

D . . . . . Dissociation

E . . . . . Evaporation

L . . . . . Liquid layer

M . . . . . Solid body

N . . . . . Component normal to leading edge

P . . . . . Melting

R . . . . . Radiation

a . . . . . Air

b . . . . . Values at boundary

e . . . . . Outer edge of boundary layer

f . . . . . External medium (except in c_f)

g . . . . . Equilibrium temperature

h . . . . . Convective heat transfer (in Chapter 11)

i . . . . . Initial value, except at h and c_f

j . . . . . Number

k . . . . . Number

l . . . . . Lower

m . . . . . Number of time-intervals

m . . . . . Model in Chapter 11

n . . . . . Normal component

n . . . . . Number of spatial intervals

p . . . . . Particular solutions

p . . . . . Prototype in Chapter 11

q . . . . . Rate of heat flow

r . . . . . Reference

s . . . . . Stagnation point or conditions

t . . . . . Total (pressure, temperature or enthalpy)

u . . . . . Upper

v . . . . . Variable thermal properties

w . . . . . Wall or boundary in solid bodies

z . . . . . Coordinates

ab . . . . . Steady state ablation

aw . . . . . Adiabatic wall

con . . . . . Free convection
ct . . . . . Contact resistence
eff . . . . . Effective (heat transfer coefficient)
ir . . . . . Irradiation
it . . . . . Internal
max . . . . . Maximum
ra . . . . . Radiative
si . . . . . Semi-infinite
sp . . . . . Spanwise (velocity)
st . . . . . Steady state
tot . . . . . Total
tr . . . . . Transition

Λ . . . . . Yaw angle
β . . . . . Penetration depth
δ . . . . . Shell with constant temperature throughout the thickness
ζ . . . . . Coordinate
λ . . . . . Wave length
ξ . . . . . Coordinate
σ . . . . . Black body
ψ . . . . . Polar angle
∞ . . . . . At infinity; ambient air conditions

Superscripts

R . . . . . Reflection
S . . . . . Transmission
c . . . . . Cylinder
m . . . . . Number of iterations in finite difference method in Chapter 6
q . . . . . Specific resistance
r . . . . . Body of revolution

PREFACE

HEAT transfer in structures has recently become of increased interest in connection with high-speed flight and nuclear engineering. As this monograph is issued in a series on aeronautical and space sciences, particular attention is given to aeronautics, but a large part of the book is also of general interest.

In a monograph of this kind it appears to some extent a matter of opinion which contents to choose and which aspects of the subject to emphasize. In view of the ever-increasing degree of specialization, an author with education as his profession would, quite naturally, put more emphasis on fundamentals and general methods than someone active in the engineering profession, who might judge many general methods more severely because of their unavoidable limitations and who would attach more value to certain special methods which are very useful in, perhaps, a limited field.

The author has endeavoured to strike a compromise between these different standpoints, although he has naturally been influenced by his work in industry during the past few years.

There is another problem in writing this monograph and it can be characterized by the following extreme approaches. Presuming the reader to have no previous knowledge about heat transfer, it would be necessary to cover a large part of this subject on which, however, a number of textbooks are already available. In the other approach the reader would be referred to other books as far as all fundamentals are concerned and the monograph would deal only with specific applications to structures; obviously, frequent reference to other sources would make tiresome reading. Now, it should be noted that heat transfer in structures is hardly an end in itself and that the temperature distributions in structures are of interest mainly for their effect on the strength of the structure and—in aeronautics—also on the internal environment of the flight vehicles. Consequently, most readers of this monograph would be primarily interested in rapid and efficient means for finding these temperature distributions. Therefore the following compromise between the two approaches was made. Those fundamental equations and well-known methods which can be found in textbooks are here only presented and explained in general but they are neither derived nor treated in detail. Less-known fundamentals and special methods important to the present subject are treated fully here, as are heat flow problems directly related to structures. Thus, because of its importance to the present subject, heat conduction in solids is the content of a large part of the monograph. The relevant analytical theory is comprehensively covered in the classical textbook of Carslaw and Jaeger, *Conduction of Heat in Solids* and, hence, analytical methods and results important for structures are merely presented here. There is, however, in the monograph a short introduction to the fundamentals of the analytical method. For other than the simplest structures and for other than simple conditions of external heat transfer, analytical methods are too complicated; some of the limitations can be overcome by using semi-analytical methods which are treated here in detail because they are new. Of more importance for practical structures are the various approximate methods and, in particular, the finite difference methods which are developed here from first principles because important advances in this field have been made only recently, and are less widely known. Some structures—or rather structural elements—are of particular interest for aeronautics and these are dealt with at length. Analogues for finding temperature distributions are only treated briefly because relevant textbooks are available. Similarity laws and model testing are covered more extensively because they are of some importance, and have been rather neglected in the literature.

This monograph does not deal with experiments and experimental equipment nor with problems related to the design of structures capable of withstanding thermal loads, and there is no systematic presentation of temperature distributions in structures. The reason for these omissions is that information on most of the designs of interest is classified and therefore not available; further, development in this field is at present so rapid that any information given now would soon become obsolete. Besides, temperature distributions in structures depend on so many diverse parameters that a systematic treatment would be difficult. Ablation is very important for severe heating conditions, but in this subject problems of external heat transfer—which belongs to aerodynamics— and of technology predominate; therefore ablation is not treated fully here, and only the fundamental equations and the heat flow inside the solid part of an ablating body are given.

So far the general aim of the monograph has been discussed; the details of its contents are as follows. In an introduction (Chapter 1) problems of the heating of structures are surveyed in general. Chapter 2 is a sum-

mary on heat transfer in high-speed flight; here the reader is assumed
to be familiar with at least the fundamental concepts of boundary layer
theory in fluid motion. The chapter deals largely with heat transfer on
simple flat plates and in the vicinity of stagnation regions; this is sufficient for many engineering purposes in connection with aerodynamic
heating. The fundamental laws of heat transfer inside structures are presented and discussed in Chapter 3. A treatment of the heat conduction
in solids and shells is followed by a section on heat transfer by free convection and thermal radiation because these modes are important for
the internal heat transfer in structures. There is also a summary on thermal conductance across interfaces and joints. Because opinions are divided on the relative merits of analytical and numerical methods for calculating the heat flow in solids, there is a general discussion on these
questions in Chapter 4. Steady heat flow is treated in Chapters 5 and 6
by analytical and numerical methods respectively. More important for
flight structures are transient heat flows for which analytical methods
and results are given in Chapter 7. Simple structural elements are
treated, such as thin shells and slabs with conditions of heat transfer both
uniformly and non-uniformly distributed on the surface. Semi-analytical methods suitable for dealing with boundary conditions of any kind
are treated in detail and the chapter is concluded by a section on heat
flow in solids with melting or evaporating surfaces. Finite difference
methods have been known and used for some time on an empirical basis, but recently, the convergence and stability of finite difference solutions have been treated from a rigorous mathematical point of view. However, the results refer to either vanishingly small differences in the independent variables or to large times. In the first case the amount of
computational work becomes infinite and as for the second case, large
times are of secondary importance for numerical computations. In Chapter 8 the behaviour of finite difference solutions is therefore investigated
in detail for varying magnitudes of the differences in space and time,
and for any times. The treatment, which is rigorous, is based on physical
considerations. The rest of this chapter deals with other aspects of the
difference methods such as accuracy, and extensions to lumped circuits;
finally, other approximate methods are summarized. A large part of Chapter 9 refers to a skin reinforced by a stiffener as a typical flight structure;
this chapter also gives a good insight into the advantages and limitations
of the analytical methods and into the possibilities of obtaining general
solutions which cover a wide range of the variables of interest. The fundamentals of those analogues most interesting for heat flow in solids-

are discussed in Chapter 10. The last chapter deals with similarity laws and model testing from a general point of view.

When preparing this monograph the author found gaps in the subject and he was stimulated to undertake a number of original investigations of varying size. The largest in extent was, perhaps, the investigation into the behaviour of finite difference solutions in Chapter 8 and the contribution in Section 7.7 to semi-analytical methods which is simpler and more general than the method of Hill. Further original contributions are included in Section 7.3.3, 7.6.2 and in Chapters 9 and 11.

As to the troublesome question of units, both metric and British units have been used in most general investigations, while in the examples the units of the original source have been retained. As a time unit the second would be more practical for structures than the hour; however, since the hour is generally used in the British system, it was retained there, while the second was used in metric units because the number of relevant papers using these units is small.

The author is indebted to M. Tideman and B. Arlinger (of SAAB Aircraft Company), and to T. Fannelöp (formerly of SAAB Aircraft Company) for reading various parts of the manuscript of this book and their comments are appreciated. Thanks are due to A. McLean (of SAAB Aircraft Company) who was so kind as to read the whole manuscript as to correctness of language. D. J. Johns of the College of Aeronautics, Cranfield, England, has carefully read the whole manuscript and his many suggestions are highly appreciated. Any short-comings in form and content are, of course, entirely the responsibility of the author.

Owing to circumstances outside the control of the author the production of this book was delayed and hence it was thought useful to add at the page–proof stage a short survey of recent developments in an Appendix.

H. SCHUH

CHAPTER 1

INTRODUCTION

1.1 General

For most materials the characteristic parameters for strength and stress, such as yield point, ultimate strength and modulus of elasticity, depend on temperature. For instance, many materials of interest for flight structures suffer a rapid loss of strength above a certain temperature. If the temperature distribution in a solid or structure is not uniform, thermal

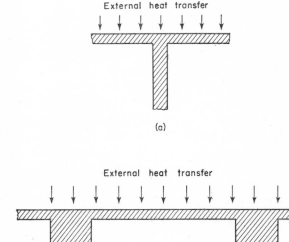

FIG. 1. 1.Two typical examples for parts of structures in which non-uniform temperatures and stresses may develop. (a) A skin reinforced by a stiffener, and (b) a skin reinforced by a frame.

stresses and thermal deformations may occur. Two typical examples of structural elements of interest in aeronautics are given in Fig. 1.1 (a and b). The first is a skin reinforced by a stiffener; if the skin is exposed to aero-

1

dynamic heating in high speed flight, it is rapidly heated, but the stiffener remains at a much lower temperature because of the time required to equalize the temperatures within the structure by internal heat transfer, particularly by heat conduction. If the joint between skin and stiffener is rigid, thermal stresses would occur during those times when the temperature distribution in the skin and stiffener is not uniform. The second example refers to a skin reinforced by a frame where both the skin and the frame are exposed to the same external heat transfer conditions at their surfaces. In both examples the temperature is, in many cases, uniformly distributed throughout the thickness except very close to the junction between them; however, the skin and the frame in the second example are at different temperatures because of the difference in thickness. Even in this case thermal stresses would develop due to the temperature differences and there is also a danger of thermal buckling.

1.2 The thermal environment of a structure

The thermal environment is defined here as the sum of the thermal influences to which the structure is exposed. When standing on the ground, structures exchange heat with the surroundings by convection and they are subject to irradiation from the sun or other heat sources, possibly including nuclear explosions. In high-speed flight, heat is developed near the surface of the structure by compression and friction in the external air flow. Due to these heat sources the structure can reach temperature levels far exceeding those of the static temperature in ambient air. Inside the structure, heat may be developed by propulsion units or electronic equipment. The large amounts of heat to which structures may be exposed due to aerodynamic heating, nuclear explosions and propulsion units etc., create new and often severe problems in aeronautical engineering.

In flight at low speeds the temperature of the structure does not deviate much from the static temperature of the air. In high-speed flight the air is compressed at wing leading edges and at fuselage noses due to the impact of the structure on the air molecules, and heat is thereby developed. However, for a large part of the structure the local angle of inclination of the surface to the flight direction is small or zero, so that the amount of compression is not large there. But heat is also developed by friction. Near the surface of the structure the air is accelerated by viscous shear forces and the air molecules in direct contact with the structure assume the same speed as the vehicle because of the non-slip condition which is valid for continuum flow. Since the viscosity of the air is small, only a thin layer

close to the surface is affected. In this layer, which in aerodynamics is called
the boundary layer, the velocity gradients are large, giving rise to appreciable shear forces at the wall which cause the frictional drag of an aircraft.
Part of the energy required to overcome the frictional drag is found in the
wake as kinetic energy, and the rest is transformed into heat in the boundary
layer through the work done by the shear forces. Because the heat conductivity of air is low, the heat developed within the boundary layer gives
rise to large increases in boundary layer temperature which thus becomes
much higher than the static temperature of the surrounding air.

Disregarding heat transfer other than that due to compression and
friction in the external air flow, the thermal environment of the structure
is given by two quantities, the adiabatic wall temperature T_{aw} and the heat
transfer coefficient h. T_{aw} is defined as the temperature of the wall when
the local rate of convective heat flow to the wall is zero. The heat transfer
coefficient is defined by the equation

$$q_w = h\,(T_{aw} - T_w) \tag{1.1}$$

where q_w is the specific rate of heat flow at and directed to the wall, and T_w
is the wall temperature. T_{aw} is equal to the steady state temperature for steady
flight conditions, if thermal radiation to the surroundings and heat transfer
within the structure can be neglected. For flight at moderate Mach numbers
T_{aw} is given approximately by Eq. (2.2.7); as an example, some numerical
values are given in Table 1.1. The heat transfer coefficient h is important
in cases of transient heating and depends, in general, in a complicated
way on the development of the boundary layer along the surface of the
structure. Typical values for h in the Mach number range 2–5 are given

TABLE 1.1. Examples for the adiabatic wall temperature T_{aw}, the heat transfer coefficient h and the equilibrium temperature T_g. Assumed: Turbulent boundary layer flow
on an ideal flat plate at zero incidence at 11 km (about 35,000 ft) altitude and standard
atmosphere (static temperature 216°K (390°R)). Also approximately valid for large
regions on slender wings or slender bodies of revolution

M	T_{aw}		h		T_g[a]	
	°C	°F	kcal / m²s°C	Btu / (ft)²h°F	°C	°F
2	98	208·4	0·06 to 0·075	44 to 55	92	197·6
3	290	554			270	518
5	855	1571			695	1283

[a] Additional assumptions for T_g: (1) A distance of 2 m (6½ ft) from the leading
edge and (2) a coefficient of emissivity for heat radiation of $\varepsilon = 0\cdot8$ which corresponds
to a suitably prepared (painted, oxidized or the like) surface.

in Table 1.1. The temperature levels of T_{aw} in this table are sufficiently low, so that dissociation of the air molecules does not occur. Dissociation is, however, important in flight at Mach numbers above 6 to 7, and in calculating the external heat transfer it is then necessary to replace temperatures by enthalpies and to use a corresponding modified heat transfer coefficient.

For practical reasons it is convenient to distinguish between moderate and severe rates of aerodynamic heating. In the first case the variations of the surface temperature T_w are of the same order of magnitude as $T_{aw} - T_i$ (with T_i as the initial temperature of the structure). For severe aerodynamic heating T_{aw} is much larger than the maximum value of T_w and the influence of changes of T_w on the rate of heat flow q_w becomes small. Hence this quantity depends, to a good approximation, only on h and T_{aw} which are both known from the external conditions. In such cases it is more convenient to use q_w directly. No definite limit between the two rates of heating is given here in terms of flight Mach numbers, since it would depend on the external heat transfer conditions as well as on the particular structure considered.

Of the other modes of heat transfer, only thermal radiation is of importance in the balance of external heat transfer. The intensity of heat radiated from the surface of a solid or structure is proportional to the coefficient of emissivity ε and to the fourth power of the surface temperature taken in degrees absolute. ε depends on the condition of the surface (for instance polished, oxidized or aged). The radiative heat losses are important when the surface temperatures become high. If thermal radiation is taken into account, the equilibrium temperatures† T_g for steady flight conditions become smaller than T_{aw}. Some values of T_g for typical flight conditions are given in Table 1.1. Because of thermal radiation T_g is less than T_{aw}; for the particular cases in Table 1.1 the differences are about 6, 20 and 160°C (or 11, 36 and 288°F). For higher altitudes than those in Table 1.1 the beneficial influence of thermal radiation becomes larger and hence the equilibrium temperatures lower. This is explained by a reduction in the rate of convective heat transfer owing to the lower density at high altitudes, while thermal radiation is unaffected by an increase in altitude.

The transient temperatures in structures during flight depend also on the initial temperatures. These are usually given by the steady state conditions of the structure either on the ground before take-off or launching of the

---

† If the surface is at the equilibrium temperature, the rate of heat flow to the wall becomes zero.

vehicle, or at a certain cruising speed in steady flight. The first case applies for instance to a fighter aircraft starting on a combat mission or to a surface-to-air missile. The second case would apply to an aircraft which cruises for a sufficiently long time at constant speed and altitude, and then is accelerated to a higher level of speed. In many cases initial temperatures may be assumed uniformly distributed in the structure. Initial temperature differences within the structure may exist due to heat developed by the engine, electronic equipment or irradiation from the sun. In steady flight the temperature distribution in the structure due to aerodynamic heating only would be approximately uniform if the amount of heat lost by heat radiation from the surface is not too important in the balance of heat flow at the surface of the structure.

1.3 Typical examples for aerodynamic heating of structures

The general considerations of the previous sections are now illustrated by typical examples. The first refers to an airplane flying for a sufficiently long time in level flight and at a constant speed. The speed is changed quickly to another level at which flight conditions are again constant for a long time. Later on the airplane is decelerated under similar conditions. Initially the temperature is assumed uniformly distributed throughout the structure. The temperatures in the structure are shown schematically in Fig. 1.2, where T_g is the equilibrium temperatnre which the structure

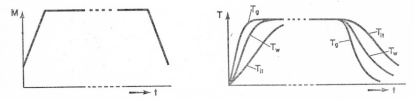

FIG. 1.2. The temperatures in a structure for a time history typical for aircraft. (M = Mach number, T = temperature, t = time, index g refers to equilibrium, w to the skin and "it" to the inside of the structure.)

would have if it were in thermal equilibrium at any instant; T_w is the temperature of the skin and T_{it} a temperature characteristic of the inside of the structure. These temperatures lie below the equilibrium temperature during acceleration and the reverse is true during deceleration. It takes some time after the end of the acceleration period for the temperature in the structure to become uniform. The largest temperature differences in the structure occur during or after the acceleration and deceleration depending on the heat transfer conditions and the dimensions of the structure. In the present case the highest temperature reached in the structure is equal to, or at least almost equal to, the equilibrium temperature.

The second case refers to an air-to-air missile which is carried by an aircraft during an initial period and then fired. Fig. 1.3 shows how the flight plan influences the temperatures in a missile skin. Uniform tempera-

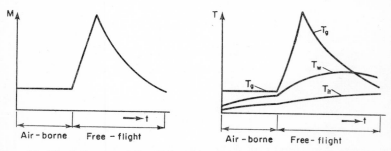

FIG. 1.3. The influence of the flight plan on the temperature of a missile skin. (Notations as in Fig. 1.2.)

ture was assumed throughout the thickness of the skin. During acceleration of the missile by a rocket engine the equilibrium temperature T_g increases to a maximum and drops again quickly. In many cases the peak values of T_g are at a level which would be too high to be tolerated in the structure, because of the reduction in strength at such high temperatures. However, a skin of finite thickness is an effective heat sink during short periods and hence its temperature T_w may remain substantially below the peak value of T_g. In that case the transient phase of heat transfer determines not only the thermal stresses and deformations but also the maximum temperature level for the strength of the material.

In the case of severe aerodynamic heating the rate of heat flow at the surface is determined only by the external heat transfer conditions, at least to a good approximation. This is the case during the re-entry of ballistic missiles or spacecraft. An important parameter determining the re-entry conditions is $K_g = W_g/(A\,C_D)$, the ratio of the weight of the vehicle W_g to the product of the cross sectional area A and the drag coefficient C_D. Heat flow histories corresponding to high (ballistic missile) and low (spacecraft) values of this parameter are given in Fig. 1.4. Obviously two thermal quantities are important: the total amount of heat transferred to the body and the maximum intensity of the heat flow. A structure can be protected against excessive heating in the following ways by (a) a heat sink, (b) heat radiation, (c) ablation and (d) transpiration cooling.

For a heat sink, a material of high heat capacity and conductivity is used so that the temperature can rise slowly and the heat can spread as quickly as possible thus keeping the surface temperatures low. For a given

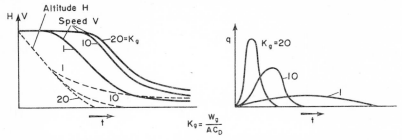

Fig. 1.4. Heat flow histories for ballistic missiles and spacecraft. (H = altitude above sea-level, V = speed, q = specific rate of heat flow, t = time; K_g in arbitrary units.)

material the effectiveness of a heat sink is limited (see Section 7.4); if it is thicker than half the penetration thickness, the surface temperatures would not be reduced any more. Because they are good conductors, metals have been used. If the surface temperature increases above the melting point, the liquid metal would soon be blown away because of its low viscosity and then the inside of the structure would be rapidly heated. Under such conditions the losses of material would be too high. Hence the surface must remain below the melting point. This requirement results in limitations on the speed and this can be obtained by using high drag shapes. Thus for ballistic missiles with re-entry bodies of the heat sink type the velocity in the lower layers of the atmosphere is comparatively small.

Using heat radiation at the surface as a means to dissipate the aerodynamic heat is effective only at high surface temperatures, because the radiative heat flow is proportional to the fourth power of the absolute temperature. The use of refractory materials is an obvious possibility. If a poor conductor is used, only a thin layer is heated. Hence these materials are not effective as a heat sink, and high thermal stresses will occur; this may be undesirable because many of these materials are brittle.

In ablation, part of the material is lost by processes which absorb heat. Thus liquefaction, evaporation and chemical reactions, possibly including even combustion, may occur. Evaporation and combustion liberate gases which by transpiring into the outside flow reduce the amount of heat transferred to the surface. In combustion the beneficial effect of transpiration must outweigh the detrimental effect due to the heat developed by combustion, if it is to be useful at all. In order to limit the loss of material it must be a poor conductor. In many cases it happens that once ablation sets in, the surface temperature does not depend much on the rate of heat flow to the surface. Then the process of ablation becomes self regulating. Among various materials, plastics have proved useful. At elevated temperatures they disintegrate chemically and develop gases. Their conductivity is poor, so that only a thin layer beneath the surface is heated. They are not brittle and have no tendency to peel off. Other possible materials are pyrolytic glasses which have no well defined melting point and become very viscous liquids at elevated temperatures. Thus they have a marked resistance against the action of the shear forces due to the air flow.

In transpiration cooling the structure can be protected by blowing gases or liquids through holes or porous surfaces whereby the heat flow to the structure is reduced. It is apparently difficult to control this process in a suitable way to maintain the structure temperature below a certain level when the rates of heat flow are large and changing rapidly.

CHAPTER 2

A SUMMARY OF EXTERNAL HEAT TRANSFER TO STRUCTURES IN HIGH SPEED FLIGHT

2.1 General

It has been stated in the introduction that in the problem of aerodynamic heating the transient heat flow in structures is more important than the steady heat flow. The question arises therefore whether steady state values for the external heat transfer can be used for calculating transient temperature distributions in structures. The magnitude of the accelerations of flight vehicles is usually such that the external air flow can be assumed to be in a steady state. This is so not only for the inviscid flow around the vehicles, but also for the viscous flow in the boundary layer at the surface of the vehicles. Assuming an instantaneous change of velocity it was found (Ref. 2.1.1) that the boundary layer quickly reaches steady state conditions. These are attained at different times for different distances from the leading edge. For wings and fuselages the order of magnitude of these times is the same as would be required by an air particle outside the boundary layer to cover these distances from the leading edge. Hence under most circumstances steady state conditions can be assumed for the external heat transfer and this is also done throughout this monograph.

For flight at not too high altitudes, continuum flow can be assumed. Then a shock wave develops in front of a body at supersonic or hypersonic speeds. For a blunt body or even a blunt leading edge, the shock is always detached from the body, while in the case of a sharp leading edge or pointed nose, the shock may be attached at the leading edge or nose depending on the included angle of the tangent wedge or tangent cone and on the Mach number. In most cases the Reynolds numbers for the vehicle would be sufficiently large so that viscous effects are restricted to a small region near the surface of the vehicle, the boundary layer; then the following is valid. For blunt bodies the stand-off distance of the shock wave will be sufficiently large so that the flow behind it can be divided into an outer inviscid region and, near the surface of the body, a viscous region which is called the boundary layer. As shown in Fig. 2.1 there are three regions: (I) The undisturbed region ahead of the shock wave within which the condition of air at rest prevails, (II) the shock layer between the shock wave and the outer edge of the boundary layer where the flow is inviscid, but rotational, and (III) the viscous boundary layer attached to the body. In passing through the shock wave the air undergoes changes in the variables of state by amounts which depend on the Mach number and on the inclination of the shock wave to the direction of flow. For cylinders symmetrical about a mid-plane or bodies of revolution at zero incidence to the undisturbed flow the streamline through the stagnation point passes through that part of the shock wave which is normal to the flow direction. Under the assumptions made the shock wave is very thin and can be treated as a discontinuity in the flow field. Across this discontinuity there is a decrease in speed and increases in pressure, density and temperature. These changes are largest when the shock is normal to the undisturbed flow direction and they decrease with the angle of inclination of the shock to the undisturbed flow direction. Hence, because of the curvature of the shock a rotational flow is introduced into the inviscid field downstream of the shock and this may affect the viscous boundary layer.

The local fluid flow at the border between the regions II and III determines the development of the boundary layer in the direction of flow. Conditions in region II can approximately be determined from the inviscid flow around the body, i.e. neglecting the boundary layer, because this is thin except at large altitudes. Consider in this assumed inviscid flow the streamline which passes through the stagnation point A and follows the contour of the body downstream (see Fig. 2.1). The conditions on this streamline downstream of the point A are a good approximation to those at the border between the regions II and III in real flow and corresponding points lie on lines normal to the surface. The inviscid flow around a body including the shock wave ahead of it can be found from theory or experiments.

So far no interactions between the inviscid flow and the boundary layer have been considered, but in reality they may occur under conditions discussed in Section 2.7.

In order to find the heat transfer far downstream of the leading edge or nose it is often convenient to consider the flow along an ideal flat plate at zero angle of incidence. The plate is assumed to be infinitely thin, so there is no shock wave, but only a Mach wave, i.e. a shock wave of infinitely small intensity; further, the pressure gradient is zero along the plate and hence the conditions at the outer edge of the boundary layer are the same as in the undisturbed free stream. The flow and heat transfer

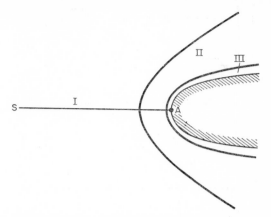

FIG. 2.1. Three regions in the flow field around a blunt body. (S stream line passing through the stagnation point A.) Not to scale.

conditions for this idealized case are well known. Thin wings at zero yaw angle differ from the ideal flat plate in two ways. First, because of the finite, though small thickness of the wing a shock wave originates which changes the flow conditions at the outer edge of the boundary layer; secondly owing to the curvature of the surface of the wing there are pressure gradients in the inviscid flow and hence also in the boundary layer.

The rate of heat flow to the surface depends not only on the flow conditions at the outer edge of the boundary layer, i.e. at the border between regions II and III in Fig. 2.1, but also on the characteristics of the boundary layer itself. The boundary layer begins in a laminar state and may become turbulent further downstream, depending on a number of quantities, in particular on the boundary layer thickness, the pressure gradient and the ratio of the wall temperature to the adiabatic wall temperature. Because of the large number of parameters and experimental difficulties, the point of transition from laminar to turbulent flow is difficult to predict (see also Section 2.6). The two types of flow differ in the velocity profile for the component parallel to the wall. For laminar flow the velocity changes rather gradually within the boundary layer whereas for turbulent flow the velocity increases very rapidly near the wall and changes much less within the remaining part of the boundary layer. A typical case for a boundary layer with zero or small pressure gradient in the flow direction is shown in Fig. 2.2. The velocity u is zero at the wall because of the non-slip condition at the wall. The temperature profiles within the boundary layer can be of different forms (see Fig. 2.3)

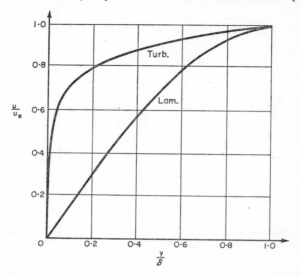

FIG. 2.2. Typical velocity profiles for laminar and turbulent boundary layer flow.

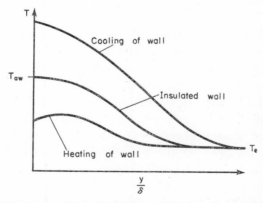

FIG. 2.3. Temperature profiles within a boundary layer in high speed flow (schematic).

depending on the amount of heat developed by friction within the boundary layer and on the wall temperature. In the case of an insulated wall the temperature profile increases from a value of T_e at the outer edge of the boundary layer to $T_w = T_{aw}$, the adiabatic wall temperature;

in this case the rate of heat flow to the wall is zero. The increase in temperature within the boundary layer is due to the heat developed by friction. Under such conditions thermal equilibrium prevails between the external flow and the surface, provided heat transfer occurs by forced convection only. The temperature profiles for $T_w > T_{aw}$ could occur during deceleration, provided the structure was sufficiently heated before retardation began. For air, the velocity and temperature boundary layers are of approximately the same thickness.

For the inviscid flow outside the boundary layer a division is made into incompressible, subsonic compressible, transonic, supersonic and hypersonic flow. The flow in each regime prevails for a certain range of the Mach number M which is the ratio of a characteristic speed to the speed of sound. The above flow regimes can be defined as follows: Incompressible $M < 0.3$, compressible $0.3 < M < 1$, transonic $M \approx 1$, supersonic $1 < M < M_{hyp}$ and hypersonic $M > M_{hyp}$. The limit M_{hyp} is difficult to give exactly; for blunt bodies it may be as low as 3 and a value of 5 is often used. Above $M = 6$ or 7 the molecules of air begin to dissociate under typical flight conditions. For subsonic flow the disturbances of a flying body propagate far upstream and downstream of the body; for supersonic flow the disturbances spread only as far as to the shock wave. In front of the shock wave the air is at rest and undisturbed by the flying object.

If there is no interaction between the boundary layer and the inviscid flow outside it, the flow in the boundary layer itself is of the same general character for all Mach numbers, i.e. a distinction between different flow regimes, as is used with inviscid flow, has no importance for the boundary layer. At any cross section the flow and the thermal properties in the boundary layer depend only on the development of the boundary layer upstream of the cross section considered, but not on that downstream. This behaviour is similar to that of the equation of heat conduction: the temperature at any point of a solid depends on the previous temperatures, but not on those of the future. The fundamental characteristics of boundary layer flow are not changed if the compressibility of the air becomes important. The difference between boundary layer flow at low and high speed lies in the heat developed by friction and compression, and in the dependence of the thermal properties of the air on temperature. Hence one would expect the same type of formulas for heat transfer to be valid for low and high speed flow.

For laminar flow the rate of heat transfer can be calculated from the fundamental equations. For turbulent flow one has to resort to experiments and semi-empirical relations. This is facilitated by the Reynolds analogy† between heat transfer and skin friction, derived from the similarity of the momentum equation for fluid flow and the equation for heat flow. Calculation of the development of the boundary layer along the surface of a body is more or less complicated, depending on the flow regime and the degree of accuracy required. The heat flow to the wall is not particularly sensitive to the precise form of the velocity profile. This often simplifies the calculation of heat transfer. In the following sections, results are given and discussed for laminar heat transfer at stagnation points and on flat plates with zero pressure gradients; in the latter case results are also given for the turbulent flow. Later in Section 2.4, an approximate, but comparatively simple method is given for calculating laminar heat transfer on bodies of arbitrary shape (see also Section 2.3.4).

2.2 Adiabatic wall temperatures

The adiabatic wall temperature is defined as the temperature which a wall assumes in thermal equilibrium, if only convective heat transfer occurs. At a stagnation point on a body of revolution, or at a stagnation line on a cylindrical body whose axis is directed normal to the flow, the adiabatic wall temperature is called the stagnation temperature T_s. At moderate Mach numbers ($M \leqslant 3$), when the air is chemically stable and the specific heats at constant pressure and at constant volume are constant, one obtains:

$$T_s = T_t = T_\infty \left(1 + \frac{\gamma - 1}{2} M_\infty^2\right) \qquad (2.2.1)$$

where T_t is the total temperature, T_∞ the ambient temperature, γ the ratio of the specific heat at constant pressure to that at constant volume (for air $\gamma = 1\cdot40$) and M_∞ the flight Mach number. The above equation is valid regardless of whether a shock wave exists ahead of the body or not. If the variation of the specific heat becomes appreciable, the stagnation temperature has to be calculated with the help of the (specific) enthalpy i which is defined as

$$i = \int_0^T c_p \, \mathrm{d}T, \qquad (2.2.2a)$$

---

† See Ref. 3.2.

provided dissociation does not occur; the stagnation enthalpy is

$$i_s = i_t = i_\infty + \frac{1}{2} u_\infty^2 \qquad (2.2.2b)$$

with u_∞ as the flight speed. In inviscid flow the total enthalpy i_t is constant along a streamline. The enthalpy of air (for numerical values see Ref. 2.2.1) is a function of the temperature and the pressure. Downstream of a shock wave, the latter quantity follows from the pressure ratio across the shock wave (see Ref. 2.2.2) on the same streamline. For moderate Mach numbers the dependence of i on the pressure is negligible.

Downstream of the stagnation point, the adiabatic wall temperature is calculated with the help of the stagnation temperature and a recovery factor η. For moderate Mach numbers η is defined by

$$\eta = \frac{T_{aw} - T_e}{T_t - T_e}, \qquad (2.2.3)$$

where T_e is the local temperature at the edge of the boundary layer. At high Mach numbers when enthalpies have to be used, η is defined by

$$\eta = \frac{i_{aw} - i_e}{i_t - i_e} \qquad (2.2.3a)$$

For attached boundary layers in two-dimensional flow on wings and bodies of revolution η for laminar boundary layers (see for instance Ref. 2.2.3) is given by

$$\eta = Pr^{1/2} \qquad (2.2.4)$$

and for turbulent boundary layers,

$$\eta = Pr^{1/3} \qquad . \qquad (2.2.5)$$

In both cases η is practically independent of the pressure gradient, of the distance from the leading edge or nose and of the Mach number. Pr is the Prandtl number and equal to $\mu c_p / k$ where μ is the dynamic viscosity and k the thermal conductivity of the external medium, all taken at a suitable reference temperature. For air under usual flight conditions only the temperature dependence of Pr is of practical importance and even this is slight (Ref. 2.2.1); it suffices therefore in most cases to use T_e as reference temperature for the Prandtl number. For air Pr is about 0·7[†] and the recovery factor η is close to unity. Hence the influence on T_{aw}

[†] Previously, values for Pr of air have been considered as uncertain and in aeronautics representative values of 0·7 to 0·75 have been used; recently values of 0·7 to 0·72 have been preferred, however this uncertainty in Pr is of little practical importance.

of variations in T_e is small, if the variations in the speed u_e at the outer edge of the boundary layer are moderate. This is the case on aircraft and missile surfaces at some distance downstream of the leading edge or nose and hence the adiabatic wall temperature there for flow in an attached boundary layer can be expressed to a good approximation by the ambient air temperature T_∞ and the flight Mach number M_∞:

$$T_{aw} = T_\infty \left(1 + \eta \frac{\gamma-1}{2} M_\infty^2\right) \tag{2.2.6}$$

with η according to Eqs. (2.2.4) or (2.2.5).

The adiabatic wall temperature on the stagnation line of yawed cylinders or wings is, for low to moderate temperatures:

$$T_{aw} = T_t - \frac{(v_{sp,\infty})^2}{2 c_p} (1 - \eta), \tag{2.2.7}$$

and for extreme temperatures, when enthalpies have to be used:

$$i_{aw} = i_t - \frac{(v_{sp,\infty})^2}{2} (1 - \eta) \tag{2.2.7a}$$

η is again a recovery factor and $v_{sp,\infty}$ is the spanwise component of the undisturbed flow velocity ahead of the cylinder or wing. η has about the same value as above (Ref. 2.2.4 and 2.2.5), i.e. as in Eq. (2.2.4), because on stagnation lines the flow is always laminar.

i_t is the total enthalpy at the stagnation line. The adiabatic wall temperatures downstream of the stagnation point are calculated as above for unyawed bodies.

2.3 Convective heat transfer coefficients in chemically stable air

2.3.1 General

The characteristics of the boundary layer determine the intensity of the convective heat transfer. While the mechanical forces on aircraft can often be found from wind tunnel tests on models, it is far more difficult to find the corresponding heat transfer characteristics from models. Experimental results are at present mainly available only for simple bodies such as cones, axisymmetric bodies with various forebodies, and flat plates. From these it is possible to estimate at least approximately the intensity of heat transfer on the surfaces of structures. In the following, a short survey of existing data is given.

2.3.2 *Ideal flat plate and cone with zero pressure gradient and constant wall temperatures*

An ideal flat plate is considered here with a sharp leading edge and with a vanishingly small thickness. Thus, at zero angle of attack no shock wave occurs at the leading edge and the pressure gradient is zero along the whole plate, if there is no interaction of the boundary layer with the external flow. Then the flow conditions at the outer edge of the boundary layer are equal to the free stream conditions. The reason for treating this apparently artificial case at length is that it is one for which the boundary layer development and the heat transfer conditions are well known.

Except at the stagnation point and its immediate surroundings the pressure gradients on slender wings are moderate and their influence on the heat transfer coefficient can in many cases be neglected. Incidentally, for turbulent boundary layers this influence is not well known. Bluntness of the leading edge influences the heat transfer coefficient along the entire wing and often this cannot be neglected, particularly at high Mach numbers. However, we can approximately dispose of that effect as well as the influence of an angle of attack by referring all quantities in this section to the local values at the outer edge of the boundary layer, which in the case of leading edge bluntness or an angle of attack may differ from the free stream values by an amount which can be estimated from Section 2.5.

For both laminar and turbulent boundary layers on flat plates, the heat transfer coefficient for constant wall temperatures can be expressed as (see for instance Ref. 2.2.3):

$$h = \frac{1}{2} f(\text{Pr}) \, \rho_e \, c_{p,e} \, u_e \, c_f \qquad (2.3.1)$$

where ρ_e and $c_{p,e}$ are the density and specific heat at constant pressure respectively, u_e is the speed; all quantities are to be taken at the outer edge of the boundary layer, c_f is the local friction coefficient and

$$f(\text{Pr}) = \text{Pr}^{-2/3} \qquad (2.3.2)$$

For air one takes $\text{Pr} = 0.72$ and hence $f(\text{Pr}) = 1.24$. For laminar flow with variable fluid properties (except for c_p which was assumed constant), but without chemical reactions, $c_f \sqrt{\text{Re}_x}$ is given in Fig. 2.4, which has been taken from Ref. 2.3.1. $\text{Re}_x = \dfrac{u_e x}{\nu_e}$ with x as the distance from the leading edge and ν_e as the kinematic viscosity at the outer edge of the boundary layer. For turbulent flow, the ratio of the compressible to the incompressible friction coefficient, c_f/c_{fi}, or the corresponding heat transfer coefficients h/h_i, was found to be practically independent of the Reynolds number,

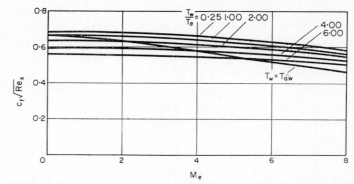

FIG. 2.4. Friction coefficient for laminar boundary layer flow on an ideal flat plate with zero pressure gradient and in chemically stable air according to van Driest (Ref. 3.3.1). M_e Mach number at the outer edge of the boundary layer.

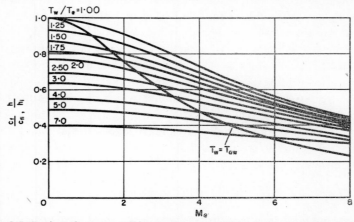

FIG. 2.5. Ratio of compressible to incompressible skin friction coefficient for turbulent boundary layer flow in chemically stable air. Also ratio of corresponding heat transfer coefficients. Otherwise as in Fig. 2.4. After Sommer and Short (Ref. 2.3.2).

based on fluid properties at the outer edge of the boundary layer. Most experimental results agreed well with a semi-empirical theory (see Ref. 2.2.3), the results of which for air are presented in Fig. 2.5†, where c_f/c_{fi} is presented

---

† Fig. 2.5 is strictly valid for an ambient air temperature $T_e = 218\,°K\,(392\,°R)$, a Reynolds number $Re_x = 1 \times 10^7$ and a temperature dependence of the viscosity of air according to Sutherland's law. The Reynolds number influence on the ratio c_f/c_{fi} is slight and it can be neglected under most flight conditions as well as any deviations from the other assumptions.

as a function of the Mach number M_e at the outer edge of the boundary layer with T_{aw}/T_e as parameter. However, reservations must be made for those parts of the figure referring to values of T_w/T_e that depart very much from T_{aw}/T_e, because experiments in these regions are too few to be decisive. The local incompressible value of c_{fi} is taken as (see Ref. 2.2.3)

$$c_{fi} = 0.288 \ (\log \ Re_x)^{-2.45} \qquad (2.3.3)$$

log is the common logarithm to the base 10. As a rough approximation $c_{fi} \sim Re_x^{-1/6}$ is often useful and hence c_{fi} and c_f depend only slightly on the distance from the leading edge x in contrast to the laminar boundary layer, for which $c_{fi} \sim Re_x^{-1/2}$ (see above).

Consider a yawed flat plate, i.e. the angle of attack is zero, but the leading edge is inclined at the yaw angle to the undisturbed flow direction. The local heat transfer conditions are now found as for the unyawed plate, but at any point the distance from the leading edge used in the formulas is taken in the undisturbed flow direction (see Fig. 2.6). This is exact

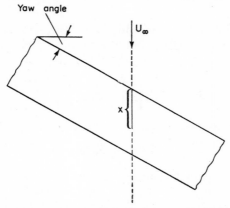

FIG. 2.6. A yawed flat plate. $x =$ distance from the leading edge in formulas for calculating heat transfer.

for laminar boundary layers (see Ref. 2.1) and approximately true for turbulent boundary layers (see Ref. 2.3.3). Hence the way a yaw angle affects aerodynamic heating of a flat plate is determined by how T_{aw} and h of an unyawed plate depend on the distance from the leading edge x. T_{aw} is independent of x (see Section 2.2); because h is proportional to the friction coefficient, h decreases with increasing x as given above for c_f and c_{fi}. Hence there is a reduction of aerodynamic heating, but only in the transient case if the radiative heat transfer is unimportant, because

T_{aw} is unaffected by the yaw. For turbulent boundary layers the reduction would not be large, because for these $h \sim c_f \sim x^{-1/6}$.

For a cone in supersonic flow Eq. (2.3.1) remains valid[†], but c_f is different. It can be found from the flat plate formulas by using for Re_x an equivalent Reynolds number which is

$$\mathrm{Re}_{x,\,\mathrm{cone}} = \frac{1}{2+l} \frac{u_e x}{\nu_e} \tag{2.3.4}$$

with $l = 1$ for laminar and 1/6 for turbulent flow[††], x is the distance from the apex measured on the surface of the cone. On a cone with finite apex angle, u_e differs from the undisturbed free stream values u_∞. u_e and ν_e can be found from the well known formulas for inviscid conical flow[‡]. For very slender cones when $u_e \approx u_\infty$ the heat transfer coefficient would be larger for cones than for flat plates by 73 per cent for laminar and 17 per cent for turbulent flow.

2.3.3 *Stagnation lines on cylinders and stagnation points on bodies of revolution*

At stagnation lines or points and their immediate surroundings§ the flow is almost always laminar and the heat transfer coefficient can be presented in the following form (Ref. 2.2.5 or 2.3.4):

$$h = G k_w \sqrt{\left[\frac{\rho_w}{\mu_w}\left(\frac{du_e}{dx}\right)_s\right]} \tag{2.3.5}$$

k, ρ and μ are the thermal conductivity, density and dynamic viscosity respectively; $\left(\dfrac{du_e}{dx}\right)_s$ is the velocity gradient at the stagnation line or point and $G = \mathrm{Nu}_w/\sqrt{\mathrm{Re}_w}$ with Nu and Re as the local Nusselt and Reynolds numbers ($\mathrm{Nu}_w = hx/k_w$, $\mathrm{Re}_w = u_e x/\nu_w$). The subscript w refers to the wall temperature. The following expressions for G are all valid for Pr $= 0.71$ (air). For a cylinder whose axis is either normal to or at a yaw

---

† Provided the shock wave is attached at the point of the cone and the angle of attack is zero.

†† For laminar flow this relation is exact and follows from Mangler's transformation (see for instance Ref. 2.1), while for turbulent flow it is approximate (unpublished results).

‡ KOPAL, Z., Tables of supersonic flow around cones, Tech. Rep. No. 1. Dept. of Elect. Eng. Mass. Inst. Tech. Cambridge, Mass. (1947).

§ More precisely in the region where $u_e = \left(\dfrac{du_e}{dx}\right)_s x$ with x as distance from the stagnation point.

angle to the undisturbed flow direction there is with good approximation:

$$G^{(c)} = 0\cdot5 \left(\frac{\rho_s \mu_s}{\rho_w \mu_w}\right)^{0\cdot44} \tag{2.3.6}$$

The subscript s refers to external flow at the stagnation line of the cylinder either yawed or unyawed. The above formula is approximately valid for values of the yaw parameter $T_t/T_{s,\Lambda}$ from 1 to about 7, see Ref. 2.2.4; $T_{s,\Lambda}$ is the temperature of the external flow at the stagnation line of a yawed cylinder. Assuming constant specific heat (approximately valid for flight up to about $M \approx 4$) $T_{s,\Lambda}$ is

$$T_{s,\Lambda} = T_\infty \left(1 + \frac{\gamma-1}{2} M_\infty^2 \cos^2\Lambda\right) \tag{2.3.7}$$

where Λ is the yaw angle. The wall pressure at the stagnation line becomes for supersonic chordwise flow:

$$\frac{p_{w,\Lambda}}{p_\infty} = \left[\frac{\gamma+1}{2} M_\infty^2 \cos^2\Lambda\right]^{\frac{\gamma}{\gamma-1}} \left[\frac{\gamma+1}{2\gamma M_\infty^2 \cos^2\Lambda - (\gamma-1)}\right]^{\frac{1}{\gamma-1}} \tag{2.3.8a}$$

and for subsonic chordwise flow:

$$\frac{p_{w,\Lambda}}{p_\infty} = \left[1 + \frac{\gamma-1}{2} M_\infty^2 \cos^2\Lambda\right]^{\frac{\gamma}{\gamma-1}} \tag{2.3.8b}$$

$\rho_s\mu_s$ in Eq. (2.3.6) is to be taken at the above temperature $T_{s,\Lambda}$ and pressure $p_{w,\Lambda}$.

For bodies of revolution one obtains from Ref. 2.3.5 and 2.3.6:

$$G^{(r)} = 0\cdot67 \left(\frac{\rho_s \mu_s}{\rho_w \mu_w}\right)^{0\cdot4} \tag{2.3.9}$$

Since the exponents 0·44 and 0·4 in Eqs. (2.3.6) and (2.3.9) are almost the same, $G^{(c)}/0\cdot5$ and $G^{(r)}/0\cdot67$ can be represented for a pressure range of 0·01 atm to 100 atm with an accuracy of ±1 per cent by one family of curves as in Fig. 2.7. The velocity gradient at the stagnation line of cylinders with the axis normal to the undisturbed flow direction (Ref. 2.2.5) and at the stagnation point of the hemispherical forebody of a cylinder in axial flow (Ref. 2.3.7) is given in Fig. 2.8. For cylindrical bodies with different forebody shapes, see Ref. 2.3.8. For a yawed cylinder the velocity gradient for the normal component of flow is to be used in the above formulas. For wings with rounded leading edges the above formulas are approximately valid, if

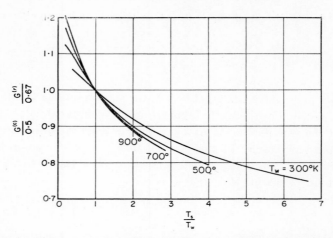

FIG. 2.7. Characteristic quantity G for laminar heat transfer in stagnation regions of cylinders (superscript c) and bodies of revolution (superscript r). Chemically stable air. Further details see text.

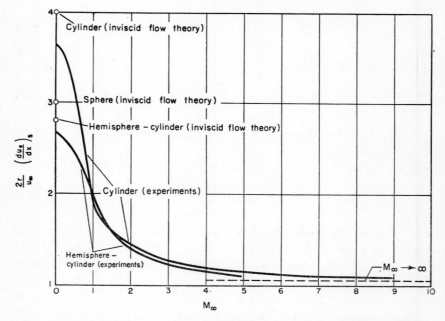

FIG. 2.8. Velocity gradient at the stagnation line of circular cylinders according to Reshotko and Beckwith (Ref. 2.3.5) and at the stagnation point of the hemispherical front part of a cylinder according to Korobkin and Gruenewald (Ref. 2.3.7). r radius of cylinder or hemisphere. For yawed cylinders replace u_∞ by its component $u_{N,\infty}$ directed normal to the cylinder axis and M_∞ by $M_{N,\infty}$ which corresponds to $u_{N,\infty}$. Chemically stable air.

the radius of the cylinder is taken as equal to the radius of curvature at the stagnation line. Similarly, in the case of rounded noses on bodies of revolution, the radius of the hemisphere is taken as equal to the radius of curvature at the stagnation line.

2.3.4 *The influence of pressure gradients on heat transfer*

Downstream of the stagnation point or line, the heat transfer conditions depend on the development of the boundary layer and on the position of the transition from laminar to turbulent flow. The latter is dealt with in Section 2.6. The development of the boundary layer depends on the shape of the body, which in turn determines the pressure distribution. For laminar boundary layers on straight or yawed wings and on bodies of revolution, a number of methods exist for calculating boundary layer development and heat transfer, see for example Refs. 2.3.9 and 2.3.10. Lees (Ret. 2.3.11) developed a comparatively simple method which originally was only meant for hypersonic flow (which is given in Section 2.4), but was also found to be useful for supersonic flow, if errors of the order of 10–15 per cent are accepted. The heat flow distribution for a circular cylinder with its axis normal to the undisturbed flow is given in Fig. 2.9 and for the hemispherical nose of a cylinder in axial flow in Fig. 2.10. The results for the

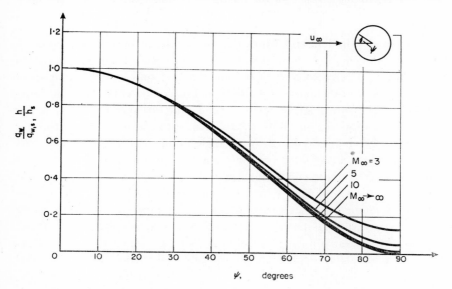

FIG. 2.9. Distribution of the rate of heat flow on the surface of a circular cylinder in transverse air flow. Laminar flow and severe rates of heating. Also approximate distribution of the heat transfer coefficient.

cylinder in transverse flow can be used to estimate the distribution of heat
flow near a rounded leading edge of a wing if the radius of curvature
at the stagnation point is equal to that of the cylinder.

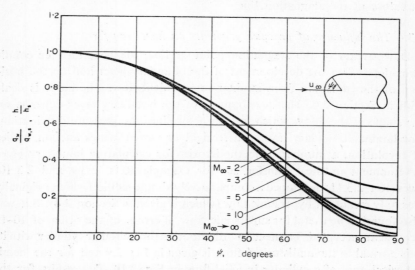

FIG. 2.10. As Fig 2.9, but for the hemispherical front part of a cylinder in
axial flow. From L. Lees (Ref. 2.3.11).

For yawed cylinders and wings the independence principle is valid for
incompressible laminar flow (see for instance Ref. 2.1), according to
which the heat transfer coefficient is determined only by the component
of flow normal to the axis of the cylinder. For compressible flow the independence principle is approximately valid and the approximation is fair
in the stagnation region (Ref. 2.2.5). Hence the laminar heat transfer
coefficient on wings is reduced by an angle of yaw and if this is large, the
reduction is substantial at least in the stagnation region. The adiabatic wall
temperature is decreased on stagnation lines, although only slightly so that
this contribution is of little practical significance (see Section 2.2). Downstream of stagnation lines the adiabatic wall temperature appears to be
unaffected by yawing. On slender yawed wings at some distance downstream of the stagnation region the heat transfer coefficient can be calculated approximately as for a yawed flat plate (see Section 2.3.2), provided
the boundary layer does not separate from the surface.

The influence of a pressure gradient on turbulent boundary layers is
rather uncertain and corresponding experiments are few; for an example
of a method of calculation see Ref. 2.3.12. Because the pressure gradients

on slender bodies and wings are small in most cases, except at the stagnation region, it is reasonable to neglect the pressure gradients in turbulent boundary layer flow. For high speed flow inside structures, such as in wind tunnels and rocket engines, the influence of pressure gradients on the heat transfer is important. In general the following type of nozzle flow is involved: subsonic flow in the inlet which is followed by a contraction with sonic flow in the narrowest cross section followed by an expansion to supersonic flow. The development of the boundary layer is determined to a large extent by the pressure distribution along the nozzle. In most cases the Reynolds number is high, so that the boundary layer flow is turbulent. The rate of heat transfer is largest close to the narrowest cross section. A method for calculating turbulent heat transfer in a nozzle is due to Bartz, Refs. 2.3.13 and 2.3.14.

2.3.5 *The influence of a non-uniform wall temperature on the heat transfer coefficient*

Suppose that a boundary layer develops from a leading edge and that the wall temperature T_w is equal to the adiabatic wall temperature T_{aw} from the leading edge to a distance x_1 from it. Hence the rate of heat flow would be zero over this distance. At the point x_1 the wall temperature

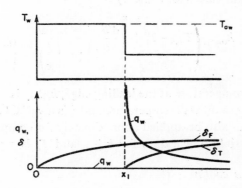

Fig. 2.11. A thermal boundary layer whose starting point lies downstream of the leading edge. (δ_F thickness of the fluid flow boundary layer, δ_T thickness of the thermal boundary layer; adiabatic surface from $x = 0$ to $x = x_1$, $T_w \neq T_{aw}$ for $x > x_1$.)

changes from T_{aw} to $T_w \neq T_{aw}$, see Fig. 2.11. A temperature boundary layer begins to develop with its origin at x_1 with the heat transfer coefficient being (theoretically) infinite at x_1. Obviously this temperature boundary layer and its heat transfer coefficient differ from the values which one would obtain for a constant wall temperature prevailing from the leading edge. If T_w changes continuously, the heat transfer coefficients are influenced in a similar way. Take for instance a flat plate with zero pressure gradient and incompressible laminar flow; suppose $T_w - T_e = Ax$ where T_e (=const.) is the temperature at the outer edge of the boundary layer, A is a constant and x is the distance from the leading edge. In that case the heat transfer coefficient increases by 65 per cent as compared with a constant wall temperature (Ref. 2.3.15). However, in most cases of interest for aerodynamic heating the conditions are such that the wall temperature variations which actually occur have a comparatively small influence on the heat transfer coefficient (see also Section 2.6).

For slender wings with a small pressure gradient, the formulas for a flat plate with zero pressure gradient may be applied approximately except in the vicinity of the stagnation region. These formulas are: for incompressible flow and a laminar boundary layer (Ref. 2.3.16)

$$q_w = -h_{\text{const.}} \left(T_{w,0} - T_e + \int_0^x \frac{\mathrm{d}T}{\mathrm{d}\xi} \frac{\mathrm{d}\xi}{\left[1 - \left(\frac{\xi}{x} \right)^{3/4} \right]^{1/3}} \right) \qquad (2.3.10)$$

and for a turbulent flow (Ref. 2.3.17)

$$q_w = -h_{\text{const.}} \left(T_{w,0} - T_e + \int_0^x \frac{\mathrm{d}T_w}{\mathrm{d}\xi} \frac{\mathrm{d}\xi}{\left[1 - \left(\frac{\xi}{x} \right)^{39/40} \right]^{7/39}} \right) \qquad (2.3.11)$$

$T_{w,0}$ is the wall temperature at the leading edge, $h_{\text{const.}}$ is the heat transfer coefficient for a constant wall temperature and ξ is a variable of integration. These formulas can also be applied approximately for compressible flow, if one uses compressible flow values for $h_{\text{const.}}$ and T_e is replaced by T_{aw}.

2.3.6 Transpiration cooling

Injection of gases through a porous surface into the boundary layer reduces the rate of heat transfer considerably. The injected gas leaves the surface at right angles to it and is usually assumed to possess the same temperature as the wall. The reduction in heat transfer becomes more effective if the injected gas has a lower molecular weight than the gas in the boundary layer. Transpiration cooling is effective for both laminar and turbulent boundary layers. For theoretical and experimental results see Refs. 2.3.18 to 2.3.22.

2.4 Convective heat transfer in dissociated air at hypersonic speeds†

In high speed flight with Mach numbers above 6 to 7 the molecules of air dissociate into atoms and energy is thereby extracted from the fluid. Hence the temperature of the air is reduced by dissociation. However, this does not necessarily mean a relief in the aerodynamic heating. In most cases the wall temperatures remain far below the temperature levels at which dissociation occurs. Hence the atoms that come close to the wall may recombine into molecules, and the dissociation energy is thereby released. Then the rate of heat flow to the wall may be the same or nearly the same whether or not dissociation takes place.

An important quantity in this connection is the speed of formation or recombination of atoms. If the speed of the chemical reactions is large in comparison to the particle speeds, steady state conditions (thermo-chemical equilibrium) can be assumed and then the degree of dissociation of the air depends only on the temperature and the pressure of the gas. If the air speed is large in comparison with the speed of the chemical reactions, non-equilibrium may prevail and in extreme cases the degree of dissociation remains fixed ("chemically frozen flow") despite changes in the variables of state. Then the heat transfer to the wall depends very markedly on whether the wall is catalytic or not. A body which is itself unaffected by a chemical reaction, but accelerates it, is called a catalyst. If there is frozen flow and the wall is catalytic, the atoms would recombine at the wall with a corresponding release of energy (heat), while for a non-catalytic wall the "frozen state" would be retained even at the wall.

The simultaneous presence of atoms and molecules complicates the analytical treatment of heat flow in the boundary layer. A gradient in the concentration of atoms and molecules gives rise to a mass transport by diffusion and the heat flow in the boundary layer is in general influenced thereby. Then there is also a "concentration" boundary layer, and simultaneous solutions of the boundary layers of fluid flow, heat flow and mass transport have to be found. In such cases the heat transfer coefficient depends also on a new non-dimensional quantity, the Lewis number

$$\text{Le} = \frac{c_p D_{12} \rho}{k} \tag{2.4.1}$$

D_{12} is the coefficient of diffusion for atoms in dissociated air.

It was mentioned earlier that at elevated temperatures the variations of the specific heat with temperature have to be taken into account by using

---

† For extensive literature see Refs. 2.4.1 and 2.4.1a.

enthalpies rather than temperatures. Further, at temperature levels which are so high that dissociation occurs, the concept of the specific enthalpy is extended to comprise also dissociation;

$$i = \int_0^T c_p \mathrm{d}T + i_D \qquad (2.4.2)$$

where c_p is the specific heat of air and i_D the dissociation enthalpy per unit mass of air. Dissociated air is predominantly a mixture of molecules and atoms of oxygen and nitrogen; therefore both c_p and i_D refer to that mixture and they depend on the temperature and the pressure.

At elevated temperatures the heat flow to the wall is defined as

$$q_w = \frac{h}{c_p}(i_{aw} - i_w) \qquad (2.4.3)$$

where on the right-hand side of the equation there is a difference of enthalpies rather than of temperatures. i_{aw} follows from Eqs. (2.2.2b), (2.2.3a) and (2.2.7a). At severe rates of aerodynamic heating i_w can often be neglected in comparison with i_{aw}. c_p is the specific heat at constant pressure and is to be taken either at T_e or at T_{aw} depending on the reference temperature for the thermal properties in the equation for h. Thus for h given by Eqs. (2.3.1) and (2.3.5) c_p is equal to $c_{p,e}$ and $c_{p,w}$ respectively.

Although the theoretical treatment of boundary layers with dissociation and diffusion is rather difficult, the results as regards heat transfer can be represented with good approximation by comparatively simple formulas for a wide range of the variables. The case of the stagnation flow treated in Section 2.3.3 has been investigated for constant Lewis numbers, for thermo-chemical conditions of equilibrium and for frozen flow with catalytic and non-catalytic walls. The influence of diffusion on the heat transfer coefficient can be taken into account by multiplying the expression for h given in Section 2.3.3 by a factor P_D (Ref. 2.3.5 and 2.3.6), which is

$$P_D = \frac{(h) \text{ with diffusion}}{(h) \text{ without diffusion}} = 1 + (B \, \mathrm{Le}^m - 1)\frac{(i_D)_e}{i_t} \qquad (2.4.4)$$

The coefficients B and m follow from Table 2.1; i_t is the total enthalpy (see Eq. 2.2.2b) which is constant at the outer edge of the boundary layer. At stagnation points, of course, $(i_D)_e = (i_D)_s$ and $i_t = i_s$. In all cases thermo-chemical equilibrium prevails at the outer edge of the boundary layer. An important result is that $P_D = 1$ for $\mathrm{Le} = 1$ in the case of thermo-chemical equilibrium and of "chemically frozen" flow with a catalytic wall.

Consider next an ideal flat plate at zero incidence. The importance of this case and its application to wings and bodies of finite thickness has

HEAT TRANSFER IN STRUCTURES

by H. Schuh

ERRATA*

Page xvii, last line: *for* solids- *read* solids

Page 5, line 20: *for* temperatnre *read* temperature

Page 23, line 13: *for* Ret. 2.3.11 *read* Ref. 2.3.11

Page 26, Eq. (2.3.10): *for* $dT/d\xi$ *read* $dT_w/d\xi$

Page 34, line 5: *for* body provided *read* body, provided

Page 38, in caption to Fig. 2.16, line 2: *for* tunnl eexperiments *read* tunnel experiments

Page 55, line 1: *for* unity *read* unity.

Page 70, line 12: *for* $\tilde{v} - \partial s_L/\partial x$ *read* $\ddot{\tilde{v}} - \partial s_L/\partial t$

Page 72, line 1: *for* eavporation *read* evaporation

Page 145, Eq. (7.5.6): *for* the numerator (in the fraction between the two equality signs) *read* $T - T_i$

Page 159, *for* Eq. (7.6.15) *read* $\Theta = (T_w - T_i)k_M/D\delta$

Page 159, last line: *delete* for

Page 165, line 4: *for* turbulentw ith *read* turbulent with

Page 174, line 9: *for* calcul ationsbecome *read* calculations become

Page 200, Table 8.3 in Footnote [b] and [c] *for* $p_{max} = 1/3$ *read* $p = 1/3$

  for $p_{max} = 1/2$ *read* $p = 1/2.$

Page 207, line 13: *for* f *read* if

Page 211, line 16: *for* $(m+1)\Delta t)$ *read* $(m+1)\Delta t,$

Page 218, line 13: *for* emperatures *read* temperatures

Page 218, line 26: *for* presen *read* present

Page 219, Eq. (8.5.8): for the denominator on the right-hand side *read* W_1

Page 225, *for* Eq. (8.7.9) *read* $b = \sqrt{(12 \varkappa t)}$

Page 267, line 10: *for* nterface *read* interface

Page 277, Eq. (9.4.11) *for the illegible subscript at D read* D_1.

Page 309, line 8: replace full stop at the end of the line by a comma.

Page 323, Footnote: *for* Ref. 8.3.6.18 *read* Ref. A.3.6.18

Page 324, line 3 from bottom: *for* tubo *read* tube

* The numbering of lines refers to lines of text excluding chapter or section headings.

NOTE: The publishers wish it to be known that, with the exception of those on pp. 26, 70, 159, 225, the author is in no way responsible for these errors which were introduced after the proofs had been approved for final correction and printing by both author and publisher.

TABLE 2.1

Thermo-chemical condition	Speed of chemical reaction	Wall	m	B
Equilibrium	Infinite	Catalytic and non-catalytic	0·52	1
Chemically frozen	Zero	Catalytic	0·63	1
Chemically frozen	Zero	Non-catalytic	—	0

been discussed previously in Section 2.1. The correction factor† for diffusion in laminar boundary layers and for thermo-chemical equilibrium is of similar form to that above and is approximately (Ref. 2.4.2):

$$P_D = 1 + (\mathrm{Le}^{1/2} - 1)\frac{(i_D)_e}{i_{\mathrm{aw}}} \qquad (2.4.5)$$

This equation differs from Eq. (2.4.4) in that $i_{\mathrm{aw}} = i_e + \frac{1}{2}\,(\mathrm{Pr})^{1/2}\,u_e^2$ takes the place of i_t. The corresponding case for turbulent flow (and also thermo-chemical equilibrium) is approximately (Ref. 2.4.3):

$$P_D = 1 + (\mathrm{Le}^m - 1)\frac{(i_D)_e}{i_t} \qquad (2.4.6)$$

This equation is tentative but if $\mathrm{Le} = 1\cdot4$ and $m = 1$ good agreement with experiments in air is obtained. For highly cooled boundary layers (see also next paragraph) the best agreement with experiments has been found if $c_f = c_{fi}$ in the equation for the heat transfer coefficient (2.3.1). c_{fi} is found from Eq. (2.3.3) with x as the distance from the stagnation point, even for blunt bodies.

The Lewis number of air has previously been considered uncertain. In Refs. 2.3.5 and 2.3.6 it was assumed constant and equal to 1·4; later on, a Lewis number varying from 1·4 for low enthalpy to 0·6 for complete dissociation was considered more realistic (Ref. 2.4.4). With the latter assumption and for wall temperatures below the dissociation level, it was found that the solutions for laminar boundary layer flow in a stagnation region and on a flat plate yield a correction factor $P_D = 1$, i.e. the Lewis number can be assumed constant and equal to 1 (Ref. 2.4.5).

So far, heat transfer at stagnation points and on flat plates with zero pressure gradient have been treated. To calculate the distribution of the

† In Fig. 2.4 $c_f \sqrt{\mathrm{Re}_x}$ is given only up to $M \approx 8$. Values for higher Mach numbers are given in Ref. 2.3.1.

rate of heat flow on a cylinder (wing) or a body of revolution, the following comparatively simple method has been developed by L. Lees (Ref. 2.3.11). We assume a non-ablating surface and first consider rather highly blunted bodies at hypersonic speeds. Because of the bluntness of the body, the static temperature behind the shock would be high, and the Mach number would be subsonic at the front part and supersonic further downstream. Assume the surface temperature to be constant and to remain low in comparison with the static temperature at the outer edge of the boundary layer. This is termed a highly cooled boundary layer although it need mean no more than that the cooling is of the heat sink type. Under such conditions, considerable simplification of the boundary layer equations can be made. The formula finally obtained by Lees is valid for two-dimensional boundary layers and for those on bodies of revolution

$$q_w = \frac{0\cdot50}{\sqrt{2}} \, \mathrm{Pr}^{-2/3} \sqrt{\left(\frac{\mu_w}{RT_w}\right)} \frac{p_e u_e r_0^j}{\left[\int\limits_0^x p_e u_e r_0^{2j} \, \mathrm{d}x\right]^{\frac{1}{2}}} (i_t - i_w) \qquad (2.4.7)$$

where R is the gas constant, p the pressure and μ the dynamic viscosity of air. The subscripts e and w refer to the outer edge of the boundary layer and the wall respectively. x is the distance from the stagnation point measured on the surface. In the case of a body of revolution r_0 is the radius of the cross section and $j = 1$, while for a two-dimensional boundary layer (for instance on a wing) $j = 0$. Calculation of q_w requires only the evaluation of an integral in which the quantities p_e and u_e are known. Because of the conditions at the stagnation point (see footnote § on page 20) one obtains there:

$$q_{w,s} = 0\cdot50 \, \mathrm{Pr}^{-2/3} \sqrt{\left(\frac{\mu_w}{RT_w}\right)} \left[p_s \left(\frac{\mathrm{d}u}{\mathrm{d}x}\right)_s (1+j)\right]^{1/2} (i_t - i_w) \qquad (2.4.8)$$

From Eqs. (2.4.7) and (2.4.8) it follows that:

$$\frac{q_w}{q_{w,s}} = \frac{p_e u_e r_0^j}{\left[2p_s \left(\frac{\mathrm{d}u}{\mathrm{d}x}\right)_s (1+j)\int\limits_0^x p_e u_e r_0^{2j} \, \mathrm{d}x\right]^{1/2}} \qquad (2.4.9)$$

In deriving Eq. (2.4.7), the following assumptions have been made: (a) thermo-chemical equilibrium, (b) Le = 1 and (c) $\rho\mu$ constant for all temperatures. It is possible to drop the restrictions (b) and (c) for Eq. (2.4.9), if values without these restrictions are taken for $q_{w,s}$. The results presented in Figs. 2.9 and 2.10 have been obtained with the help of Eq. (2.4.9).

2.5 The influence of bluntness and angle of attack on heat transfer in supersonic flight

It has already been remarked in Section 2.3.2 that the simple heat transfer formulas for the ideal flat plate (with zero pressure gradient along the surface) can be applied approximately to slender wings and to those parts of a body of revolution which do not deviate too much from the cylindrical form. This is so provided that the development of the boundary layer, and in particular the heat flow to the wall, is not much influenced by the pressure gradient which, of course, is present on bodies of finite thickness. The neglect of the pressure gradient along the surface implies that the flow conditions at the outer edge of the boundary layer be constant along the surface. However, they are not always well approximated by the free stream values (these are the conditions of state for the undisturbed air) and the flight speed, for two reasons. An angle of attack and blunting of the leading edge may influence the flow characteristics on the whole wing or body, even if the pressure gradient along the major part of the wing or body is zero. Of course, if the effect of blunting or of angle of attack is small, their influence may be of the same order of magnitude as that of the neglected pressure gradient, but in many cases the angle of attack and the bluntness cannot be neglected.

The shock wave in front of bodies of finite thickness influences the inviscid flow conditions at the surface which—as mentioned earlier—are in most cases assumed equal to those at the outer edge of the boundary layer. If the leading edges or noses are sharp and the shock is attached, the inviscid flow characteristics at the surface are determined by the attached oblique shock and they differ therefore from the undisturbed flow conditions ahead of the body. In order to investigate these differences, a flat plate at an angle of incidence φ_i† and a cone with an included angle at the apex χ_0 were considered. Corrections to the undisturbed flow values have been calculated for the adiabatic wall temperatures and for the heat transfer coefficients in laminar and turbulent flow for undissociated air. The results which can be applied directly to wedges and cones are given in Figs. 2.12, 2.13a and 2.13b.‡ In these $(T_{aw})_\infty$ and T_∞ are

---

† At a negative angle of incidence (suction side of a flat plate) the shock is replaced by an expansion fan, see later on.

‡ When calculating the correction for the heat transfer coefficient h, a representative mean value was assumed for the wall temperature; as such the arithmetic mean of the two values $T_w = T_{aw}$ at a certain Mach number and $T_w = T_{aw}$ at $M = 0.9$ (cruising speed in high speed flight) was chosen (see also Figs. 2.4 and 2.5). The influence of

the adiabatic wall temperature and the static temperature respectively, both for undisturbed flight conditions; P_c is the ratio of the heat transfer

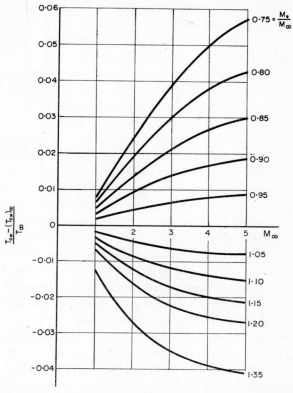

FIG. 2.12. The influence of the local flow Mach number M on the adiabatic wall temperature T_{aw} on wedges and cones. Subscript ∞ refers to undisturbed flow conditions. Turbulent boundary layer with $\eta = 0.90$. Air with $\varkappa = 1.40$. (Approximately also valid for slender bodies and wings of arbitrary form.)

coefficients for local and undisturbed flight conditions. For slender wings and bodies with a sharp leading edge or point, respectively, these corrections would apply only to the wedge-like or conical front part.

If the wing or body is blunted, the shock wave is detached and ahead of the stagnation region it is directed normal to the flow. For inviscid and symmetric flow, the conditions at the surface of the body are now influenced by the fact that the surface stream line ahead of the body passes through the normal part of the shock wave (see Fig. 2.1).

the choice of T_w on the heat transfer ratio P_c is only moderate for turbulent and unimportant for laminar boundary layers.

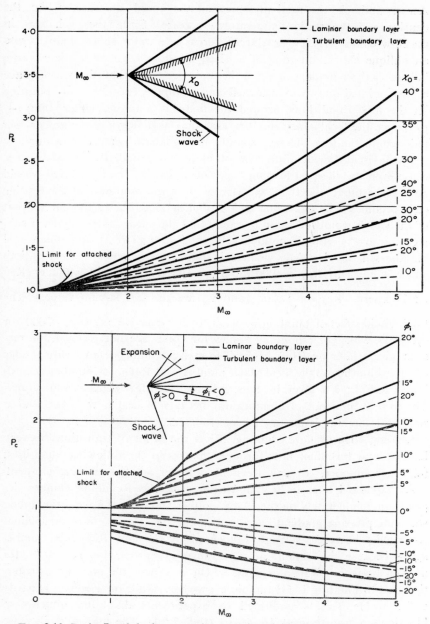

FIG. 2.13. Ratio P_c of the heat transfer coefficient for local and for undisturbed flow conditions in laminar and turbulent boundary layers on cones with included angle χ_0 (above), and on flat plates with an angle of incidence φ_i (below). $\varphi_i > 0$ pressure side, $\varphi_i < 0$ expansion side. Air with $\varkappa = 1\cdot40$.

Across a shock, the total pressure and the speed decrease, while the density and the static temperature increase. Since these changes in the flow characteristics are larger across a normal shock than across an oblique shock, blunting of a sharp leading edge or a sharp nose influences the boundary layer on the body provided that the shock wave at the pointed body was attached and oblique. The effect of blunting on the flow conditions around the body is — among other things — to reduce the local Mach number and the local Reynolds number per unit length, and to increase slightly the adiabatic wall temperature.

For inviscid flow, an influence of bluntness would always occur, because even the sharpest leading edge which can be manufactured would have some bluntness. If in real viscous flow the bluntness of the leading edge becomes very small, the region of shear flow due to the curved part of the shock would be small in extent and the shear layer may then submerge into the viscous boundary layer. Hence there is no influence of bluntness, if its size d (as defined in Fig. 2.14) is below a certain limit which is given by $Re_d \leqslant 6000$ for cones and $Re_d \leqslant 80$ for cylinders (Ref. 2.5.1) where $Re_d = \dfrac{u_\infty d}{\nu_\infty}$ (u_∞ and ν_∞ are the free stream values). The full inviscid effect of blunting appears to be effective at $Re_d \geqslant 3000$ for cylinders, while corresponding values for cones are not reached, for reasons given later on (Ref. 2.5.1). The inviscid influence of leading edge or nose blunting on the local Mach number and Reynolds number according to Ref. 2.5.2 is given in Figs. 2.14 and 2.15 for wedges and cones. The overall influence of blunting on the rate of heat flow at the wall is small for laminar boundary layers (Ref. 2.5.2).

Leading edge or nose blunting affects the point of transition between laminar and turbulent flow through changes in the following quantities: (a) Mach number, (b) unit Reynolds number and (c) pressure gradient.

As explained later in Section 2.6 the *transition* Reynolds number depends only moderately on the Mach number and the *unit* Reynolds number, while the pressure gradient has a large influence. The length of the laminar run x_{tr} is, however, strongly influenced by the unit Reynolds number u_e/ν_e, because, by definition, x_{tr} is inversely proportional to u_e/ν_e for a given transition Reynolds number. On a cylinder the pressure distribution due to blunting is favourable everywhere, while on a cone it is partly unfavourable. This is confirmed by experiments about the influence of blunting on transition at $M_\infty = 3 \cdot 1$ (Ref. 2.5.1). The maximum increase in the length of the laminar run due to blunting was found to be 30 per cent for a cone with included angle of 10°, but 200 per cent for a hollow

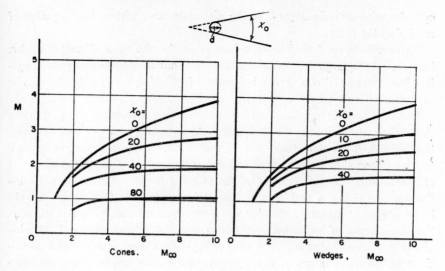

Fig. 2.14.

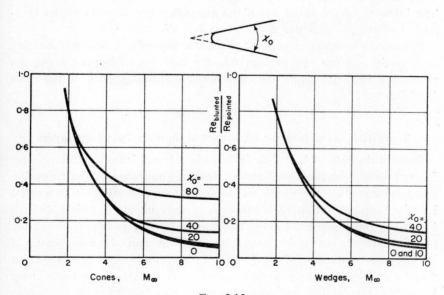

Fig. 2.15.

FIGS. 2.14 and 2.15. Influence of leading edge or nose blunting on the surface Mach number M and the surface Reynolds number of wedges and cones in inviscid flow. χ_0 wedge or cone included angle. Chemically stable air with $\varkappa = 1{\cdot}40$ and an ambient temperature of 218° K (392° R) for the Reynolds number.

cylinder with an axis aligned to the airstream and with a leading edge of semi-circular form.

These effects on transition are important for the rate of heat transfer, because of the large differences between laminar and turbulent heat transfer. But there is also a direct influence of blunting on the heat transfer as discussed previously.

The effect of an angle of attack on the flow around a wing of finite thickness is to increase the strength of the shock wave on one side and to diminish it on the other side. If the leading edge is sharp, the shock on the upper side may be replaced by an expansion fan. If the angle of attack is small, its influence is of the same order of magnitude as the influence of thickness and may therefore be neglected. For comparatively large angles of attack, a slender wing may be replaced by a flat plate at the same angle of incidence and hence Fig. 2.13b may be used. The inviscid flow conditions on each side of this plate are equal to the conditions at the outer edges of the respective boundary layers. The flow conditions on the pressure and suction side follow respectively from the oblique shock and the (Prandtl–Meyer) expansion around a sharp corner. The intensity of the shock or of the expansion corresponds to the inclination of the plate to the undisturbed flow direction.

For slender cones at an angle of attack the flow pattern becomes complex and maxima in the rate of heat transfer have been observed along the stagnation line and along the opposite leeward generatrix of the cone (Ref. 2.5.3).

2.6 Transition from laminar to turbulent flow in boundary layers

Because the rate of heat flow in boundary layers is many times greater for turbulent flow than for laminar flow, a knowledge of the transition point is important for problems of aerodynamic heating of structures. Despite large efforts in both theory and experiment, it is still difficult to predict transition accurately. The reason for this is the large number of parameters upon which transition depends and—in many cases of interest—the difficulty of controlling infinitesimal disturbances, which may be amplified, if the boundary layer flow is unstable, and finally cause transition. The laminar boundary layer becomes unstable to disturbances at a point where the Reynolds number based on a characteristic boundary layer thickness exceeds a certain value, which generally depends on many flow parameters. This point of instability is different from and lies upstream of, the point of transition. If the level of disturbances is low, the distance is large between the instability and the transition point; the latter is, however, important for the heat flow to the wall. In most cases transition does not occur at a fixed point, but spreads over a region which may be considerable in extent. Observations seem to indicate that the instantaneous flow at any point and at any time is either fully laminar or fully turbulent. In the transition region the flow fluctuates between the laminar and turbulent states, turbulent spots originating at random and flowing downstream with the fluid while spreading in size. These turbulent spots coalesce and finally yield a completely turbulent flow. If the flow conditions are kept constant, the probability of finding turbulent flow at a certain point can be found from a sufficient number of instantaneous observations.

The parameters controlling transition in compressible flow can be grouped as follows: (1) Mach number, (2) Unit Reynolds number, (3) Pressure gradient, (4) The heat flow at the wall, (5) The geometry of the leading edge or nose, the angle of attack or sweep and the cross flow, (6) Suction or blowing at the wall, (7) Free stream turbulence, sound and lateral contamination, and (8) The surface roughness. The parameters covered by (1) to (6) refer to the characteristics of the boundary layer flow, the rest to external disturbances. In free flight there is no free stream turbulence—except in particular cases—while sound and surface roughness are always present, at least to some extent. Most experiments have been made in wind tunnels, and despite efforts to avoid external disturbances, some are always present, and they are difficult to identify, particularly if their level is low.

It is, however, desirable for aeronautical applications to know at least roughly the position of the transition point or its most forward and most aft point. Space permits only the presentation of a few results: otherwise the reader is referred to the few survey articles, Refs. 2.6.1, 2.6.2 and 2.6.3, from which most of the extensive literature may be gathered.

In the following figures results are presented for the influence on transition of a number of parameters, taken one at a time. In these experiments particular efforts were made to keep external disturbances at as low a level as possible. The Reynolds number $\mathrm{Re}_{tr} = \dfrac{u_e\, x_{tr}}{\nu_e}$ is used as a transition parameter with x_{tr} as the point at which the flow is turbulent 50 per cent of the time. In Fig. 2.16 wind tunnel results for cones and flat plates are presented; in these experiments the pressure gradient and the rate of heat flow at the wall were zero, and the model was aerodynamically smooth. Further, the turbulence level of the tunnel was low and in some cases it had been verified that its influence was negligible. The noise level was not measured. In flight, higher values of the transition Reynolds number may be obtained, because there the residual noise level

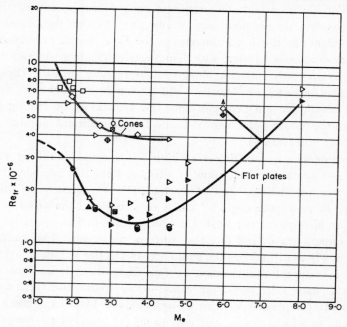

Cones:

   ○ Evvard et al., J.A.S. 1954. 10° cone.
   ▷ Laufer, Marte, J.P.L. Rep. 20—96.
   ◇ Van Driest, Boison, J.A.S. 1957. 10° cone.
   ⬦ Jack, NACA TN 4313, Fig. 15. 18° cone.
   □ Czarnecki, Jackson, NACA TN 4388. 10° cone.
   ⊠ Brinich, Sands, NACA TN 3979. 10° cone.

Flat Plates:

   ○ Coles, J.A.S. 1954.
   □ Brinich and Sands, NACA TN 3979.
   △ O'Donnel, NACA TN 3122.
   ◇ Korkegi, J.A.S. 1956.
   ▷ Potter and Whitfield, AEDC-TR-60-5.
   Open symbols: original data.
   Closed symbols: Corrected for leading edge bluntness effects.

FIG. 2.16. Influence of Mach number on transition Reynolds number as obtained by wind tunnl eexperiments. Zero pressure gradient, zero heat flow at the wall and aerodynamically smooth surfaces.

may be lower. Fig. 2.17 shows how strongly the transition Reynolds number is influenced by the heat flow to the wall while other conditions are the same as above. If the pressure falls in flow direction, a laminar boundary layer is stabilized and it is destabilized for an increasing pressure. Few systematic experiments have been made on the influence of a pressure gradient. On swept or delta wings the transition Reynolds number is

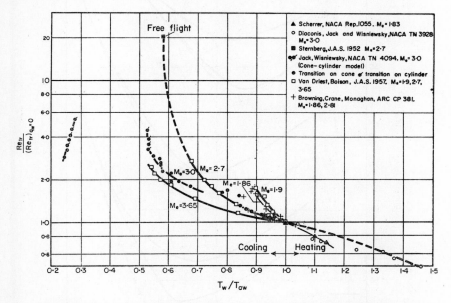

FIG. 2.17. Influence of the surface rate of heat flow on the transition Reynolds number of cones. Zero pressure gradient and aerodynamically smooth surfaces.

reduced by the sweep angle, see Ref. 2.6.4. Another important parameter is the maximum allowable roughness before transition is affected (Ref. 2.6.5 and Fig. 2.18).

Transition can also be caused by "transverse" contamination in a laminar boundary layer with a local disturbance, for instance from an isolated roughness or from a side-wall having a turbulent boundary layer. The latter case may occur on a wing with a laminar boundary layer near the junction to the fuselage. Turbulence from isolated roughness spreads approximately in wedge form with an included angle χ_0 (see Fig. 2.19) and from turbulent side walls it spreads with half this angle or $\chi_0/2$ (see Fig. 2.20). For an isolated roughness of sufficient size placed in a laminar boundary layer at $M = 1\cdot61$, χ_0 is about $12°$ for the fully turbulent core and about $22°$ for the region embracing intermittent turbulence;

for $M = 2 \cdot 0$ corresponding figures are 9° and 16° (Ref. 2.6.6). For transverse contamination from a side wall the angle $\chi_0/2$ for the region embracing intermittent turbulence was 9·5° at low subsonic speed (Ref. 2.6.7), 9° at $M = 1 \cdot 4$ (Ref. 2.6.8), 5° increasing downstream to 7° for a Mach number of 1.76 (Ref. 2.6.10) and 5·5° at $M = 5 \cdot 8$ (Ref. 2.6.9).

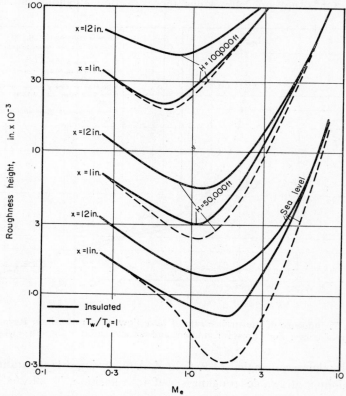

FIG. 2.18. Maximum tolerable roughness not affecting transition on a flat plate ($x = $ distance from leading edge). From Ref. 2.6.5.

In many cases it is important to know the minimum Reynolds number for which turbulent flow can exist. Generally accepted values for incompressible flow on flat plates are $\mathrm{Re}_x = 300,000$ to $500,000$ (with x as the distance from the leading edge). So far, only rough estimates appear to be available for high speed flow, which confirm the values given above (Ref. 2.6.11) even for stagnation point flow. For turbulent flow actually to exist at these low Reynolds numbers, the laminar boundary layer must be subjected to large disturbances which would normally be due to roughness.

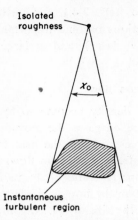

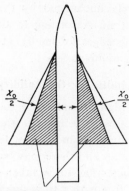

FIG. 2.19. Turbulent contamination from an isolated roughness element.

FIG. 2.20. A fuselage and a highly swept wing as an example where transition by transverse contamination may occur.

2.7 Interaction of boundary layers with external flow

The interaction may be classified (Ref. 2.4.1) as (a) "boundary layer" induced, (b) "shock" induced, and (c) "bluntness" induced. In the first case the boundary layer interacts with an otherwise undisturbed inviscid flow by displacement of the streamlines. In the second case a shock wave is present in the inviscid flow and encounters a boundary layer somewhere downstream of the leading edge. In the third case the pressure and vorticity field developed by a bluntness of the leading edge interacts with the boundary layer. The last case has been discussed in Section 2.5 for a boundary layer small in comparison with the vorticity layer.

Only an interaction of type (a) above and with a laminar boundary layer will be briefly treated here. The parameter characterizing this type of interaction is

$$\chi = \frac{M_\infty^3 \sqrt{C_\infty}}{\sqrt{\mathrm{Re}_{x,\infty}}} \qquad (2.7.1)$$

where $C_\infty = \dfrac{\mu_w}{\mu_\infty} \dfrac{T_\infty}{T_w}$ and $\mathrm{Re}_{x,\infty} = \dfrac{u_\infty x}{\nu_\infty}$. μ and ν are the dynamic and kinematic viscosity respectively, u is the speed, w and ∞ refer to wall and free stream conditions respectively. The interaction is classified as weak if $\chi < 4$ and as strong if $\chi > 4$. For weak interactions the adiabatic wall temperatures and the local heat transfer coefficient remain approximately unchanged by the interaction. See Ref. 2.4.1 for further information. According to Eq. (2.7.1) interactions become important near leading edges (x small), at high altitudes (ν_∞ large) and at large flight Mach numbers.

2.8 Limits for the validity of the continuum flow

At high altitudes the static pressure and density become so low that air ceases to behave as a continuum. In rarefied gases the movement of the individual molecules determines the forces on, and the heat transfer to, bodies and there may be large differences from continuum flow. A new parameter has to be taken into consideration: the ratio of the molecular mean free path λ to a characteristic length L in the flow field. Three flow regions can be distinguished, depending on the size of λ/L: (a) Slip flow (slightly rarefied $\dfrac{\lambda}{L} \approx 0\cdot01$ to $0\cdot1$), (b) transition flow (moderately rarefied $\dfrac{\lambda}{L} \approx 0\cdot1$ to 10) and (c) free molecule flow (highly rarefied $\dfrac{\lambda}{L} > 10$). In the first flow regime continuous viscous effects predominate, and the only important non-continuum effect is a modification of the boundary conditions at the wall: the velocity component parallel to the wall is no longer zero and there is a temperature jump between the gas and the wall. In free molecule flow the impact of isolated molecules on the wall determines the forces and heat transfer according to the kinetic gas theory. The fundamental laws for this type of flow are different from the continuum theory. The transition flow lies between (a) and (c), and both free molecule and continuum flow effects occur.

The importance of the slip boundary correction is, however, small in practice. Under conditions when it would be important, other effects due to a low Reynolds number become more important. The boundary layer becomes relatively thick and its displacement of the stream lines would cause pressure gradients to develop. In addition the region of vorticity behind the shock would become important. For not too low Reynolds numbers, the characteristic length L for the onset of slip flow is equal to the boundary layer thickness δ. For large Mach numbers, both λ and δ differ appreciably at different places on a body. On blunt bodies, ordinary boundary layer equations without slip at the wall have been found to give satisfactory results even for Reynolds numbers as low as a few hundred, Ref. 2.8.1. For more details see Refs. 2.4.1 and 2.8.1, in which an extensive literature on this subject may also be found.

It is of interest in aeronautical applications to know how the molecular mean free path changes with altitude. This relation depends on the season, and whether it is day or night (Ref. 2.8.2). As a rough guide at ambient air conditions on a summer day λ is for the Earth's atmosphere 10^{-7}, 10^{-4}, 10^{-2} and 1 m (3×10^{-7}, 3×10^{-4}, 3×10^{-2} and 3 ft), for respective altitudes of 0, 50, 100 and 150 km (0, 160,000, 320,000 and 480,000 ft). The rate of heat flow is small at altitudes where rarefied gas effects become important. In general these problems are mainly of interest for flight near the outer edge of the Earth's or another planet's atmosphere.

2.9 Heat transfer by forced convection and thermal radiation. Equilibrium temperatures

Heat transfer between the structure and the surroundings can occur not only by convection but also by thermal radiation. The radiative heat losses on the surfaces are:

$$q_{\mathrm{ra}} = \varepsilon \, C_\sigma \, T_w^4 \qquad (2.9.1)$$

where ε is the hemispherical emissivity, C_σ the Boltzmann constant (equal to the radiation constant of a black body, see also Section 3.6). ε is a material constant which is treated more extensively in Section 3.6. The surface also receives heat by irradiation from the surroundings and this contribution may be large in the case of a nuclear explosion. For irradiation, the spectral distribution of the oncoming radiation energy $q_{\mathrm{ir},\lambda}$ must be known. If $\alpha_\lambda(T_w)$ is the absorptivity of the material for a wave length λ at a temperature T_w, the energy received by the surface from irradiation is

$$q_w = \int_0^\infty \alpha_\lambda(T_w) \, q_{\mathrm{ir},\lambda} \mathrm{d}\lambda \qquad (2.9.2)$$

and depends not only on the characteristics of the surface, but also on the spectral distribution of the oncoming radiation. For a grey body† α_λ in Eq. (2.9.2) can be replaced by ε using Kirchhoff's law by which the spectral absorptivity is equal to the spectral emissivity. Radiation from the sun acts approximately as coming from a black body. Irradiation from the natural surroundings on an aircraft surface may be complex, but it is of low intensity and so has little influence on the heat balance. Hence for simplicity this irradiated energy is assumed to be $\varepsilon C_\sigma T_\infty^4$ with T_∞ as the ambient air temperature.

---

† For the definitions of a grey or black body see Section 3.6.

If both heat convection and radiation are important, the equilibrium temperature T_g follows from

$$h(T_{aw} - T_g) = \varepsilon\, C_\sigma\, (T_g^4 - T_\infty^4) \tag{2.9.3}$$

Since h may vary appreciably along the surface of flight structures, the equilibrium temperature T_g would also do so. For a structure at rest on the ground, h would depend only on free convection (see Section 3.5) and the balance must be extended to include also irradiation from the surroundings.

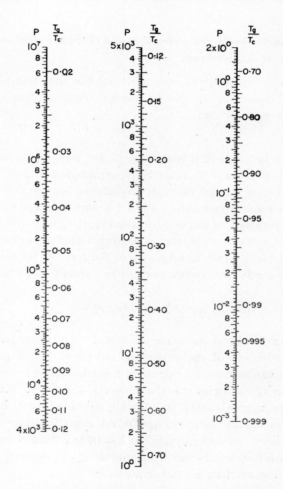

FIG. 2.21. A nomogram for determining equilibrium temperatures of a surface with forced convection and radiative heat transfer.

The solution of Eq. (2.9.3) is facilitated by rewriting it as follows.

$$P\left(\frac{T_g}{T_c}\right)^4 + \frac{T_g}{T_c} - 1 = 0 \tag{2.9.4}$$

with

$$P = \frac{\varepsilon C_\sigma}{h} T_c^3 \tag{2.9.5}$$

and

$$T_c = T_{\mathrm{aw}} + \frac{\varepsilon C_\sigma}{h} T_\infty^4 \tag{2.9.6}$$

A general solution of Eq. (2.9.4) in the form of a nomogram is given in Fig. 2.21.

2.10 On the heat transfer at the surface of high speed vehicles

Because of the difficulty of simulating flight conditions on models of aircraft and missiles in wind tunnels, most experiments are made on flat plates, wings, cones and bodies of revolution. Flight tests on the full scale aircraft or missile are rather to be considered as a final check of earlier temperature predictions. Besides experiments, there are also theories for convective heat transfer on simple bodies, particularly for laminar flow. On the basis of this knowledge the heat transfer on the surfaces of structures can be predicted. It is important to note that at present the accuracy of convective heat transfer measurements on these simple bodies is at best $\pm$ 10 per cent in most cases. A somewhat larger uncertainty is to be expected for aircraft and missiles.

In the following, some general remarks are given concerning the procedure for approximately predicting convective heat transfer on actual structures from data for simple bodies. At sharp leading edges or noses, the local heat transfer coefficient is, at least theoretically, infinite. Hence, after changing the flight speed the equilibrium temperature is attained instantaneously, if the material of the edge or nose is a perfect insulator for heat conduction; for good conducting materials such as metals, it takes a certain although short time before the equilibrium temperature is reached. At rounded leading edges the rate of heat transfer is finite and is given in Section 2.3.3.

Swept wings can be treated as infinite yawed wings (see Sections 2.3.2 and 2.3.4) except at the roots and tips. In the stagnation region, the sweep of the wing has no important influence on the adiabatic wall temperature but reduces the heat transfer coefficient substantially for a sufficiently large sweep angle. On slender wings, heat transfer conditions at some distance from the stagnation region are approximately the same as on a flat plate at the same distance from the leading edge, if measured in the undisturbed flow direction. Thus no difficulties occur at the root of the wing, where the "independence principle" (see Section 2.3.4) for infinite yawed wings would not be applicable. The extent of the laminar run of the boundary layer is apparently reduced by sweeping (see Section 2.6) and thus turbulent flow may be established earlier and then a larger part of the surface would be exposed to the high rates of heating associated with turbulent flow.

On bodies of revolution (fuselages) variations in the diameter are important for the development of laminar boundary layers, but less so for turbulent boundary layers.

Except for flight at very large altitudes the boundary layer on the greater part of the surface of aircraft or missiles can be assumed turbulent; in the stagnation region the flow is almost always laminar. On highly swept wings a large part of the surface may be affected by transverse contamination from a turbulent boundary layer on the fuselage (see Section 2.6).

Whether the rate of heat transfer is largest at the stagnation point or in the turbulent boundary layer region downstream depends on the radius of curvature at the leading edge and on the speed. The formulas of Sections 2.2 to 2.4 are valid for attached boundary layers. If the boundary layer separates, the heat transfer coefficient may decrease considerably (Ref. 2.10.1), while the adiabatic wall temperature does not change much. In practical applications it will often be impossible to predict the heat transfer conditions at all points, so that a more or less arbitrary interpolation will be necessary, and of course this involves inaccuracies.

References

General:

2.1   SCHLICHTING, H., *Boundary Layer Theory*, 4. ed., McGraw-Hill, New York (1960) or an edition in German: SCHLICHTING, H., *Grenzschicht-Theorie*, 3. Auflage, G. Braun, Karlsruhe (1958).

2.2   TRUITT, R. W., *Fundamentals of Aerodynamic Heating*, The Ronald Press, New York (1960).

Individual:

2.1.1 MOORE, F. K., Unsteady laminar boundary-layer flow, NACA TN 2471 (1951).

2.2.1   HILSENRATH, J. *et al.*, *Tables of Thermodynamic and Transport Properties of Air, Argon, Carbon Dioxide, Carbon Monoxide, Hydrogen, Nitrogen, Oxygen and Steam*, Pergamon Press (1960).

2.2.2   FELDMAN, S., Hypersonic gas dynamic charts of equilibrium air, Avco Research Lab., Everett, Mass, Techn. Rep. 40, (1957).

2.2.3   MONAGHAN, R. J., On the behaviour of boundary layers at supersonic speeds, Fifth International Aeronautical Conference, Los Angeles, U.S.A., (1955), see also Inst. Aero. Sci., Preprint 557 (1955).

2.2.4   BECKWITH, I. E., Similar solutions for the compressible boundary layer on a yawed cylinder with transpiration cooling, NACA TN 4345 (1958).

2.2.5   RESHOTKO, E. and BECKWITH, I. E., Compressible laminar boundary layer over a yawed infinite cylinder with heat transfer and arbitrary Prandtl number, NACA Rep. 1379 (1958).

2.3.1   VAN DRIEST, E. R., Investigation of the laminar boundary layer in compressible fluids using the Crocco method, NACA TN 2597 (1952).

2.3.2   SOMMER, C. S. and SHORT, B. J., Free-flight measurements of turbulent-boundary-layer skin friction in the presence of severe aerodynamic heating at Mach numbers from 2·8 to 7·0, NACA TN 3391 (1955).

2.3.3   ASHKENAS, H. and RIDDELL, F. R., Investigation of the turbulent boundary layer on a yawed flat plate, NACA TN 3383 (1955).

2.3.4   BECKWITH, I. E., The effect of gas properties on the heat transfer in stagnation flows, *J. Aero. Sci.* **25**, 8, 533–534 (1958).

2.3.5   FAY, J. A., RIDDELL, F. R. and KEMP, N. H., Stagnation point heat transfer in dissociated air flow, *Jet Prop.* **27**, 6, 672–674 (1957).

2.3.6   FAY, J. A. and RIDDELL, F. R., Theory of stagnation point heat transfer in dissociated air, *J. Aero. Sci.* **25**, 2, 73–85 (1958).

2.3.7   KOROBKIN, I. and GRUENEWALD, K. H., Investigation of local laminar heat transfer on a hemisphere for supersonic Mach numbers at low rates of heat flux, *J. Aero. Sci.* **24**, 3, 188–194 (1957).

2.3.8   BOISON, J. C. and CURTISS, H. A., An experimental investigation of blunt body stagnation point velocity gradient, *A.R.S. J.* **29**, 2, 130–135 (1959).

2.3.9   RESHOTKO, E., Simplified method for estimating compressible laminar heat transfer with pressure gradient, NACA TN 3888 (1956).

2.3.10 ENGLERT, G. W., Estimation of compressible boundary-layer growth over insulated surfaces with pressure gradient, NACA TN 4022 (1957).

2.3.11 LEES, L., Laminar heat transfer over blunt-nosed bodies at hypersonic flight speeds, *Jet Prop.* **26**, 4, 259–269, 274 (1956).

2.3.12 RESHOTKO, E. and TUCKER, M., Approximate calculation of the compressible turbulent boundary layer with heat transfer and arbitrary pressure gradient, NACA TN 4154 (1957).

2.3.13 BARTZ, D. R., An approximate solution of compressible turbulent boundary-layer development and convective heat transfer in convergent–divergent nozzles, *Trans. A.S.M.E.* **77**, 1235–1245 (1955).

2.3.14 BARTZ, D. R., A simple equation for rapid estimation of rocket nozzle convective heat transfer coefficients, *Jet Prop.* **27**, 1, 49–51 (1957).

2.3.15 CHAPMAN, D. and RUBESIN, M., Temperature and velocity profiles in the compressible laminar boundary layer with arbitrary distribution of surface temperature, *J. Aero. Sci.* **16**, 9, 547–565 (1949).

2.3.16 LIGHTHILL, M. J., Contributions to the theory of heat transfer through a laminar boundary layer, *Proc. Roy. Soc.* A **202**. 359–377 (1950).

2.3.17 RUBESIN, M. W., The effect of an arbitrary surface-temperature variation along a flat plate on the convective heat transfer in an incompressible turbulent boundary layer. NACA TN 2345 (1951).

2.3.18 PAPPAS, C. C., Effect on injection of foreign gases on the skin friction and heat transfer of the turbulent boundary layer, IAS Rep., No. 59–78 (1959).

2.3.19 HOWE, J. T. and MERSMAN, W. A., Solutions of the laminar compressible boundary-layer equations with transpiration which are applicable to the stagnation regions of axisymmetric blunt bodies, NASA TN D-12 (1959).

2.3.20 RUBESIN, M. W., An analytical estimation of the effect of transpiration cooling on the heat-transfer and skin-friction characteristics of a compressible, turbulent boundary-layer, NACA TN 3341 (1954).

2.3.21 GREEN, L., JR. and NALL, K. L., Experiments on porous-wall cooling and flow separation control in a supersonic nozzle, IAS Rep., No. 59–38 (1959).

2.3.22 MICKLEY, H. S., ROSS R. C. and SQUYERS, A. L., Heat, mass and momentum transfer for flow over a flat plate with blowing or suction, NACA TN 3208 (1954).

2.4.1   HAYES, W. D. and PROBSTEIN, R. F., *Hypersonic Flow Theory*, Academic Press, New York (1959).

2.4.1a. DORRANCE, W. H., *Viscous hypersonic flow, Theory of reacting and hypersonic boundary layers*, McGraw-Hill, New York (1962).

2.4.2   MONAGHAN, R. J., CRABTREE, L. F. and WOODS, B. A., Features of hypersonic heat transfer, Royal Aircraft Establishment. Technical Memo., No. Aero 607 (1958).

2.4.3   ROSE, P. H., PROBSTEIN, R. F. and ADAMS, MAC C., Turbulent heat transfer through a highly cooled, partially dissociated boundary layer, *J. Aero. Sci.* **25**, 12, 751–760 (1958).

2.4.4   HANSEN, C. F., Approximations for the thermodynamic and transport properties of high-temperature air, NASA TR R-50 (1959).

2.4.5   COHEN, N. B., Boundary-layer similar solutions and correlation equations for laminar heat-transfer distribution in equilibrium air at velocities up to 41,100 feet per second, NASA TR R-118 (1961).

2.5.1   BRINICH, P. F. and SANDS, N., Effect of bluntness on transition for a cone and a hollow cylinder at Mach 3·1, NACA TN 3979 (1957).

2.5.2   MOECKEL, W. E., Some effects of bluntness on boundary-layer transition and heat transfer at supersonic speeds, NACA Rep. 1312 (1958).

2.5.3   BURBANK, P. B. and HODGE, B. L., Distribution of heat transfer on a 10° cone at angles of attack from 0° to 15° for Mach numbers of 2·49 to 4·65 and solution of the heat transfer equation that permits complete machine calculations, NASA MEMO 6-4-59L (1959).

2.6.1   PROBSTEIN, R. F. and LIN, C. C., A study of the transition to turbulence of the laminar boundary layer at supersonic speeds, Instit. of the Aeron. Sciences Preprint No. 596 (1956).

2.6.2   MICHEL, R. Connaissances actuelles sur la transition aux grandes vitesses, *La Recherche Aéronautique*, No. 71, 29–36 (1959).

2.6.3   FANNELÖP, T., Unpublished.

2.6.4   DUNNING, R. W. and ULMANN, E. F., Effects of sweep and angle of attack on boundary-layer transition on wings at Mach number 4·04, NACA TN 3473 (1955).

2.6.5 SMITH, A.M.O. and CLUTTER, D. W., The smallest height of roughness capable of affecting boundary-layer transition, *J. Aero/Space Sci.* **26**, 4, 229–245 (1959).

2.6.6 BRASLOW, A. L., KNOX, E. C. and HORTON, E. A., Effect of distributed three-dimensional roughness and surface cooling on boundary-layer transition and lateral spread of turbulence at supersonic speeds, NASA TN D-53 (1959).

2.6.7 CHARTERS, A. C., JR, Transition between laminar and turbulent flow by transverse contamination, NACA TN 891 (1943).

2.6.8 LIEPMANN, H. W., ROSHKO, A. and DHAWAN, S., On the reflection of shock waves from boundary layers, NACA TN 2334 (1951).

2.6.9 KORKEGI, R. H., Transition studies and skin friction measurements on an insulated flat plate at a Mach number of 5·8, *J. Aero. Sci.* **23**, 2, 97–107 (1956).

2.6.10 MORKOVIN, M. V., On transition experiments at moderate supersonic speeds, *J. Aero. Sci.*, **24**, 7, 480–486 (1957).

2.6.11 VAN DRIEST, E. R., On the aerodynamic heating of blunt bodies, *ZAMP* **IX b**, 233–248 (1958).

2.8.1 SCHAAF, S. F., Recent progress in rarefied gas dynamics research, *Proceedings Sixth Midwestern Conference on Fluid Mechanics*, Texas, (Sept. 1959).

2.8.2 TSIEN, H. S., Superaerodynamics, mechanics of rarefied gases, *J. Aero. Sci.* **13**, 12, 653–664 (1946).

2.10.1 LARSON, H. K., Heat transfer in separated flows, *J. Aero/Space Sci.* **26**, 11 731–738 (1959).

CHAPTER 3

FUNDAMENTAL LAWS FOR HEAT TRANSFER WITHIN STRUCTURES

3.1 Heat conduction in solids

3.1.1 *General*

Heat flow in an isotropic solid is governed by the following differential equation expressed in rectangular Cartesian coordinates (Ref. 3.1.1):

$$\rho c \frac{\partial T}{\partial t} = \frac{\partial}{\partial x}\left(k \frac{\partial T}{\partial x}\right) + \frac{\partial}{\partial y}\left(k \frac{\partial T}{\partial y}\right) + \frac{\partial}{\partial z}\left(k \frac{\partial T}{\partial z}\right) + S \qquad (3.1.1)$$

T is the temperature, t the time, ρ the density, c the specific heat, k the thermal conductivity, S the heat per unit time and unit volume either absorbed or released within the body and x, y, z the distances along the axes of the coordinate system. For most substances the thermal properties of the solid, ρ, c and k, vary with temperature. The temperature in a solid is completely determined by Eq. (3.1.1), if the initial temperature distribution and the conditions at the boundaries are given.

In most problems steady state conditions exist initially. In aeronautical applications this is the case when a structure has been exposed for a sufficiently long time to a constant thermal environment; this may happen when the vehicle is standing on the ground in natural surroundings, or in flight, if the speed and the altitude are constant.

The steady temperatures are uniform if internal heat sources are absent and if the local equilibrium temperature for the external heat transfer does not vary along the surface. On the ground, solar irradiation and internal heat sources are mainly responsible for non-uniform temperature distributions. In flight, the local equilibrium temperatures have only slight to moderate variations along the surfaces of aircraft structures, if thermal radiation is not a very important part of the total external heat transfer. If this is the case and internal heat sources are absent, the steady temperatures are almost uniformly distributed throughout the structure.

The form of the boundary conditions in steady and transient heat flow depends on the mode of heat transfer on the surfaces of the structure.

All three modes: forced convection, free convection and thermal radiation may occur either singly or in any combination, although forced and free convection rarely occur together. Heat can be exchanged (a) between the outer surfaces of a structure and its surroundings, mainly the ambient air, (b) between different parts of the surface of a structure which are at different temperature levels, (c) between the inner surfaces of a structure and parts of the load inside the cavities of this structure, such as fuel, equipment and "payload", and (d) between parts of a structure and an internal flow system. An illustration of possible ways of heat transfer on the surfaces of an airborne structure is given in Fig. 3.1(a). In flight,

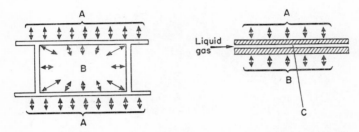

Fig. 3.1(a). Examples of modes of heat transfer possibly occurring on surfaces of structures.

A External heat transfer between the structure and its environment due to (a) compression and friction of the air flowing over the surface of the structure, (b) irradiation from the sun, atomic explosions etc., (c) thermal radiation from the surface of the structure to the ambient space.

B Internal heat transfer by free convection and heat radiation between different parts of the structure, between the structure and gases, liquids or parts of the "payload".

C Heat transfer between the structure and a gas or liquid flowing in channels or passages inside the structure.

external heat input to the structure is caused by heat due to compression and friction of the external air flow, which is transferred to the surface by forced convection. Heat may also be transferred from the hot exhaust gases of jets close to the surface of an aircraft. In the external flow the rates of heat transfer due to free convection are quite negligible in flight compared with those due to forced convection. However, free convection to ambient air is important for a structure standing still on the ground. External heat transfer by radiation may be important both in flight and on the ground. In general the direction of the radiative heat flow is from the hot structure to the ambient air and the thermal input due to aerodynamic heating is thereby alleviated, but the direction is reversed for irradiation from the sun, from nuclear explosions or from nearby hot surfaces. Heat transfer by radiation may even occur between external surfaces facing each other; for instance between parts of the fuselage and the wing (Fig. 3.1(b)). Across cavities inside the structure heat is mainly exchanged by free convection and radiation. In internal

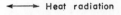

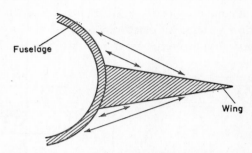

FIG. 3.1(b). Heat transfer by radiation between a fuselage and a wing, if these are at different temperatures.

flow systems heat is transferred by forced convection; such as, for instance, in the fuel system which may even be specially designed to cool the structure. Separate cooling systems have also been proposed for this purpose.

3.1.2 *Simple boundary conditions*

Difficulties in solving Eq. (3.1.1) may arise for certain boundary conditions, particularly when analytical methods are used. The simplest boundary conditions are those for which the temperature or the rate of heat flow is constant in the time and uniformly distributed over the surface. Among these is the important case in which the heat flow is zero at the surface; this can be expressed as

$$\left(\frac{\partial T}{\partial \bar{n}}\right)_w = 0 \tag{3.1.2}$$

The subscript w means surface values and $\bar{n}$ a distance inside the solid body measured from the surface on a straight line normal to it. This boundary condition occurs on a surface thermally insulated against its surroundings. It is also used at a plane of symmetry in cases with symmetrical heat flow when only half the structure or solid need be considered.

Next in increasing order of complexity come the following boundary conditions:

$$T_w = f(x_w, y_w, t) \tag{3.1.3}$$

and

$$q_w = -k\left(\frac{\partial T}{\partial n}\right)_w = g(x_w, y_w, t) \qquad (3.1.4)$$

in which either the temperature T_w or the specific rate of heat flow q_w at the surface of the structure is given. In these equations x_w, y_w are the coordinates of a point on the surface and f, g are given functions of the variables x_w, y_w and t. Although Eqs. (3.1.3) and (3.1.4) do not correspond to the general laws of external heat transfer, they can in certain cases be used as approximations in order to facilitate finding solutions of Eq. (3.1.1).

3.1.3 Boundary conditions for external heat transfer

If heat transfer occurs at the surface of a structure by convection or thermal radiation or both, the general form of the boundary condition is

$$-k\left(\frac{\partial T}{\partial n}\right)_w = g(T_w, T_r, x_w, y_w, t \ldots) \qquad (3.1.5)$$

T_r is a reference temperature of the external medium and the dots indicate possible further parameters of the external heat transfer. One essential difference between the previous boundary condition Eq. (3.1.4) and Eq. (3.1.5) is that the surface temperature T_w now also occurs on the right-hand side of the equation. It is usually possible to choose a reference temperature T_r for the external medium such that the heat flow at the surface vanishes for $T_w = T_r$. Then it is often useful to write Eq. (3.1.5) in the following form

$$-k\left(\frac{\partial T}{\partial n}\right)_w = h(T_w, T_r, x_w, y_w, t \ldots)(T_r - T_w) \qquad (3.1.6)$$

where h is the heat transfer coefficient which in general depends on the same number of variables as the function g in Eq. (3.1.5).

This name for h is rather a misnomer which was introduced at a time when it was not yet realized how many parameters h depended on, and when available methods for solving the differential equation (3.1.1) required constant values of h. The concept of the heat transfer coefficient is indeed most useful if h is either independent of T_w or depends on it only to a moderate degree. If analytical solutions are sought by the usual methods, h must at least be independent of T_w, otherwise the boundary conditions would become non-linear.

Further, analytical solutions become cumbersome or difficult to obtain unless h is constant; hence whenever possible this is assumed and then

Eq. (3.1.6) is simplified to

$$q_w = -k\left(\frac{\partial T}{\partial \bar{n}}\right)_w = h(T_r - T_w) \tag{3.1.7}$$

Therefore the more important modes of external heat transfer may be briefly reviewed with respect to their dependence on the surface temperature T_w. For heat transfer by forced convection, as for instance occurs at the outer surfaces of aircraft in flight, h depends on T_w/T_e, because the material properties of the air depend on temperature (see Chapter 2). T_e is the temperature at the outer edge of the boundary layer. The degree to which h depends on T_w/T_e can be seen in Fig. 2.4 and 2.5 which refer respectively to a laminar and a turbulent boundary layer both with zero pressure gradients and constant wall temperatures. Such conditions prevail approximately on slender wings and bodies at moderate Mach numbers, and at some distance from the leading edges and noses respectively.

Consideration is next given to a boundary condition with heat transfer by free convection; here convection of the fluid is caused by density differences in the presence of gravity or other mass forces. In such cases

$$h \sim (|T_r - T_w|)^a \tag{3.1.8}$$

"a" in this equation denotes a constant which is usually between $1/3$ and $1/4$ (for further details see Section 3.5). If heat transfer by free convection occurs on the boundary of a solid body whose temperature distribution is to be calculated, T_w is unknown at first and an approximation must be assumed for the expression on the right hand side of Eq. (3.1.8). Improved values of T_w can be found by iteration and this procedure converges quickly, because the exponent in the above expression is small.

If radiative heat transfer occurs between the surface of the structure and another radiator at the temperature T_r, Eq. (3.1.5) reads:

$$-k\left(\frac{\partial T}{\partial \bar{n}}\right)_w = C_R(T_r^4 - T_w^4) \tag{3.1.9}$$

C_R is a radiation coefficient depending on the geometry and, in general, also on the temperatures T_r and T_w. This dependence on temperature may, however, be neglected for certain temperature regions (see Section 3.6). It is possible to write Eq. (3.1.9) in the same form as Eq. (3.1.6) with an effective heat transfer coefficient:

$$h_{eff} = C_R T_r^3\left[\left(\frac{T_w}{T_r}\right)^3 + \left(\frac{T_w}{T_r}\right)^2 + \left(\frac{T_w}{T_r}\right) + 1\right] \tag{3.1.10}$$

If a constant mean value can be assumed for the expression within the square brackets, Eq. (3.1.9) can be "linearized", but, except for rough estimates, it is only useful if T_w/T_r does not deviate too much from unity Values for the expression $h_{eff}/C_R T_r^3$ can be found in Fig. 3.2.

If heat transfer by both forced convection and thermal radiation occurs, the boundary condition is of the form

$$-k\left(\frac{\partial T}{\partial n}\right)_w = h(T_{r1}-T_w)+C_R(T_{r2}^4-T_w^4) \qquad (3.1.11)$$

where the reference temperatures T_{r1} and T_{r2} for the two modes of heat transfer are different. Such conditions prevail at the outer surfaces of structures in high speed flight with T_{r1} equal to the adiabatic wall tem-

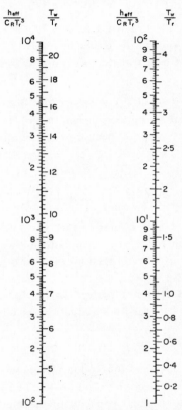

Fig. 3.2. The "effective" heat transfer coefficient h_{eff} in the "linearized" law for radiation as a function of T_w/T_r; T_w surface temperature, T_r temperature of the radiator and C_R radiation coefficient.

perature T_{aw} and T_{r2} equal to the effective radiation temperature of the surroundings, usually assumed for simplicity to be equal to the ambient air temperature T_∞. In some cases T_{r2} and T_∞ may differ considerably, nevertheless this is usually unimportant for the heat transfer because if the contribution of the radiative component in Eq. (3.1.11) is appreciable, then also $T_{r2}^4 \ll T_w^4$ and the exact magnitude of T_{r2} need not be known. In order to "linearize" Eq. (3.1.11) use can be made of the equilibrium temperature T_g, which is obtained by putting the left-hand side of Eq. (3.1.11) equal to zero and solving for $T_w = T_g$. This calculation is facilitated by using Eqs. (2.9.3) to (2.9.6)† and Fig. 2.21. In the "linearized" form Eq. (3.1.11) reads

$$-k\left(\frac{\partial T}{\partial \bar{n}}\right)_w = (h + h_{\text{eff}})(T_g - T_w) \tag{3.1.12}$$

where h_{eff} is given in Eq. (3.1.10), but with T_r in that equation replaced by T_g. Similar expressions can easily be derived for any combinations of the three modes of heat transfer: forced and free convection, and heat radiation.

3.1.4 Boundary conditions at a contact surface between two solids

When two solids are in perfect thermal contact with each other, the temperatures and the rates of heat flow are continuous at the contact surface:

$$(T_1)_w = (T_2)_w \tag{3.1.13}$$

$$-k_1\left(\frac{\partial T_1}{\partial \bar{n}_1}\right)_w = k_2\left(\frac{\partial T_2}{\partial \bar{n}_2}\right)_w \tag{3.1.14}$$

where the subscripts 1 and 2 refer to the two different solids. We extend the previous definition for $\bar{n}$ also to $\bar{n}_1$ and $\bar{n}_2$, which quantities consequently increase in opposite directions and this explains the negative sign in Eq. (3.1.14).

If the thermal contact is not perfect, as for bolted, riveted or certain welded‡ joints, the first of the above equations is replaced by

$$-k_1\left(\frac{\partial T_1}{\partial \bar{n}_1}\right)_w = h_{\text{et}}[(T_2)_w - (T_1)_w] \tag{3.1.15}$$

where h_{et} is the conductance at the interface between the two surfaces. About this quantity see Section 3.7. For Eq. (3.1.15) to be valid, even in transient heat flow, the heat capacity of the medium sandwiched between the two solids must be negligible. This is true in most cases, and particularly if there is only air in the cavities between the two solid surfaces.

---

† In these equations T_{aw}, T_∞ and εC_σ correspond respectively to T_{r1}, T_{r2} and C_R.
‡ Mainly spot and seam welded joints.

3.1.5 *One-dimensional transient heat conduction and its importance for heat transfer in structures*

In many cases the thermal properties of structural materials can be assumed approximately constant and, if internal heat sources are absent, Eq. (3.1.1) yields for linear heat flow

$$\frac{\partial T}{\partial t} = \varkappa \frac{\partial^2 T}{\partial x^2} \qquad (3.1.16)$$

where the diffusivity $\varkappa$ is

$$\varkappa = \frac{k}{\rho c} \qquad (3.1.17)$$

Eq. (3.1.16) can be applied to simple and composite slabs with heat flow directed normal to the surfaces. It is presumed that the heat transfer conditions are constant along the surfaces. The same equation can also be applied to a shell of constant thickness with heat flowing parallel to its

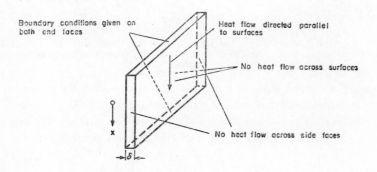

(a) Slab

(b) Shell

Fig. 3.3. Direction of one-dimensional heat flow and boundary conditions in a slab and in a shell without surface heat transfer.

surfaces which are assumed thermally insulated. Then the temperature is constant in the cross-section of the shell. The two cases are illustrated in Fig. 3.3. Shells with external heat transfer are treated later in Section 3.2. Eq. (3.1.16) can even be used in the case of heat flow normal to the

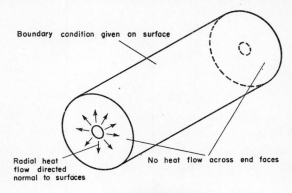

Cylinder

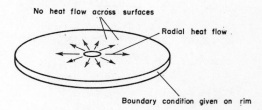

Ring frame

Fig. 3.4. One-dimensional radial heat flow in a cylinder (for instance a thick fuselage) and a plane shell (for instance a ring frame) without surface heat transfer.

surface of a curved shell of cylindrical form provided its radius of curvature is large compared with the thickness of the shell.

The differential equation for one-dimensional radial heat flow in cylindrical and spherical layers is for variable thermal properties:

$$\rho c \frac{\partial T}{\partial t} = \frac{1}{r^j} \frac{\partial}{\partial r} \left(k r^j \frac{\partial T}{\partial r} \right) \tag{3.1.18}$$

r is the radius of curvature, $j = 1$ for a cylindrical and $j = 2$ for a spherical coordinate system. At the centre of a solid cylinder or sphere the temperature must be finite. This property is often expressed in the form: $r = 0$, $r\dfrac{\partial T}{\partial r} = 0$ and used as a boundary condition at $r = 0$. Eq. (3.1.18) can be used to obtain solutions for radial heat flow normal to surfaces, for instance in cylindrical and spherical parts of a fuselage whose thickness is comparable to the radius of curvature. Further, it can be used for radial heat flow parallel to the surfaces of frames of annular form such as those used inside fuselage structures, provided there is no heat flow through the surface of the frame (Fig. 3.4). One-dimensional heat flow in a structure is in many cases a good approximation to the real conditions with two- and three-dimensional heat flow. For instance heat transfer conditions vary along the surfaces of flight structures with the distance from the leading edges or noses, but this variation is often moderate. This is particularly so if the boundary layer at the surface is turbulent and if places are considered which are not too close to the transition point between laminar and turbulent flow. Calculation of the heat flow in the structure is facilitated by the fact that in most cases the component normal to the surface is not greatly influenced by the component parallel to the surface. Hence for the normal component it suffices to assume one-dimensional heat flow with local heat transfer conditions at the surface. However, near a stagnation point or line, heat transfer conditions may vary considerably as is also the case near the transition point.

3.1.6 *Heat conduction with variable thermal properties*

The thermal properties of almost all materials vary with temperature. Depending upon the material, mean values can be used as a good approximation within a certain range of temperature. When the temperature differences in a body or structure become very large, which is often the case when melting or evaporation occurs at the surface, variable thermal properties must be taken into account. The finding of solutions in such cases may be simplified (Ref. 3.1.2) to some degree as follows. Introducing a new variable, instead of the temperature by

$$\Theta_v = \int\limits_0^T \frac{k}{k_0}\,\mathrm{d}T \tag{3.1.19}$$

where k_0 is a fixed reference value, Eq. (3.1.1) can be transformed to

$$\rho c \frac{\partial \Theta_v}{\partial t} = k\left(\frac{\partial^2 \Theta_v}{\partial x^2} + \frac{\partial^2 \Theta_v}{\partial y^2} + \frac{\partial^2 \Theta_v}{\partial z^2} \right) \tag{3.1.20}$$

However, ρ, c and k are still functions of the temperature and Eq. (3.1.20) is non-linear even in Θ_v. For other analytical methods and results see Ref. 3.1.3.

3.2 Heat flow in shells with uniform temperature throughout the thickness

3.2.1 *Plane and quasi-plane shells*

In thin sheet structures the temperature can often be assumed uniform throughout the sheet thickness and the calculations can be simplified. The conditions when this is possible are now investigated. Assuming heat flow to occur parallel and normal to the surface of a plate in the x- and y-direction respectively, the equation of heat conduction for constant thermal properties is according to Eq. (3.1.1):

$$\rho c \frac{\partial T}{\partial t} = k \left(\frac{\partial^2 T}{\partial x^2} + \frac{\partial^2 T}{\partial y^2} \right) \tag{3.2.1}$$

It is assumed that the shell has constant thickness and that the heat transfer at the outer surface $y = 0$ occurs according to Eq. (3.1.7) with a coefficient h and a medium temperature T_f. The boundary condition thus becomes:

$$y = 0; \quad -k \frac{\partial T}{\partial y} = h(T_f - T) \tag{3.2.2}$$

The other surface, at $y = \delta$, is thermally insulated:

$$y = \delta; \quad \frac{\partial T}{\partial y} = 0 \tag{3.2.3}$$

Integrating each term in Eq. (3.2.1) with respect to y from $y=0$ to $y=\delta$ and using Eq. (3.2.2) yields

$$\rho c \delta \frac{\partial \overline{T}}{\partial t} = \delta k \frac{\partial^2 \overline{T}}{\partial x^2} + h(T_f - T_u) \tag{3.2.4}$$

$\overline{T}$ is the mean value of the temperature throughout the thickness of the shell and T_u the temperature at the surface $y=0$. If

$$\left| \frac{T_u - \overline{T}}{T_f - \overline{T}} \right| \ll 1 \tag{3.2.5}$$

Eq. (3.2.4) reduces to an equation for one-dimensional unsteady heat flow with "internal" sources of intensity $h(T_f - \overline{T})$:

$$\rho c \delta \frac{\partial \overline{T}}{\partial t} = \delta k \frac{\partial^2 \overline{T}}{\partial x^2} + h(T_f - \overline{T}) \tag{3.2.6}$$

It is assumed that h and T_f vary appreciably only within distances which are large in comparison with the thickness of the shell, i.e.

$$\left|\frac{\partial h}{\partial x}\right| \ll \frac{h}{\delta} \quad \text{and} \quad \left|\frac{\partial T_f}{\partial x}\right| \ll \left|\frac{T_f - T_i}{\delta}\right| \tag{3.2.7}$$

where T_i is the initial temperature which is assumed constant. Then one need only consider one-dimensional heat flow normal to the surfaces. For thin shells $\mathrm{Bi}_\delta = (h\delta)/k$ is small and hence from Eq. (7.5.3) and (7.5.4) it follows in the present notation (y-coordinate normal to the surfaces) that:

$$\frac{T - T_f}{T_i - T_f} \approx \cos\left\{\left(1 - \frac{y}{\delta}\right)\sqrt{\mathrm{Bi}_\delta}\right\}e^{-\mathrm{Bi}_\delta \tau} \tag{3.2.8}$$

$\overline{T}$ is found by integrating Eq. (3.2.8) with respect to y/δ between the limits 0 and 1, and T_u is found by putting $y=0$ in Eq. (3.2.8). With the help of these values for $\overline{T}$ and T_u Eq. (3.2.5) can be written in the following form

$$\frac{T_u - \overline{T}}{T_f - \overline{T}} \approx \frac{1}{2}\mathrm{Bi}_\delta \ll 1 \tag{3.2.9}$$

This is the condition when the temperatures in shells are uniform throughout the thickness.

For modes of heat transfer which lead to non-linear boundary conditions these estimates are also valid if linearized expressions are used, as for instance in Section 3.1.

In an analogous way the following equation can be obtained for two-dimensional heat flow in a thin shell with uniform temperature throughout the thickness. Rectilinear Cartesian coordinates x and z lying in the mid-plane of the shell are used. The thickness of the shell and the thermal properties of the material may vary. One obtains thus:

$$\rho c \delta \frac{\partial \overline{T}}{\partial t} = \frac{\partial}{\partial x}\left(\delta k \frac{\partial \overline{T}}{\partial x}\right) + \frac{\partial}{\partial z}\left(\delta k \frac{\partial \overline{T}}{\partial z}\right) + g \tag{3.2.10}$$

g stands for a general form of external heat transfer including not only that by forced convection as above but also other modes. Eq. (3.2.10) is also valid for shells of any form which could be obtained from plane sheets by pure bending without strain. Examples are box type or cylindrical structures, even a conical shell, but in this case a polar coordinate system is more practical. If the thickness δ of the sheet is discontinuous, separate solutions have to be used, each covering a region within which δ is continuous; at the discontinuity the temperature and the rate of heat flow $k\delta\dfrac{\partial T}{\partial n}$ must be continuous ($\bar{n}$ is directed normal to the cross-section at the discontinuity). Solutions would be only approximate within a distance of the order of magnitude $\dfrac{\delta_1+\delta_2}{2}$ from the plane of discontinuity. At the end faces of the sheets any of the boundary conditions discussed before can occur, but in most cases the temperature gradient is zero if conditions are as in Eq. (3.1.7). Further, in metal structures the regions for heat flow may be connected in many ways and new types of boundary conditions arise as for instance where two sheets join to form a T-section (Fig. 3.5). Three separate solutions, one for each of the three arms, are to be

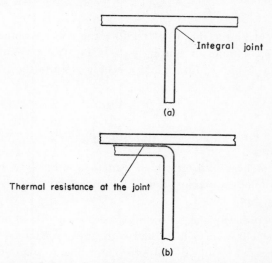

FIG. 3.5. Two metal sheets forming a T-section with (a) an integral joint and (b) a bolted, riveted or welded joint.

sought. If the arms are joined without thermal resistance, then at the junction the three separate solutions must have the same temperature and the amounts of inflowing and outflowing heat must be balanced. Usually one arm is welded, bolted, riveted or bonded to a continuous sheet. There is then a temperature discontinuity across the joint. However, since sheets in such a structure overlap for some distance, heat flow conditions are more complicated and the reader is referred to Ref. 9.13.

3.2.2 Two-dimensional heat flow in shells of revolution

In this section uniform temperature $\bar{T}$ throughout the thickness is assumed. The following equations were obtained in the usual way (see, for instance, Ref. 3.1.1) by considering the heat balance in an infinitely small element of the shell.

For a conical shell of thickness δ with included angle χ_0 at the apex and with $\bar{x}$ as the distance from the apex, one has

$$\rho c \delta \frac{\partial \bar{T}}{\partial t} = \frac{1}{\bar{x}} \frac{\partial}{\partial \bar{x}} \left(\bar{x} \delta k \frac{\partial \bar{T}}{\partial \bar{x}} \right) + \frac{1}{\bar{x}^2 \sin^2 \frac{\chi_0}{2}} \frac{\partial}{\partial \psi} \left(\delta k \frac{\partial \bar{T}}{\partial \psi} \right) + g \quad (3.2.11)$$

ψ is the polar angle in any cross-section (Fig. 3.6). The solutions for the temperature must be periodic in ψ with the period 2π.

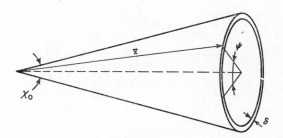

FIG. 3.6. Coordinate system for two-dimensional heat flow in a conical shell.

For an axially symmetric shell one has

$$\rho c \delta \frac{\partial \bar{T}}{\partial t} = \frac{1}{r} \frac{\partial}{\partial \bar{x}} \left(r \delta k \frac{\partial \bar{T}}{\partial \bar{x}} \right) + \frac{1}{r^2} \frac{\partial}{\partial \psi} \left(\delta k \frac{\partial \bar{T}}{\partial \psi} \right) + g \quad (3.2.12)$$

$\bar{x}$ is the distance from the nose measured mid-way between the two surfaces of the shell and r the radius in the cross-section. Again, if the shell is closed, the solutions must be periodic in ψ with the period 2π (Fig. 3.7).

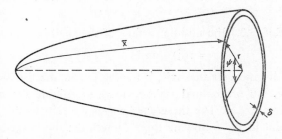

FIG. 3.7. Coordinate system for two-dimensional heat flow in an axially symmetric shell.

For a spherical shell the equation of heat conduction in spherical polar coordinates is

$$\varrho c \delta \frac{\partial \overline{T}}{\partial t} = \frac{1}{r_0^2 \sin \varphi} \frac{\partial}{\partial \varphi} \left(\delta k \sin \varphi \frac{\partial \overline{T}}{\partial \varphi} \right) + \frac{1}{r_0^2 \sin^2 \varphi} \frac{\partial}{\partial \chi} \left(\delta k \frac{\partial \overline{T}}{\partial \chi} \right) + g \quad (3.2.13)$$

where r_0 is the mean radius of the shell, φ the latitude and χ the azimuth (Fig. 3.8).

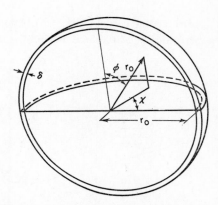

FIG. 3.8. Coordinate system for two-dimensional heat flow in a spherical shell.

3.3 Three-dimensional heat flow in shells of revolution

The temperature throughout the thickness of the shell is now assumed non-uniform, but the shell is still assumed thin, i.e. its thickness is to be small as compared with the radius in the cross-section. The temperature gradients normal to the surfaces of the shell can become large; this may occur for non-metals at all rates of the surface heat flow which are of interest in aeronautics, but for metals it can occur only for severe intensities of heating as for instance during re-entry of vehicles into the Earth's atmosphere.

Following Ref. 3.3.1 the middle surface of the shell is assumed given by

$$z = z(\xi) \quad \text{and} \quad r = r(\xi) \quad (3.3.1)$$

where z is a distance on the axis, r the radius in the cross-section and ξ a parameter. An orthogonal right-handed coordinate system is defined as shown in Fig. 3.9(a). The three axes corresponding to the coordinates ξ, ψ and ζ point in the following three directions: the tangent to the meridian, the tangent to the circle of revolution in the cross-section and the normal to the middle surface.

In order to find the expression for an elemental volume of the shell consider first an infinitely small surface element in the middle surface. This is of rectangular form with the sides $r_\psi d\psi' = rd\psi$ and $gd\xi$ and its

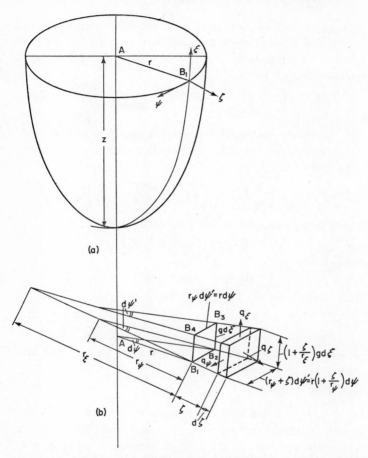

FIG. 3.9. Coordinate system for three-dimensional heat flow in a shell of revolution. (a) Middle surface of the shell, (b) a differential volume element in the shell.

four corners are denoted by B_1, B_2, B_3 and B_4 in Fig. 3.9(b) in which also the angle $d\psi'$ can be seen. r_ψ is the radius of curvature in the middle surface intersecting the ψ–ζ plane and

$$g = \sqrt{\left[\left(\frac{dz}{d\xi}\right)^2 + \left(\frac{dr}{d\xi}\right)^2\right]} \qquad (3.3.2)$$

At a distance ζ from the corners B_1 to B_4 and in a direction normal to the middle surface lies the base of the volume element with the height $d\zeta$. According to Fig. 3.9(b) the sides of the base are $G_1\,d\xi$ and $G_2\,d\psi$ with

$$G_1 = g\left(1 + \frac{\zeta}{r_\xi}\right) \quad \text{and} \quad G_2 = r\left(1 + \frac{\zeta}{r_\psi}\right) \qquad (3.3.3)$$

where r_ξ is the radius of curvature in the middle surface intersecting the ξ–ζ plane. If the sides of the differential volume element are known, the components of heat flow in the coordinate system follow easily (Ref. 3.1.1); in the present case they are

$$q_\xi = -\frac{k}{G_1}\frac{\partial T}{\partial \xi}, \quad q_\psi = -\frac{k}{G_2}\frac{\partial T}{\partial \psi} \quad \text{and} \quad q_\zeta = -k\frac{\partial T}{\partial \zeta} \qquad (3.3.4)$$

Since the coordinate system is orthogonal, the elemental volume of Fig. 3.9(b) is a parallelepiped for which the heat flow balance yields, for constant thermal properties

$$\frac{\partial T}{\partial t} = \frac{\varkappa}{G_1 G_2}\left\{\frac{\partial}{\partial \xi}\left(\frac{G_2}{G_1}\frac{\partial T}{\partial \xi}\right) + \frac{G_1}{G_2}\frac{\partial^2 T}{\partial \psi^2} + \frac{\partial}{\partial \zeta}\left(G_1 G_2 \frac{\partial T}{\partial \zeta}\right)\right\} \qquad (3.3.5)$$

For thin shells as assumed at the beginning of this section

$$\zeta \ll r_\xi \quad \text{and} \quad \zeta \ll r_\psi \qquad (3.3.6)$$

and consequently

$$G_1 \approx g \quad \text{and} \quad G_2 \approx r. \qquad (3.3.7)$$

With these simplifications Eq. (3.3.5) becomes

$$\frac{\partial T}{\partial t} = \varkappa\left\{\frac{1}{gr}\frac{\partial}{\partial \xi}\left(\frac{r}{g}\frac{\partial T}{\partial \xi}\right) + \frac{\partial^2 T}{r^2 \partial \psi^2} + \frac{\partial^2 T}{\partial \zeta^2}\right\} \qquad (3.3.8)$$

where r and g are functions of ξ according to Eqs. (3.3.1) and (3.3.2).

3.4 Ablation

If the surface of a solid or a structure is subjected to severe rates of aerodynamic heating, the melting or evaporation temperature of the material may be reached. In the case of melting, a liquid layer is formed at the surface and the liquid material is swept away by the aerodynamic forces acting on the surface. In the case of sublimation, direct evaporation takes place from the solid into the gaseous state, by-passing the liquid state. The whole process of ablation involves heat transfer in the external air flow, heat flow through the liquid layer of the molten material (in the case of melting ablation) and heat flow into the solid. In this section the fundamental equations of ablation are given except those for the external heat transfer which are complicated and outside the scope of this monograph.

In the following treatment† we assume a coordinate system fixed relative to the solid (see Figs. 3.10 and 3.11). We consider only ablation of short duration, so that the ablated layer is thin, i.e. it is small in com-

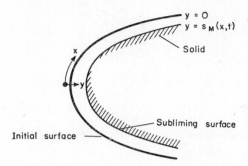

FIG. 3.10. Schema for subliming ablation.

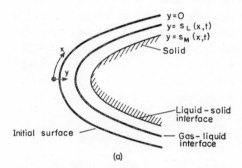

FIG. 3.11(a). Schema for melting ablation.

parison to the distance along the surface and the radius of curvature of the body. Then a rectangular coordinate system can be used; the initial surface of the body (before the start of ablation) is at $y = 0$ and x is measured along this surface. y increases in the direction towards the inside of the solid. All conditions are either the same in planes parallel to the x–y plane for cylindrical bodies or are rotationally symmetric for bodies of revolution. Because a thin layer of ablation is assumed, a number of simplifications in the fundamental equations can be made. One is that the interfaces in Figs. 3.10 and 3.11 are inclined at only a small angle to surfaces $y = $ const. Therefore the equations for the liquid layer in melting ablation can be simplified and they become of the same form

---

† Complete fundamental equations for ablation have apparently not yet been published, but extensive treatments are given in Refs. 3.4.1 to 3.4.5.

as for the usual boundary layer equations in fluid flow. In deriving the boundary conditions the normal component of any vector can be replaced by the component of the same vector in the y-direction, if both

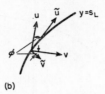

(b)

FIG. 3.11 (b). Velocity components at the surface.

the x- and the y-component of the vector are of the same order of magnitude. Inside the solid the heat is assumed to penetrate only to a small depth, and the curvature of the body can then be neglected approximately in calculating the heat flow there, and the rectangular coordinate system introduced above can also be used inside the solid. Otherwise the right-hand side of Eq. (3.4.2) must be replaced by an expression for div (k grad T) in a suitable coordinate system. In the following equations a homogeneous solid is assumed with well defined melting and evaporation temperatures. If sublimation occurs, material is lost at the surface of the solid by evaporation and the surface at $y = s_M (x, t)$ moves towards the inside of the body (see Fig. 3.10). If heat radiation is neglected, the boundary conditions at the surface are

$$q_w(x, t) = - k_M \frac{\partial T_M}{\partial y} + \rho_M S_E \frac{\partial s_M}{\partial t}$$ (3.4.1a)

$$T(s_M) = T_M(s_M) = T_E$$ (3.4.1b)

$q_w(x, t)$ is the rate of the external heat flow directed towards the surface of the solid; it is, incidentally, much influenced by the rate of evaporation. k and ρ are the heat conductivity and density respectively. S_E is the latent heat of evaporation and T_E the evaporation temperature. Quantities without large-letter subscripts refer to the external air and those with the subscript M to the solid. Inside the solid the equation of heat conduction in the present notation is,

$$\rho_M c_M \frac{\partial T_M}{\partial t} = \frac{\partial}{\partial y} \left(k_M \frac{\partial T_M}{\partial y} \right)$$ (3.4.2)

c_M is the specific heat of the solid. If the solid is not homogeneous and if it is composed of substances with different evaporation temperatures, the substance with the lowest evaporation temperature may evaporate inside the solid. The vapour produced may then pass through cracks to the surface of the solid and from there diffuse into the gas. In this case the surface temperature may be higher than the evaporation temperature of the most volatile substance, and the above equations may have to be modified, but this is not considered here.

When the body melts at the surface, a liquid layer is formed there. The gas–liquid interface is assumed at $y = s_L(x, t)$ and the liquid–solid interface at $y = s_M(x, t)$. As mentioned above, the thickness of the liquid layer is small as compared with its extent parallel to the surface of the solid; hence the motion and the heat flow in the liquid layer are governed by the usual boundary layer equations. Since in many cases the acceleration terms in the flow of liquids are not negligible, the boundary layer equations are given here for the transient state. The equation of motion for laminar flow and that of continuity are

$$\rho_L \frac{\partial u_L}{\partial t} + \rho_L u_L \frac{\partial u_L}{\partial x} + \rho_L v_L \frac{\partial u_L}{\partial y} = -\frac{dp}{dx} + a_g \rho_L + \frac{\partial}{\partial y}\left(\mu_L \frac{\partial u_L}{\partial y}\right) \quad (3.4.3)$$

$$\frac{\partial}{\partial x}(\rho_L u_L r_0) + \frac{\partial}{\partial y}(\rho_L v_L r_0) = 0 \quad (3.4.4)$$

u and v are the velocities of the liquid parallel and normal to the surface, p the pressure in the liquid, μ the viscosity, r_0 the radius of curvature in the cross-section in the case of a body of revolution ($r_0 = $ constant in the case of cylindrical bodies), a_g is a mass force, for instance due to acceleration or deceleration; the subscript L refers to the liquid layer. If the forces of surface tension in the liquid are negligible, the pressure inside the liquid layer is the same as that on the gas–liquid interface (Ref 3.4.4). The temperature distribution in the liquid layer is determined by

$$\rho_L c_{p,L} \frac{\partial T_L}{\partial t} + \rho_L c_{p,L} u_L \frac{\partial T_L}{\partial x} + \rho_L c_{p,L} v_L \frac{\partial T_L}{\partial y} =$$

$$= \frac{\partial}{\partial y}\left(k_L \frac{\partial T_L}{\partial y}\right) + u_L \frac{dp}{dx} + \mu_L \left(\frac{\partial u_L}{\partial y}\right)^2 \quad (3.4.5)$$

where $c_{p,L}$ is the specific heat of the liquid at constant pressure. The last two terms on the right-hand side of Eq. (3.4.5) are due to the heat developed by compression and by friction; both terms are negligible in most cases.

When deriving the boundary conditions at the interfaces, use is made of the fact that the inclination of the interfaces is small under the assumptions made earlier in this section. Hence velocities and shear forces parallel to the interfaces can be replaced by corresponding quantities in the

x-direction. Similarly, the heat flow component normal to interfaces can be replaced by that in the y-direction. However, the velocity components normal to interfaces in boundary layers are small as compared with the longitudinal component; therefore at interfaces the normal component of the velocity is in general not equal to the component in the y-direction. If $\tilde{u}$ and $\tilde{v}$ denote the velocity components parallel and normal to an interface and u and v are the components of the same velocity in the x- and y-directions (see Fig. 3.11(b)), there exists the relation

$$\left.\begin{aligned} \tilde{u} &= u \cos \varphi + v \sin \varphi \approx u \\ \tilde{v} &= -u \sin \varphi + v \cos \varphi \approx -u \frac{\partial s_L}{\partial x} + v \end{aligned}\right\} \qquad (3.4.6)$$

where the approximate expressions on the right-hand side of Eq. (3.4.6) follow from the assumptions of a thin ablation layer: $\frac{\partial s_L}{\partial x} \approx \varphi \ll 1$. At the gas–liquid interface the velocity relative to the interface and in a direction normal to it is $\tilde{v} - \frac{\partial s_L}{\partial x}$ on the gas side and $\tilde{v}_L - \frac{\partial s_L}{\partial t}$ on the liquid side. The continuity of mass flow normal to the interface requires that

$$\rho\left(\tilde{v} - \frac{\partial s_L}{\partial t}\right) = \rho_L\left(\tilde{v}_L - \frac{\partial s_L}{\partial t}\right). \qquad (3.4.7)$$

With the help of Eq. (3.4.6) the Eq. (3.4.8c) below is obtained. The other boundary conditions at the gas–liquid interface follow from the non–slip condition at the surface (Eq. 3.4.8a) and the equality of the shear stress on both sides of the interface (Eq. 3.4.8b). Summarizing, we have at the gas–liquid interface, $y = s_L(x, t)$, the following boundary conditions for the fluid field:

$$u = u_L \qquad (3.4.8a)$$

$$\mu \frac{\partial u}{\partial y} = \mu_L \frac{\partial u_L}{\partial y} \qquad (3.4.8b)$$

$$\rho\left(v - u \frac{\partial s_L}{\partial x} - \frac{\partial s_L}{\partial t}\right) = \rho_L\left(v_L - u_L \frac{\partial s_L}{\partial x} - \frac{\partial s_L}{\partial t}\right) \qquad (3.4.8c)$$

If the surface tension in the liquid layer can be neglected, no additional boundary condition for continuity in the normal stresses is necessary. From the continuity of heat flow and the condition for evaporation at $y = s_L(x, t)$ the following equations are obtained,

$$q_w(x, t) = -k_L \frac{\partial T_L}{\partial y} + \rho_L S_E \frac{\partial s_L}{\partial t} \qquad (3.4.9a)$$

$$T = T_L = T_E \tag{3.4.9b}$$

where S_E and T_E are the latent heat and the temperature of evaporation respectively.

By observing that the coordinate system is fixed relative to the solid, we obtain the following flow quantities at the solid–liquid interface

$$u_L = 0 \tag{3.4.10a}$$

$$\rho_L \left(v_L - \frac{\partial s_M}{\partial t} \right) = -\rho_M \frac{\partial s_M}{\partial t} \tag{3.4.10b}$$

The boundary condition for the temperature field is analogous to Eq. (3.4.9a):

$$-k_L \frac{\partial T_L}{\partial y} = -k_M \frac{\partial T_M}{\partial y} + \rho_L S_P \frac{\partial s_M}{\partial t} \tag{3.4.11a}$$

$$T_L = T_M = T_P \tag{3.4.11b}$$

where S_P and T_P are the latent heat of fusion and the melting temperature respectively.

Inside the solid the equation of heat conduction is given by Eq. (3.4.2). If the penetration depth is small, the solid can be assumed infinite and the boundary condition at $y \to \infty$ is:

$$T_M = T_i \tag{3.4.12}$$

where T_i is the initial temperature in the solid; T_i is assumed uniform.

For melting and evaporation one has to add the boundary layer equations for the external air flow, including in general also the diffusion equation for the gases developed by the ablated material. Thus a large number of equations are obtained and simplifications are therefore desirable. The speed of the molten layer is usually small in comparison to the speed of air inside the boundary layer. Hence it is possible to put $u = 0$ at the gas–liquid interface when calculating the external boundary layer. In some cases it suffices to assume steady state conditions in the external boundary layer and in the boundary layer of the molten liquid; hence one may put $\frac{\partial}{\partial t} = 0$ in Eqs. (3.4.3) and (3.4.5). When treating melting abla-

tion, evaporation can often be neglected at the liquid–gas interface and then the left-hand side of Eq. (3.4.8c) is zero. Thus for a number of cases the above system of equations can be considerably simplified. On the other hand there are cases in which some of the assumptions made in deriving the above equations are not valid; for instance, when the solid

is a mixture of substances with different melting and eavporation temperatures, or if there is no well defined melting temperature as in the case
of glass.

3.5 Heat transfer by free convection

3.5.1 *General*

If the density of a fluid varies with temperature and body forces exist,
a fluid flow can be maintained by buoyancy forces, provided that the
density differences are sufficiently large. Centrifugal and gravitational
forces are the most important body forces; only the latter type are treated
here. In a steady state the temperature differences causing free convection
are constant; they are given either between a wall and the undisturbed
fluid, or between different parts of the surface of an enclosure. From
dimensional analysis it follows that both the fluid flow and the heat flow
are determined by two non-dimensional quantities: the Grashof number
Gr and the Prandtl number Pr which are defined by

$$\mathrm{Gr}_L = \frac{gL^3\beta_f|T_1-T_2|}{\nu_f^2} \left.\begin{array}{c} \\ \\ \\ \end{array}\right\}$$

$$\mathrm{Pr} = \frac{\mu_f c_{pf}}{k_f}$$

(3.5.1a)

The heat transfer coefficient h is usually given in the non-dimensional
form

$$\mathrm{Nu}_L = (hL)/k_f \qquad (3.5.1b)$$

L is a characteristic length, k the thermal conductivity, g the gravity acceleration, β the coefficient of volume expansion, T_1 and T_2 two temperatures characteristic of the buoyancy forces in free convection flow,
ν the kinematic viscosity, and the subscript f refers to the fluid. In Nu,
k as used in this section refers to the thermal conductivity of the fluid,
as distinct from the sections on heat flow in solids where k refers to the
solid. The product Gr · Pr is called the·Rayleigh number Ra. If the distribution of the heat transfer coefficient is non-uniform, differences between local and mean values are in general not large. The latter quantity
is in most cases given here.

3.5.2 *Horizontal layers between parallel walls*

Suppose a horizontal layer of thickness d to be contained between
parallel walls of which the lower is heated and at a temperature T_1, while

the upper is cooled and at a temperature T_2. If the temperature difference between the two walls is sufficiently small, only heat transfer by conduction is important. This is the case, if the Rayleigh number

$$\mathrm{Ra} = \frac{g\beta_f |T_1 - T_2| d^3}{\nu_f \chi_f} \tag{3.5.2}$$

is less than 1700. If it is larger, free convection becomes important for the heat transfer. Up to a Rayleigh number of 40,000 the free convection flow is laminar and occurs in the form of regular cells. This form of movement has already been treated by Rayleigh (Ref. 3.5.1). For $\mathrm{Ra}_d > 40{,}000$ the flow is turbulent, but the transition from laminar to turbulent flow is not accompanied by a sudden increase in the rate of heat transfer as is the case in forced convection flow.

Graaf and Held (Ref. 3.5.2) obtained the following correlation of the results of their own experiments in air ($\mathrm{Pr} = 0\cdot71$) as well as those of Mull and Reiher (Ref. 3.5.3):

$$\left.\begin{array}{ll} \mathrm{Nu}_d = 1 \ldots \ldots & \mathrm{Gr}_d < 2\times10^3 \\ \mathrm{Nu}_d = 0\cdot0507\,\mathrm{Gr}_d^{0\cdot40} & 2\times10^3 < \mathrm{Gr}_d < 5\times10^4 \\ \mathrm{Nu}_d \approx 3\cdot8 \ldots\ldots\ldots & 5\times10^4 < \mathrm{Gr}_d < 2\times10^5 \\ \mathrm{Nu}_d = 0\cdot0426\,\mathrm{Gr}_d^{0\cdot37} & 2\times10^5 < \mathrm{Gr}_d \end{array}\right\} \tag{3.5.3}$$

In these equations all fluid properties are taken at the mean temperature $T_{\mathrm{mean}} = 1/2\,(T_1 + T_2)$. Hence for a gas such as air $\beta = 1/T_{\mathrm{mean}}$.

If the upper wall is heated and the lower cooled, stable layers are obtained; then heat is transferred mainly by conduction in the case of liquids and by both conduction and thermal radiation in the case of gases.

3.5.3 *Vertical and inclined layers between parallel walls*

Consider first vertical layers between parallel walls at different temperatures. Again, Graaf and Held's measurements (Ref. 3.5.2) and the earlier measurements of Mull and Reiher can be correlated by the following equations† valid, for air:

$$\left.\begin{array}{ll} \mathrm{Nu}_d = 1 \ldots \ldots & \mathrm{Gr}_d < 7\times10^3 \\ \mathrm{Nu}_d = 0\cdot0384\,\mathrm{Gr}_d^{0\cdot37} & 7\times10^3 < \mathrm{Gr}_d < 1\times10^5 \\ \mathrm{Nu}_d \approx 2\cdot8 \ldots\ldots & 1\times10^5 < \mathrm{Gr}_d < 2\times10^5 \\ \mathrm{Nu}_d = 0\cdot0317\,\mathrm{Gr}_d^{0\cdot37} & 2\times10^5 < \mathrm{Gr}_d \end{array}\right\} \tag{3.5.4}$$

---

† Compared with Ref. 3.5.2 minor adjustments have been made in the presentation of results.

In these equations there is no dependence of Nu_d on the ratio L/d (L = height of layer, d its width) and this fact is in contradiction to the work of other authors who found Nu to be proportional to $(L/d)^{-l}$ with l being about $\dfrac{1}{9}$. The influence of L/d on Nu is, however, so small that it lies almost within the scatter of experimental values.

Next consider air layers between parallel walls inclined at an angle φ_i to the horizontal. The following results are also due to Graaf and Held (Ref. 3.5.2): If the flow is laminar ($Gr < 5 \times 10^4$) heat transfer and fluid flow are the same as for horizontal layers if $0° \leqslant \varphi_i \leqslant 20°$, and the same as for vertical layers if $70° \leqslant \varphi_i \leqslant 90°$. Linear interpolation between the values for horizontal and vertical layers can be made for angles of φ_i lying between 20° and 70°

$$Nu_{d,\varphi_i} = Nu_{d,0°} + (Nu_{d,90°} - Nu_{d,0°})\frac{\varphi_i - 20}{50} \tag{3.5.5}$$

For turbulent flow ($Gr_d > 10^5$) one obtains:

$$Nu_{d,\varphi_i} = Nu_{d,0°} + (Nu_{d,90°} - Nu_{d,0°})\frac{\varphi_i}{90} \tag{3.5.6}$$

Cylindrical layers were investigated by Beckmann (Ref. 3.5.4); in his experiments only the inner cylinder was heated.

3.5.4 Heat transfer from plates and from the outer surfaces of cylinders

In this section free convection on plates and cylinders in a (theoretical) unlimited fluid is considered. The free convection flow is now confined to a boundary layer attached to a heated or cooled wall with the speed outside the boundary layer (and on its outer edge) being zero in free convection flow. The results can also be applied approximately to surfaces inside structures, if the thicknesses of the boundary layers remain small as compared with the dimensions of the enclosure. The heat transfer from vertical cylinders is the same as from vertical plates, if the boundary layer thickness is small as compared with the diameter of the cylinder.

The local Nusselt number on plates and cylinders varies with the distance x from the leading edge and the stagnation point respectively and is of the general form

$$Nu_x = C(Gr_x \cdot Pr)^a \tag{3.5.7}$$

From this equation and Eq. (3.5.1) it follows that h is proportional to x^{3a-1}. Because a is between 1/3 and 1/4, h is constant or varies at most as $x^{-1/4}$. Therefore local and mean values differ by a constant factor of at most 4/3. In the following, mean values $\overline{\mathrm{Nu}}$ are given as is customary. From these the local values can easily be found if necessary.

A correlation of experimental values due to McAdams (Ref. 3.3), is given in Fig. 3.12. In the Nusselt and Grashof numbers L is the height of a vertical plate or cylinder and the Nusselt number $\overline{\mathrm{Nu}}_L$ refers to the

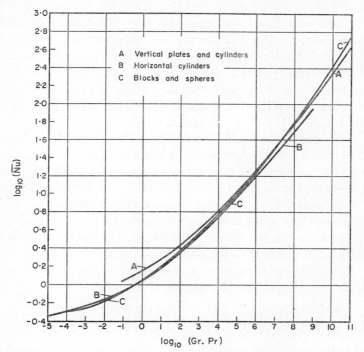

FIG. 3.12. Correlation for free convection around horizontal cylinders, vertical plates and blocks, and spheres according to Ref. 3.1 and 3.3. The characteristic length in $\overline{\mathrm{Nu}}$ and Gr is (a) the length L for vertical planes and cylinders, (b) the diameter D for horizontal cylinders and spheres and (c) the edge length for blocks.

mean values along the length L of the plate. The curve in Fig. 3.12 can be approximated as follows for $\mathrm{Gr}_L \cdot \mathrm{Pr} > 10^4$:

$$\left. \begin{array}{l} \overline{\mathrm{Nu}}_L = 0\cdot59(\mathrm{Gr}_L \cdot \mathrm{Pr})^{1/4} \dots 10^4 < \mathrm{Gr}_L \cdot \mathrm{Pr} < 10^9 \\ \overline{\mathrm{Nu}}_L = 0\cdot13(\mathrm{Gr}_L \cdot \mathrm{Pr})^{1/3} \dots 10^9 < \mathrm{Gr}_L \cdot \mathrm{Pr} < 10^{12} \end{array} \right\} \quad (3.5.8)$$

The first line refers to laminar and the second to turbulent flow.

For horizontal cylinders the characteristic length in the expressions for Nu and Gr is the diameter of the cylinder D. The mean values of the

Nusselt number are (Ref. 3.3):

$$\overline{\mathrm{Nu}}_D = 0{\cdot}4 \ \text{.} \ \ldots \ldots \qquad 0 < \mathrm{Gr}_D \cdot \mathrm{Pr} < 10^{-5} \left.\right\}$$

$$\overline{\mathrm{Nu}}_D = 0{\cdot}525(\mathrm{Gr}_D \cdot \mathrm{Pr})^{1/4} \qquad 10^4 < \mathrm{Gr}_D \cdot \mathrm{Pr} < 10^9 \qquad (3.5.9)$$

$$\overline{\mathrm{Nu}}_D = 0{\cdot}129(\mathrm{Gr}_D \cdot \mathrm{Pr})^{1/3} \qquad 10^9 < \mathrm{Gr}_D \cdot \mathrm{Pr} < 10^{12}$$

Values of $\overline{\mathrm{Nu}}$ in the range $10^{-5} < \mathrm{Gr}_D \cdot \mathrm{Pr} < 10^4$ can be taken from Fig. 3.12. The second and third equations refer to laminar and turbulent flow respectively. In Fig. 3.12 the relations between Nusselt numbers and $\mathrm{Gr} \cdot \mathrm{Pr}$ for horizontal cylinders, spheres and blocks are very similar to those for the vertical plate.

These results can partly be explained by the moderate influence on the heat transfer coefficient h of the gravity acceleration g and the characteristic length in the above formulas.

For horizontal plates the flow pattern is not so well defined and no theories are available. It is obvious that free convection flow exists above a heated plate facing upwards or below a cooled plate facing downwards; this is, however, not the case for heated plates facing downwards or cooled plates facing upwards. In the latter two cases the fluid layer is stable on an infinite plate, but at the ends of a finite plate the heated layers can flow upwards and the cooled layers downwards. The following results for square plates of finite size were given by Fishenden and Saunders (Ref. 3.5.5). For the upper surfaces of heated plates or the lower surfaces of cooled plates one has ($L =$ side length of square):

$$\overline{\mathrm{Nu}}_L = 0{\cdot}54(\mathrm{Gr}_L \cdot \mathrm{Pr})^{1/4} \ \cdots \ \ 10^5 < \mathrm{Gr}_L \cdot \mathrm{Pr} < 2 \times 10^7 \left.\right\}$$
$$\overline{\mathrm{Nu}}_L = 0{\cdot}14(\mathrm{Gr}_L \cdot \mathrm{Pr})^{1/3} \ \cdots \ \ 2 \times 10^7 < \mathrm{Gr}_L \cdot \mathrm{Pr} < 3 \times 10^{10} \qquad (3.5.10)$$

For the lower surface of heated plates or the upper surface of cooled plates one has:

$$\overline{\mathrm{Nu}}_L = 0{\cdot}25(\mathrm{Gr}_L \cdot \mathrm{Pr})^{1/4} \ \cdots \ \ 10^5 < \mathrm{Gr}_L \cdot \mathrm{Pr} < 2 \times 10^7 \qquad (3.5.11)$$

In this case no values are given for $\mathrm{Gr}_L \cdot \mathrm{Pr} > 2 \times 10^7$.

3.5.5 *On calculating heat transfer by free convection inside structures*

The results of the preceding sections referred to simple bodies. It was observed that bodies of various shapes differed only by 10 to 15 per cent in the value of the Nusselt number referred to a suitably chosen characteristic length. Apparently, free convection flow is not very sensitive to the form of the body. This fact can be used, of course with due caution, for calculating the heat transfer inside structures, if simplifications and assumptions are made.

A case of practical importance not yet fully investigated experimentally is free convection inside cylinders having a horizontal axis. This corresponds to free convection inside empty fuselages. Because the Nusselt numbers on vertical plates and horizontal cylinders do not differ much when L and D are taken as the characteristic lengths, one may as an approximation use the formulas for the mean value of $\overline{\text{Nu}}$ for either of the two cases. However, locally there may be large differences: During transient heating the heat transfer will be lower at the top of the cylinder (fuselage) and higher at the bottom than the above mean value. At the bottom, heat transfer is probably similar to that on a heated plate facing upwards.

In many cases the conditions for free convection in empty spaces inside structures will be similar to those in horizontal, vertical or inclined layers.

3.6 Heat transfer by thermal radiation†

3.6.1 *Black body radiation*

A black body is defined as one which absorbs all oncoming radiation and reflects none. Suppose a small disc of a black body to be inside an isothermal enclosure at the same temperature as the body. From the second law of thermodynamics it follows that (a) the rate of heat flow received by the black body per unit area must be equal to that emitted and (b) that the thermal conditions must remain unchanged if the body is rotated through any angle. Because of (b) the intensity of heat flow in the enclosure is everywhere the same or, in other words, it is isotropic. Then the specific rate of heat flow emitted from the disc in any direction must be proportional to the parallel projection of the area of the disc on a plane normal to the direction considered. This immediately yields Lambert's cosine law.

$$q'_\sigma = q'_{\sigma,n} \cos \varphi_n \qquad (3.6.1)$$

where, generally,

$$q' = \frac{dq}{d\omega} \qquad (3.6.2)$$

q is the total rate of heat flow radiated from a surface per unit area, q' the fraction of q radiated into a certain direction per solid angle ω (or the radiation intensity), φ_n the angle between the normal to the surface and the direction considered. The subscripts σ and n refer to a black body and the normal component of the radiation intensity respectively. By integrating Eq. (3.6.1) with respect to the solid angle, one obtains

---

† Only heat transfer between opaque bodies is treated in this Section.

a relation between the total rate of heat flow and the normal component of the radiation intensity:

$$q_\sigma = \pi q'_{\sigma,n} \qquad (3.6.3)$$

The relation between the temperature and the rate of heat flow emitted per unit area of a black body is given by a law due to Stefan and Boltzmann:

$$q_\sigma = C_\sigma T^4 \qquad (3.6.4)$$

The spectral distribution of the radiation from a black body is a function of the temperature only. $C_\sigma = 1{\cdot}354 \times 10^{-11} \dfrac{\text{kcal}}{\text{m}^2\text{s}(°\text{K})^4} (= 0{\cdot}1714 \times 10^{-8}$ Btu/[(ft)^{2}h(°R)^4]) is the radiation constant of a black body (Ref. 3.2).

3.6.2 *Grey body radiation*

For a grey body the ratio of the total emitted energy at any temperature to that of a black body is a constant

$$\varepsilon = \frac{q(T)}{q_\sigma(T)} \qquad (3.6.5)$$

and this is valid also for each spectral component of the radiation. Further, Lambert's cosine law is valid. If a small grey disc is placed in an isothermal enclosure instead of the black body as previously, it follows, again from the second law of thermodynamics, that

$$\varepsilon = \alpha \qquad (3.6.6)$$

where α is the ratio of absorbed to incident radiation. From Eqs. (3.6.5) and (3.6.4) it follows that the emitted total rate of heat flow is:

$$q = \varepsilon C_\sigma T^4 \qquad (3.6.7)$$

3.6.3 *Solid body radiation*

The thermal behaviour of real bodies deviates in general from both black and grey radiators. The spectral distribution of the radiation differs from that of a black body; further, relation (3.6.6) is only valid for monochromatic radiation, that is $\varepsilon_\lambda = \alpha_\lambda$; both quantities ε_λ and α_λ vary with the wave length λ. If α is defined as the ratio of the total absorbed to the total incident radiative energy, α differs in general from ε. Eq. (3.6.7) is still valid, as it stands, for the total emitted energy and ε is called the total emissivity.† It is also often called the "hemispherical" emissivity to distinguish it from the directional emissivity which is

$$\varepsilon'(\varphi_n) = \frac{q'}{q'_\sigma} \qquad (3.6.8)$$

---

† Sometimes it is called the "mean effective" emissivity (mean referring to the wavelength of the radiation).

and is a function of the angle φ_n between the normal to the surface and the direction of radiation. If Lambert's law is valid, ε' is independent of φ_n. Most solids deviate, however, from Lambert's law. For non-metals ε' is approximately constant from $\varphi_n = 0$ to about $60°$ and decreases for larger angles; for metals ε' is approximately constant from $\varphi = 0$ to $40°$ and increases at larger angles φ_n. In Table 3.1 the total "normal" emissivity (i.e. the emissivity in a direction normal to the surface of the body) and the total absorptivity for solar radiation are given for some materials of interest in aeronautics. Further information, particularly on spectral emissivity is given in Refs. 3.6.1, 3.6.2 and 3.6.2a.

TABLE 3.1. Total normal emissivity and absorptivity of solar radiation for some structural materials

Material	Ref.	Emissivity		Absorptivity of solar radiation α_n
		Temp. °F	ε_n	
Metals				
Aluminium, polished			0·08	0·10
Aluminium, oxidized			0·18	—
Copper, polished	3.6.2	1000	0·18	0·26
Copper, oxidized			0·18	—
Iron, polished			0·13	0·45
Iron, oxidized			0·78	
Alloys				
24–54 aluminium alloy weathered		100–700	0·33	—
53–50 aluminium alloy weathered		150–700	0·75–0·58	—
18–8 stainless steel unpolished	3.6.1	350–750	0·21	—
18–8 stainless steel sand blasted, weathered		250–650	0·84	—
J. H. magnesium alloy weathered		150–550	0·57	—
MH–42 magnesium alloy weathered		150–750	0·69–0·42	—
Pigments				
Lampblack			0·97	0·97
White Al_2O_3		750	0·79	0·16
White ZnO	3.6.2		0·91	0·18
White $PbCO_3$			0·71	0·12
Red Fe_2O_3		750	0·70	0·74
Yellow PbO			0·49	0·48

3.6.4 *Heat exchange between black bodies*

The heat exchange between two black bodies is easily found as the difference between the emitted and absorbed rates of heat flow for each body (see Fig. 3.13):

$$d^2 Q_{1-2} = \frac{\cos \varphi_{1n} \cos \varphi_{2n}}{\pi r^2} dA_2 dA_1 C_\sigma (T_2^4 - T_1^4) \ . \tag{3.6.9}$$

$d^2 Q_{1-2}$ is the rate of heat flow gained by body 1.

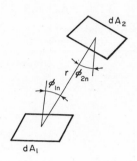

F̧IG. 3.13. Two surface elements in radiative heat exchange.

For simplification a shape factor is introduced:

$$dF_{1-2} = \frac{\cos \varphi_{1n} \cos \varphi_{2n}}{\pi r^2} dA_2 \tag{3.6.10}$$

For the heat transfer between an infinitesimal area dA_1 and a finite area A_2 the shape factor becomes:

$$F_{1-2} = \int_{A_2} \frac{\cos \varphi_{1n} \cos \varphi_{2n}}{\pi r^2} dA_2 \tag{3.6.11}$$

For two finite areas A_1 and A_2 a mean shape factor is defined as:

$$\overline{F}_{1-2} = \frac{1}{A_1} \int_{A_1} F_{1-2} dA_1 \tag{3.6.12}$$

Hence there is the following general relation

$$A_1 \overline{F}_{1-2} = A_2 \overline{F}_{2-1} \tag{3.6.13}$$

For some simple geometrical configurations the shape factors are given in Fig. 3.14, for other cases see Ref. 3.3. In more general cases graphical and experimental methods are available (see, for instance, Ref. 3.2).

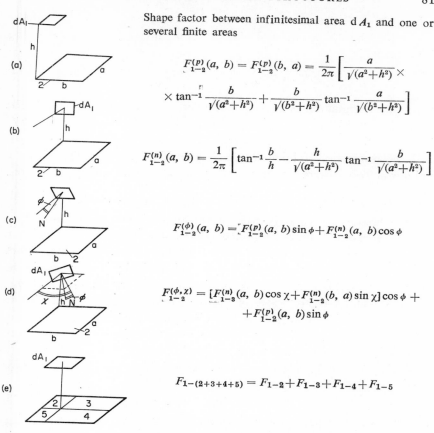

Shape factor between infinitesimal area dA_1 and one or several finite areas

$$F_{1-2}^{(p)}(a,\,b) = F_{1-2}^{(p)}(b,\,a) = \frac{1}{2\pi}\left[\frac{a}{\sqrt{(a^2+h^2)}}\times\right.$$
$$\left.\times\tan^{-1}\frac{b}{\sqrt{(a^2+h^2)}} + \frac{b}{\sqrt{(b^2+h^2)}}\tan^{-1}\frac{a}{\sqrt{(b^2+h^2)}}\right]$$

$$F_{1-2}^{(n)}(a,\,b) = \frac{1}{2\pi}\left[\tan^{-1}\frac{b}{h} - \frac{h}{\sqrt{(a^2+h^2)}}\tan^{-1}\frac{b}{\sqrt{(a^2+h^2)}}\right]$$

$$F_{1-2}^{(\phi)}(a,\,b) = F_{1-2}^{(p)}(a,\,b)\sin\phi + F_{1-2}^{(n)}(a,\,b)\cos\phi$$

$$F_{1-2}^{(\phi,\chi)} = [F_{1-3}^{(n)}(a,\,b)\cos\chi + F_{1-2}^{(n)}(b,\,a)\sin\chi]\cos\phi +$$
$$+ F_{1-2}^{(p)}(a,\,b)\sin\phi$$

$$F_{1-(2+3+4+5)} = F_{1-2}+F_{1-3}+F_{1-4}+F_{1-5}$$

Shape factor between two finite areas

$$\overline{F}_{1-3} = \frac{2}{ab\pi}\left[b\sqrt{(h^2+a^2)}\tan^{-1}\frac{b}{\sqrt{(a^2+h^2)}} + a\sqrt{(b^2+h^2)}\times\right.$$
$$\times\tan^{-1}\frac{a}{\sqrt{(b^2+h^2)}} - bh\tan^{-1}\frac{b}{h} - ah\tan^{-1}\frac{a}{h} - \frac{h^2}{2}\times$$
$$\left.\times\ln\frac{(h^2+a^2+b^2)h^2}{(a^2+h^2)(b^2+h^2)}\right]$$

$$\overline{F}_{2-3} = \frac{1}{\pi}\left[\tan^{-1}\frac{b}{h} + \frac{a}{h}\tan^{-1}\frac{b}{a} - \frac{\sqrt{(a^2+h^2)}}{h}\times\right.$$
$$\times\tan^{-1}\frac{b}{\sqrt{(a^2+h^2)}} + \frac{h}{4b}\ln\frac{(a^2+b^2+h^2)h^2}{(a^2+h^2)(b^2+h^2)} + \frac{a^2}{4bh}\times$$
$$\left.\times\ln\frac{(a^2+b^2+h^2)a^2}{(a^2+b^2)(a^2+h^2)} - \frac{b}{4h}\ln\frac{(a^2+b^2+h^2)b^2}{(a^2+b^2)(h^2+b^2)}\right]$$

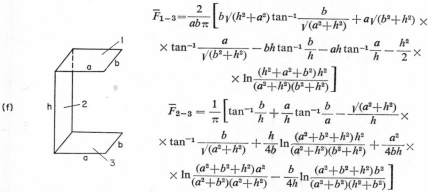

FIG. 3.14(a–f). Shape factors for some simple configurations. ($N =$ direction normal to element dA_1.) From Ref. 3.2 except (d). Misprints in Ref. 3.2 have been corrected.

In order to calculate the heat transfer inside enclosures the surfaces are divided into N elements. The rate of heat flow $Q_{w,k}$ conveyed to the kth element is

$$Q_{w,k} = \sum_j A_k \overline{F}_{k-j} C_\sigma (T_j^4 - T_k^4) \tag{3.6.14}$$

where the summation is to be made over all N elements. Assume that either the rate of heat flow $Q_{w,k}$ (often equal to zero) or the temperature T_k is given at the surfaces of each element. Hence for the N elements a system of N linear equations follows for those quantities $Q_{w,k}$ and T_k^4 which are unknown. This system can be solved by standard calculating procedures.

3.6.5 *Heat exchange in an enclosure consisting of grey walls*

Grey bodies absorb only part of the oncoming radiative heat flow, while the rest is diffusely reflected. Hence the heat transfer between two surface elements cannot be treated independent of the other surface elements as is the case for black bodies. This difficulty is overcome in the following way. First, two new quantities are introduced: $q_{k\leftarrow}$ and $q_{k\rightarrow}$ which are the respective rates of the total radiative heat flow impinging on and leaving the unit area of the kth element. Each of the wall-elements of the enclosure is now assumed to have on its surface a uniform distribution of temperature and the above specific rates of heat flow impinging on and leaving the surface. By definition the rate of heat flow gained by the kth element is

$$q_{w,k} = q_{k\leftarrow} - q_{k\rightarrow} \tag{3.6.15}$$

For the radiative heat flow leaving the surface, one obtains

$$q_{k\rightarrow} = (1 - \varepsilon_k) q_{k\leftarrow} + \varepsilon_k C_\sigma T_k^4 \tag{3.6.16}$$

where the first term is the reflected part of the oncoming heat flow. ε_k is the total emissivity of the surface element k; further, use has been made of Eq. (3.6.6) which is valid for grey bodies. The balance of heat flow at the surface of the kth element yields

$$q_{w,k} = \left(\sum_j F_{k-j} q_{j\rightarrow} \right) - q_{k\rightarrow} \tag{3.6.17}$$

where the first term is the sum of the heat flows impinging on the kth element and the second is the rate of heat flow leaving the same element.

The shape factor was previously defined in connection with black body radiation and since the radiative heat flow from a black surface at uniform temperature is uniformly distributed in all directions, then in Eq. (3.6.14) there is no restriction on the size of an element; it is only required that its temperature be uniform. However for grey surfaces the radiative heat flow leaving the surface of an element is according to Eq. (3.6.16) composed of two parts, the emissive component depending on the temperature only and the reflected component depending on the intensity of the oncoming heat flow, which in turn depends on the geometry of the enclosure. Consequently, elements must in general be small in size as compared to their spacing, if the intensity of the oncoming heat flow is to be uniformly distributed on each element. To be accurate one should replace in Eq. (3.6.17) F_{k-j} by dF_{k-j} (see Eqs. (3.6.10) and (3.6.11)), and the sum by an integral. In an approximate analysis particularly for surfaces whose emissivities are near 1, one uses finite surfaces and replaces F_{k-j} by a mean value $\overline{F}_{k-j}$ as defined by Eq. (3.6.12). For numerical calculations it is useful to note that $\sum_j F_{k-j} = 1$ and $\sum_j \overline{F}_{k-j} = 1$, if in both cases the sum is taken over all N surface elements of the enclosure.

For each element k there are four unknowns $q_{w,k}$, $q_{k\leftarrow}$, $q_{k\rightarrow}$ and T_k^4. One of the first three unknowns may be eliminated immediately with the help of Eq. (3.6.15). There thus remain three unknowns and two equations, (3.6.16) and (3.6.17). A third equation follows from a boundary condition at the walls of the enclosure which yields a relation between $q_{w,k}$ and T_k. In simple cases either the $q_{w,k}$ or the T_k are given and then $2N$ equations result which are linear, provided T_k^4 is treated as one of the unknowns. The solution can be obtained by standard methods or analogues (Ref. 3.6.3).

As a simple illustration of the method consider two parallel plates which are denoted as 1 and 2. The distance between the plates is to be small as compared with their extent. Because there are now only two surface elements, the following relations exist: $q_{w,1} = -q_{w,2}$, $q_{1\leftarrow} = q_{2\rightarrow}$ and $q_{1\rightarrow} = q_{2\leftarrow}$. If these relations are used and Eq. (3.6.16) is written for each of the two surfaces, $k = 1$ and $k = 2$, one obtains:

$$\left. \begin{array}{l} q_{1\rightarrow} = (1-\varepsilon_1)q_{1\leftarrow} + \varepsilon_1 C_\sigma T_1^4 \\ q_{1\leftarrow} = (1-\varepsilon_2)q_{1\rightarrow} + \varepsilon_2 C_\sigma T_2^4 \end{array} \right\} \qquad (3.6.18)$$

Eq. (3.6.18) may easily be solved for $q_{1\rightarrow}$ and $q_{1\leftarrow}$. Using these solutions one obtains from Eq. (3.6.15) the rate of heat flow per unit area of both surfaces:

$$q_{w,1} = -q_{w,2} = \frac{\varepsilon_1 \varepsilon_2 C_\sigma}{\varepsilon_1 + \varepsilon_2 - \varepsilon_1 \varepsilon_2} (T_2^4 - T_1^4) \qquad (3.6.19)$$

Consider one surface completely enclosing a second surface which is not concave. The two surfaces are assumed to be at uniform though different temperatures. In the case of two concentric cylindrical or spherical surfaces the rate of radiative heat flow between the two surfaces is exactly (Ref. 3.1):

$$Q_{w,1} = - Q_{w,2} = \frac{C_\sigma A_1 (T_2^4 - T_1^4)}{\dfrac{1}{\varepsilon_1} + \dfrac{A_1}{A_2}\left(\dfrac{1}{\varepsilon_2} - 1\right)} \qquad (3.6.20)$$

The subscripts 1 and 2 refer to the smaller and larger surface respectively and the large letter Q refers to the total rate of heat flow between the two surfaces. For other geometrical configurations Eq. (3.6.20) is still approximately valid. In some of these cases exact solutions have been found and the results are compared in Ref. 3.1 with those of Eq. (3.6.20). If the area of surface 1 is much smaller than that of surface 2, i.e. $A_2 \gg A_1$, the second term in the denominator vanishes and the rate of heat flow becomes independent of the emissivity and of the area of the enclosure.

3.6.6 *General remarks on heat exchange between solid bodies*

Real solids differ from ideal grey bodies in ways which have been explained in Section 3.6.3. A procedure for real bodies similar to those of the previous section would become very cumbersome and would in many cases perhaps not be worthwhile, because the emissivities and absorptivities are sensitive to surface impurities which in practice are only approximately known. For the same reasons the division into surface elements is often made coarse. To be accurate the preceding equations should be written in differential form, i.e the sums should be replaced by integrals but this would, of course, still further complicate the procedure.

3.7 Thermal conductance across interfaces and joints

3.7.1 *Rigid surfaces*

Heat flow takes place between two plane rigid surfaces in contact with each other mainly by (a) conduction through those parts of the surfaces in direct contact with each other, (b) conduction through the thin gas layer between the surfaces and (c) thermal radiation across the cavity of the interface. The contribution of each mode of heat transfer is determined by (a) the contact pressure, (b) the roughness and the overall flatness of the surfaces, and (c) the temperature level. The contact pressure, the roughness and the overall flatness of the surfaces determine the effective contact area and the thickness of the gas layer between the surfaces. The temperature level of the surfaces has a large influence on the intensity of the radiative heat transfer; it increases with the temperature as follows from Section 3.6.

TABLE 3.2. Thermal conductance across interfaces of clean rigid surfaces in contact; air in the cavities between interfaces

Material	Roughness root mean square μ in.	Ref.	Pressure p.s.i.	Temperature °F	Conductance $\frac{Btu}{(ft)^2 h °F}$	Temperature °F	Conductance $\frac{Btu}{(ft)^2 h °F}$
Aluminium	10–40		7	200	750–1000	450	1000–1300
Aluminium	60–90	3.7.1	7	200	450–650	450	700–900
Stainless steel	20–60		7	200	800–1400	500	1000–1400
Stainless steel	100–120		7	200	250	500	380

Material	Roughness root mean square μ in.	Ref.	Temperature °F	Pressure p.s.i.	Conductance $\frac{Btu}{(ft)^2 h °F}$	Pressure p.s.i.	Conductance $\frac{Btu}{(ft)^2 h °F}$
Aluminium	10		200	7	1400	400	4500
Aluminium	10		400	7	2000	400	8000
Aluminium	120		200	7	300	400	2200
Aluminium	120	3.7.2	400	7	500	400	5000
Stainless steel	30		200	7	1200	400	1800
Stainless steel	30		400	7	1700	400	2400
Stainless steel	100		200	7	380	400	550
Stainless steel	100		400	7	480	400	700
Carbon steel	4		room	ca. 2	3000	300	5000
Carbon steel	1000	3.7.3	room	ca. 2	200–300	200	350–500

TABLE 3.3. Thermal conductance across interfaces of some joints; air in the cavities between interfaces

| Material | Joint | Number of types of rivets | Ref. | Thickness | | Rivet pitch in. | Thermal conductance $\dfrac{\text{Btu}}{(\text{ft})^2 \text{ h } {}^\circ\text{F}}$ | Temperature at interface °F |
				Skin in.	Stringer or second skin in.			
Aluminium	riveted	3	3.7.5	0·06–0·25	0·06–0·37	1·5	150–1300	100–450
Aluminium	riveted	3	3.7.6	0·06–0·5	0·06–0·25	0·75–1·5	250–1000†	100–450
Aluminium	riveted	3	3.7.7	0·02–0·125	0·05–0·125	0·75–1·5	130–2000 / 120–500 ‡	ca. 80
Aluminium	riveted	1	3.7.8	0·08	0·08	0·8–1	200–500 ‡	160
Stainless steel	riveted	1	3.7.8	0·08	0·08	0·5–1	40–70	160
Stainless steel	spot welded		3.7.8	0·08	0·08	—	45	160
Aluminium	riveted	—§	3.7.9	0·16	1·25	1·0	100–1100	300
Aluminium	riveted	1	3.7.9	0·16	1·25	1·0	800 ‖	100
Aluminium	riveted	1	3.7.9	0·16	1·25	1·0	600 ‖	200
Aluminium	riveted	1	3.7.9	0·16	1·25	1·0	400 ‖	400

† Omitting a few values with exceptionally high scatter.
‡ Mean values for each specimen from measurements on about 20 samples.
§ A large number of different types of rivets.
‖ A series of measurements on one specimen to find influence of interface temperature.

The dependence of the interface conductance on the above parameters is not known, nor is a general correlation of the experiments available. From the experimental results given in Table 3.2 and from Ref. 3.7.1 to 3.7.4 the following conclusions can be drawn:

(1) The interface conductance increases with increasing contact pressure. The influence of the contact pressure is larger for light alloys than for steel. The increase of the conductance with the contact pressure is appreciable at low pressure, but becomes smaller at high contact pressures.

(2) The interface conductance increases with increasing temperature levels.

(3) At any pressure level the interface conductance increases as the surface roughness decreases. However, surface roughness is not alone dominant, the overall flatness may be more important. There is less experimental scatter for rough than for smooth surfaces.

(4) A metal foil sandwiched between the plane surfaces of two solids appears to increase the interface conductance, if the metal foil is softer than the material of the solids. If two surfaces are bonded by a layer of a poor conductor, the conductance is practically equal to that of the layer of the bonding material.

(5) The interface conductance has a tendency to increase with time over long periods, other conditions being the same. When the joint is cooled the initial value of the conductance is almost regained.

3.7.2 *Joints in metal sheets*

The results of the previous section are only of limited value for structural joints in thin metal sheets which are riveted, bolted, welded or bonded together. The reasons for this are that the contact pressures are unknown and their local variations are very probably large for joints of the above types. Non-uniformities in the temperature distributions result in non-uniform thermal expansions and these are likely to affect the contact pressures. Complicated paths for the heat flow may also arise owing to the presence of rivets or bolts or to local variations in the thermal contacts in welded joints. However, the thermal conductances for bonded joints are probably the same for metal sheets as for rigid surfaces.

There is considerable scatter in the available results; one reason for this is the large number of parameters determining the interface conductance and another the individual differences in the joints, even when these are made of the same material and have the same dimensions (Refs. 3.7.8, 3.7.9). Variations may occur from one test run to the next, and even during a given test of short duration (Ref. 3.7.5). In order to obtain accurate data for a design it would be necessary to test a large number of samples made under production conditions. Thus mean values as well as maximum and minimum deviations could be found. In most of the known experiments the number of samples for each specimen was low, usually not exceeding six. In analyzing experiments it is therefore difficult to distinguish between the individual scatter in samples of the same specimen and the influence of parameter variations. In Table 3.3 a footnote has been attached to all those values of the interface conductance for which the individual scatter is reduced or eliminated, or when one specimen only was investigated. The values in Table 3.3 are meant to give some information on the order of magnitude only of the interface conductance and its scatter. Results on aluminium joints from different sources agree reasonably well. Further general results from different sources can be summarized as follows:

(1) There is some tendency for the interface conductance to decrease with increasing skin thickness (Ref. 3.7.6).

(2) Joints between hard materials such as stainless steel, Inconel X and 6A1–4V titanium alloy give lower values for the interface conductance than aluminium (Refs. 3.7.8 and 3.7.9).

(3) The type of connection across the joint (rivet, bolt or weld) has an appreciable influence, and values of the interface conductance may vary as much as 10:1 to 25:1. Alloy steel screws, high-shear pins and lockbolts give the highest values, while blind and exploding type rivets give the lowest values with occasional exceptions (Ref. 3.7.9).

(4) In a particular case (see last three values in Table 3.3 a decrease of interface conductance with increasing temperature was observed (Ref. 3.7.9). This is in contrast to experiments for rigid surfaces.

References

Fundamental books on heat transfer:

3.1   JAKOB, M., *Heat Transfer*, Vols. I and II, John Wiley, New York (1949 and 1957).

3.2   ECKERT, E. R. G. and DRAKE JR., R. M., *Heat and Mass Transfer*, McGraw-Hill, New York (1959).

3.3   MCADAMS, W. H., *Heat Transmission*, Third edition, McGraw-Hill, New York (1954).

Individual references:

3.1.1 CARSLAW, H. S. and JAEGER, J. C., *Conduction of Heat in Solids*, Clarendon Press, Oxford, first ed. (1947), second ed. (1959).

3.1.2   EYRES, N. R., HARTREE, D. R., INGHAM, J., JACKSON, R., SARJANT R. J. and
WAGSTAFF, J. B., The calculation of variable heat flow in solids, *Phil. Trans.
Roy. Soc. London* A **240**, 1–57 (1946–1948).

3.1.3   CRANK, J., *The Mathematics of Diffusion*, Clarendon Press, Oxford (1956).

3.3.1   BRULL, M. A. and VINSON, J. R., Approximate three-dimensional solutions
for transient temperature distributions in shells of revolution, *J. Aero/
Space Sci.* **25**, 12, 742–750 (1958).

3.4.1   LANDAU, H. G., Heat conduction in a melting solid, *Quart. Appl. Math.* **8**, 81–94
(1950).

3.4.2   SUTTON, G. W., The hydrodynamics and heat conduction of a melting surface, *J. Aero/Space Sci.* **25**, 1, 29–32, 36 (1958).

3.4.3   LEES, L., Similarity parameters for surface melting of a blunt nosed body in
a high velocity gas stream, *ARS Journal* **29**, 5, 345–354 (1959).

3.4.4   GOODMAN, T. R., Aerodynamic ablation of melting bodies, *Proc. Third. U. S.
Nat. Congress Appl. Mech.*, 735–745 (1958).

3.4.5   ROBERTS, L., A theoretical study of stagnation-point ablation, NASA TR R-9
(1959).

3.5.1   RAYLEIGH, LORD: On convection currents in a horizontal layer of fluid, when
the higher temperature is on the under side, *Phil. Mag.* **32**, 6, 529–546 (1916).

3.5.2   DE GRAAF, J. G. A. and VAN DER HELD, E. F. M., The relation between the heat
transfer and the convection phenomena in enclosed plane air layers, *Appl.
Sci. Res.* A **3**, 6, 393–409 (1953).

3.5.3   MULL, W. and REIHER, H., Der Wärmeschutz von Luftschichten. Seine expe-
rimentelle Bestimmung und graphische Berechnung, *Gesundh. Ing.*, Beiheft 28,
Reihe I, 1–26 (1930).

3.5.4   BECKMANN, W., Die Wärmeübertragung in zylindrischen Grenzschichten bei
natürlicher Konvektion, *Forsch. a. d. Gebiet d. Ingenieurswes.* **2**, 165–178 (1931).

3.5.5   FISHENDEN, M. and SAUNDERS, O. A., *An Introduction to Heat Transfer*, Clarendon, Oxford Press, (1950).

3.6.1   SNYDER, N. W., GIER, J. T. and DUNKLE, R. V., Total normal emissivity measurements on aircraft materials between 100 and 800°F, *Trans. ASME* **77**,
1011–1019 (1955).

3.6.2   SLOTE, L. and MURRAY, W. D., A method of predicting skin, compartment,
and equipment temperatures for aircraft, WADC TR 53–119 (1953).

3.6.2a SINGHAM, J. R., Tables of emissivity of surfaces, *Int. J. Heat Mass Transfer*,
5, 67–76 (1962).

3.6.3   OPPENHEIM, A. K., Radiation analysis by the network method, *Trans. ASME*
78, 4, 725–735 (1956).

3.7.1   BARZELAY, M. E., TONG, K. N. and HOLLO, G., Thermal conductance of contacts in aircraft joints, NACA TN 3167 (1954).

3.7.2   BARZELAY, M. E., TONG, K. N. and HOLLOWAY, G. F., Effect of pressure on
thermal conductance of contact joints, NACA TN 3295 (1955).

3.7.3   BRUNOT, A. W. and BUCKLAND, F. F., Thermal contact resistance of laminated
and machined joints, *Trans. ASME* **71**, 3, 253–257 (1949).

3.7.4   KOUWENHOVEN, W. B. and POTTER, J. H., Thermal resistance of metal contacts, *The Welding Journal* **27**, 10, Supplement 515–520 (1948).

3.7.5   BARZELAY, M. E. and HOLLOWAY, G. F., Effect of an interface on transient
temperature distribution in composite aircraft joints, NACA TN 3824 (1957).

3.7.6   BARZELAY, M. E. and HOLLOWAY, G. F., Interface thermal conductance of twenty-seven riveted aircraft joints, NACA TN 3991 (1957).

3.7.7   COULBERT, C. D. and CHIEN LIU, Thermal resistance of aircraft structure joints, WADC Tech. Note 53–50 (1953).

3.7.8   SCHUH, H., Unpublished.

3.7.9   BARZELAY, M. E., Range of interface thermal conductance for aircraft joints, NASA TN D-426 (1960).

CHAPTER 4

ON METHODS OF CALCULATING TEMPERATURE DISTRIBUTIONS IN STRUCTURES

4.1 General

Temperature distributions in solids are determined by using the equation of heat conduction, which is a partial differential equation of parabolic type in the transient case and of elliptic type in the two- or three-dimensional steady case; together with suitable boundary conditions. There is no doubt that these equations exactly describe the heat flow in solids. Hence, the temperature distributions in solids and in structures can be found as solutions of the differential equations, provided that the boundary conditions and—in the case of transient heat flow—also the initial temperatures are known. Boundaries are interfaces between the solid and a surrounding medium (gas or liquid), or interfaces inside a body between different parts in contact with each other.

In most cases general laws for the external heat transfer are known from experiments and from theory. The heat transfer across interfaces inside bodies can be determined only by experiments. Obviously the most direct way to find the temperature distributions in structures would be to measure the temperatures in the structures themselves when exposed to the real environment. In aeronautics flight, measurements would be needed on a specimen of the design. This procedure is uncertain, because successful flights at the high speeds where aerodynamic heating is important would very likely presume sufficient knowledge about the temperature distribution in the test vehicle already when it is designed. Besides, flight measurements are difficult to make, liable to errors and costly; they should however be made as a final check of the accuracy of the temperature predictions underlying the design.

Hence temperature distributions in structures and solids are best found by an approach using singly or in combination: (a) laboratory experiments, (b) analogues and (c) calculations. In the laboratory it is in general more convenient to determine the external heat transfer separately from the internal heat flow in structures.

One reason for this is that the external heat transfer can be found, with an accuracy sufficient for engineering purposes, from tests made in wind tunnels and using simplified models of small size. The heat flow inside the structure can be simulated by exposing the outer surfaces to suitably controlled heat sources such as radiant heating lamps. Simulation of aerodynamic heating in structures is usually made with a view to experiments on the strength and stiffness of structures at elevated temperatures, because the temperature distribution itself can be found more easily with the help of analogues or by calculations.

Suitable analogues to heat flow exist in mechanics, electricity and other subjects. The same laws are valid for the flow of electricity as for heat, if the electrical currents, potentials and conductivities are assumed as quantities analogous to heat flow, temperatures and thermal conductivities. Therefore thermal quantities can be determined by measuring electrical currents and potentials in an electrical conductor of analogous form and with analogous boundary conditions (see also Section 10). An advantage is that electrical measurements are easier to make and yield more accurate results than thermal measurements.

Lastly, the distribution of heat flow within structures can also be found by calculation, even for complex structures, if high speed calculating machines are used, and at costs which are in general far less than those for corresponding experiments.

In steady heat flow it is fairly obvious which methods are most suitable in a particular case. For one-dimensional heat flow the analytical methods are preferable in all cases with "linear" laws of heat flow and of external heat transfer. In two-dimensional heat flow the analytical method is only suitable for bodies of the simplest geometrical form. In all other cases numerical methods (in particular the relaxation method), or analogues, are commonly used.

In transient heat flow the relative merits of some of the more important methods of calculation are less evident. They are therefore discussed here in general terms. Because the amount of computational work usually increases with the required accuracy, a general paragraph comes first on the accuracy desired for temperature distributions in structures.

It is useful to note that in most cases the temperatures rather than the rates of heat flow are important for structures at elevated temperatures. The accuracy of the final solution depends not only on the errors incurred in solving the equation of heat conduction, but also on the accuracy of the data on external heat transfer and on the thermal properties of the solid. Convective heat transfer is the most important mode of external heat transfer. Of its two parameters the heat transfer coefficient is the least accurate and is at the present state of the art uncertain to about ± 10 per cent, or more, on simple bodies such as flat plates, cones and so on. Somewhat larger errors are to be expected for the surfaces of aircraft. If thermal radiation is important, an uncertainty may arise because the coefficient of emissivity is sensitive to the condition of the surface (cleanness, degree of oxidation, etc.) and may not be known accurately. Among the thermal properties of materials the heat conductivities are the least accurately known, in general not better than to within a few per cent. Hence it would not seem worthwhile to require solutions of the temperatures to an accuracy better than a few per cent, if the amount of computational work becomes large as a result. The accuracy in the temperatures refers to temperature increases above the initial temperature which is usually constant.

4.2 Analytical and semi-analytical methods in transient heat flow

Analytical methods for solving the partial differential equation of heat conduction are well known and are comprehensively presented in the standard book by Carslaw and Jaeger, (Ref. 3.1.1.). These methods, including the method of separation of variables, Laplace or other transforms, and the methods of sources and sinks can be applied only if the equation of heat conduction and the boundary conditions are linear. This is so, if the thermal properties of the solids are independent of temperature and if at the boundaries one of the following quantities is given: (a) the temperature, (b) the rate of heat flow or (c) a linear relation between the temperature and the rate of heat flow at the surface is valid, for instance in heat transfer by forced convection. Analytical solutions can be given in closed form for only the most simple cases; in general they are obtained in the form of series. In many cases these do not converge sufficiently rapidly for the whole range of parameters and it is often necessary to use two different series, of which one converges rapidly for small times and the other for large times. The numerical calculation of these series is often laborious.

For simple bodies such as slabs, cylinders, spheres and for simple boundary conditions, such as instantaneously applied heat transfer at the surface, the number of non-dimensional parameters is small so that it is possible to construct general charts for a wide range of parameters. Solutions for composite bodies become difficult and general charts would be too voluminous. In certain cases of one-dimensional heat flow it is possible to obtain solutions even for highly complex bodies by a method using heat waves which are transmitted and reflected at interfaces; these solutions are, however, only valid for small times.

No exact analytical methods are yet known which are applicable when the thermal properties depend on temperature. Non-linear boundary conditions such as thermal radiation and heat transfer by free convection at surfaces can be dealt with by integral equations.

Except in a few fundamental cases, analytical solutions and, in particular, their numerical evaluations are laborious and they are not practical for bodies with complicated geometries or boundary conditions which are other than simple; this is still more true of structures whose geometry is usually complex, and in aeronautics the boundary conditions may be non-linear and time-dependent. Therefore more flexible but approximate methods appear more suitable for such structures. Among these methods is a so-called semi-analytical method which is based on analytical solutions for constant and linear boundary conditions. The time is divided into equal intervals and during each interval the external heat transfer conditions are assumed constant although in general they are different for different time intervals. By superposing suitable partial solutions for each time interval the final solution is obtained with good accuracy even for comparatively large time steps.

4.3 Methods using finite differences and lumped circuits

In finite difference methods the body is divided into sections of finite size and this yields a certain lumping error. There is still little known about it, although many papers have appeared on finite difference calculations during the past 15 years. Hence the lumping error can in general not be improved upon other than by repeating the whole calculation with a finer division into smaller sections. Another important point with methods using finite differences in both space and time concerns the convergence and stability of solutions. The number of sections in a finite body is usually decided with respect to the lumping error but if the size of the time step is chosen too large, oscillations may occur in some finite difference methods, among them one which is most widely used. If the oscillations increase in amplitude with increasing time, such solutions are called unstable. Conditions for convergence and stability of finite difference methods have been investigated extensively in recent times and found in general to be simple. However, these conditions alone are not always sufficient to obtain solutions which are everywhere satisfactory from a thermodynamic point of view. This requirement can be met by increasing the severity of the convergence and stability conditions.

A finite difference method has been used first by Binder and Schmidt (Ref. 8.3). This method is of the explicit type and still most widely used. In his classical paper Schmidt considered a slab of constant initial temperature which is suddenly exposed to external heat transfer and a surprisingly coarse division was used. The number of sections for one half of the symmetrically heated slab was only 4 at the beginning of the heat transfer, later on it was 2 and during the final period it was only 1. Nevertheless, the error did not exceed 3 per cent of the initial temperature difference between the external medium and the body. This result is important, because in this method the amount of numerical computations increases as the third power of the number of sections as will be shown later in Chapter 8. For a long time Schmidt's favourable result has apparently been considered as fortuitous rather than of general importance. Recently it was shown that a division into four or even two sections is sufficient for most engineering purposes. The division refers to a "penetration" depth or the whole slab, depending on whether temperature increases have respectively occurred only in a part of the slab (during the initial phase) or in the whole slab (during the later phase of heating). A division into 20 or more sections has been used in examples quoted previously in the literature. It is interesting to note that the minimum volumes of numerical calculations for division of a slab into 20 and 4 sections are in the ratio of 125:1 for the present method. In other finite difference methods the amount of numerical work increases less rapidly with the number of sections, but there are other disadvantages in these methods.

In many cases it is convenient to use spatial differences of unequal length. Then it is only one step further to replace the solid by a series of lumped elements of heat capacities and heat resistances. This method is particularly convenient for composite bodies and structures. The mathematical procedure is similar to that for spatial differences of equal length, the only difference being that the coefficients in the difference equations are variable in space.

A large number of problems important in the heating of structures can be solved by one-dimensional heat flow. If a high speed calculating machine is used, a general programme can be used for all cases in which the heat flow is either normal to the surfaces of composite layers or parallel to the surfaces of thin shells with uniform temperature throughout the thickness and with external heat transfer at the surface. Similar programming can be made for two- and three-dimensional heat flow, but the requirements on the memory of the machine are larger than for one-dimensional flow. Many cases can even be solved using a desk calculating machine and within a reasonable time if care is taken to make the divisions as coarse as the required accuracy permits. Due to their flexibility the finite difference methods appear very useful in all cases where other than the simplest structures are investigated under realistic flight conditions. Other approximate methods have apparently not yet become as important in this connection.

CHAPTER 5

STEADY HEAT FLOW I: ANALYTICAL METHODS

5.1 General

Steady heat flow in structures can occur during steady flight owing to variations in the local equilibrium temperatures along the surfaces of the flight vehicles. This case, however, is not important in practice for the following reasons. At moderate supersonic speeds the equilibrium temperature does not deviate greatly from the adiabatic wall temperature of the boundary layer flow and this temperature in turn does not vary much with distance from the stagnation point or line (see Section 2.2). At hypersonic speeds higher wall temperatures may be obtained and then the variations in the equilibrium temperature are larger due to the influence of thermal radiation from the wall. However, in hypersonic flight the speeds are in most cases not steady at all or, except at high altitudes, they are steady only for times which are not long enough to permit thermal equilibrium to be attained in the structure.

Frequent causes of steady heat flow are internal heat sources such as propulsion units and electronic equipment, and typical cases are: (a) the heat flow from an engine through a ring frame to the skin of the vehicle and (b) the heat flow from electronic equipment through insulating layers to the skin of the vehicle. Sometimes unsteady heat flow can be treated as quasi-steady. Such conditions prevail for the heat flow to or from a fuel tank because of the large heat capacity of the fuel. More seldom, perhaps, steady heat flow occurs at very high altitudes owing to irradiation from the sun.

5.2 One-dimensional heat flow in composite slabs and shells

The fundamental law of heat conduction in solids is

$$q = -k \frac{\partial T}{\partial x} \qquad (5.2.1)$$

where q is the intensity of heat flow in the x-direction and k the conductivity. Assume a slab of thickness δ without internal heat sources and with constant k; its surfaces 1 and 2 are to be at the temperatures $T_{w,1}$ and $T_{w,2}$. Then Eq. (5.2.1) yields:

$$q = k \, \frac{T_{w,1} - T_{w,2}}{\delta} \tag{5.2.2}$$

The heat flow q is directed normal to the surfaces of the slab and x increases from surface 1 to 2. The specific thermal resistance† of the slab is defined as

$$R^{(q)} = \frac{\delta}{k} \tag{5.2.3}$$

If the slab is composed of layers of different materials with perfect thermal contact at the interfaces, the thermal resistance $R^{(q)}$ between the surfaces of the slab is equal to the sum of the resistances of the component layers. The intensity of heat flow is

$$q = \frac{T_{w,1} - T_{w,2}}{R^{(q)}_{tot}} \tag{5.2.4}$$

q being known and constant, the temperature distribution within the slab follows from Eq. (5.2.1). If heat resistances are present at the interfaces, they can be taken into account by adding their resistances to those of the solid layers, provided that the heat transfer across the interfaces obeys a linear law (see Section 3.7).

For a shell (or a bar) with adiabatic surfaces and with constant temperature in the cross-section the rate of heat flowing through the cross-section and parallel to the surfaces is

$$Q = -kF \frac{dT}{dx} \tag{5.2.5}$$

where F is the area of the cross-section. If F is constant, the resistance to heat flow for a shell between two cross-sections a distance l apart is

$$R = \frac{l}{kF} \tag{5.2.6}$$

---

† Later on in this monograph we shall drop superscripts at R and not distinguish between specific resistances, resistances per unit length and resistances themselves. This is not likely to cause any confusion, since one uses only resistances of the same kind in a particular case.

For the general case of variable cross-section, but constant k, it follows from Eq. (5.2.5) that

$$T_{w,1} - T_{w,2} = \frac{Q}{k} \int_{x_1}^{x_2} \frac{\mathrm{d}x}{F} \qquad (5.2.7)$$

Hence the heat resistance between x_1 and x_2 is

$$R_{12} = \frac{1}{k} \int_{x_1}^{x_2} \frac{\mathrm{d}x}{F} \qquad (5.2.8)$$

If the shell is composed of longitudinal sections of different materials or if the cross-section is discontinuous in certain places, one can proceed as for the composite slab and calculate the total resistance between the end faces from the resistance of the component sections. Hence Q is known and the temperature distribution follows from Eq. (5.2.5).

If external heat transfer of the forced convection type occurs from the surfaces of a shell, the equation of heat conduction for variable cross-section and variable heat conductivity reads:

$$\frac{\mathrm{d}}{\mathrm{d}x}\left(kF\frac{\mathrm{d}T}{\mathrm{d}x}\right) + Uh(T_f - T) = 0 \qquad (5.2.9)$$

where h is the heat transfer coefficient and T_f is the temperature of the external medium. U is the total length of that part of the circumference which is exposed to external heat transfer. A general solution of Eq. (5.2.9) for constant values of k, F, U, h and T_f can readily be obtained

$$T - T_f = B_1 \cosh \gamma x + B_2 \sinh \gamma x \qquad (5.2.10)$$

with

$$\gamma = \sqrt{\left(\frac{hU}{kF}\right)} \qquad (5.2.11)$$

The constants B_1 and B_2 can be determined from the boundary conditions at the end faces of the shell. For heat transfer by heat radiation or free convection at the side faces of the shell numerical methods must be used (see Chapter 6).

Consider a composite shell with constant, but different, values of k, F and h in the axial sections; for each of these a solution of the type of Eq. (5.2.10) is obtained where B_1 and B_2 are replaced by $B_1^{(n)}$ and $B_2^{(n)}$ with the superscript n referring to section n. At the inner boundaries of the sections the temperature and the heat flow must be continuous,

if the thermal contact is perfect at the interfaces. Considering also the boundary conditions at both end-faces of the shell, one obtains for N sections a system of $2N$ equations for the $2N$ unknown coefficients $B_1^{(n)}$ and $B_2^{(n)}$.

This system of equations is of such a form that it can be solved by step-wise elimination or by recurrence formulas; both procedures are analogous to the methods presented later on in Section 6.3, and details are not given here.

5.3 Radial heat flow in cylindrical or spherical layers

Heat flow in a cylindrical rocket charge is an example of radial heat flow. The equation of heat flow for a cylinder or cylindrical layer of length L is

$$Q = -2\pi L k r \frac{dT}{dr} \qquad (5.3.1)$$

r is the radius and Q the rate of heat flow. Hence one obtains by integrating Eq. (5.3.1)

$$Q = 2\pi L k \frac{T_{w,1} - T_{w,2}}{\ln(r_2/r_1)} \qquad (5.3.2)$$

where ln denotes the natural logarithm. From Eq. (5.3.2) it follows that the thermal resistance R of the cylinder is

$$R = \frac{\ln(r_2/r_1)}{2\pi k L} \qquad (5.3.3)$$

For spheres and spherical layers the equation of heat conduction is

$$q = -k r^2 \frac{dT}{dr} \qquad (5.3.4)$$

where q is the intensity of heat flow per unit solid angle. The equation is also valid for conical heat flow in a solid cone having adiabatic surfaces. By integration of Eq. (5.3.4) the thermal resistance between radii r_1 and r_2 per unit solid angle ($r_2 > r_1$) is obtained as

$$R = \frac{r_2 - r_1}{k r_1 r_2} \qquad (5.3.5)$$

The overall resistance and the temperature distributions in simple and composite cylindrical and spherical layers can be calculated in the same way as for linear heat flow in Section 5.2.

5.4 Radial heat flow in shells

A ring frame with adiabatic surfaces is an example of radial heat flow in a shell of constant thickness δ without external heat transfer. Then Eqs. (5.3.1) to (5.3.3) are valid, if L is replaced by δ. If δ varies, the resistance is calculated by

$$R = \frac{1}{2\pi k} \int_{r_1}^{r_2} \frac{dr}{r\delta} \qquad (5.4.1)$$

For a shell with external heat transfer by forced convection occurring on its surfaces the balance of heat flow yields, with k and δ constant,

$$k\delta \frac{1}{r} \frac{d}{dr} \left(r \frac{dT}{dr} \right) + 2h(T_f - T) = 0 \qquad (5.4.2)$$

If h and T_f are also constant Eq. (5.4.2) can be re-written as

$$\frac{d^2 T^*}{dr^2} + \frac{1}{r} \frac{dT^*}{dr} - \gamma^2 T^* = 0 \qquad (5.4.3)$$

where

$$T^* = T - T_f \qquad (5.4.4)$$

and

$$\gamma = \sqrt{\left(\frac{2h}{k\delta} \right)} \qquad (5.4.4a)$$

For a circular disc, the solution is of the form

$$T^* = B I_0(\gamma r) \qquad (5.4.5)$$

where I_0 is the modified Bessel function† of the first kind and of zero order. The constant B follows from the boundary conditions at the outer rim $(r = a)$. For a ring frame the solution is

$$T^* = B_1 I_0(\gamma r) + B_2 K_0(\gamma r) \qquad (5.4.6)$$

where K_0 is the modified Bessel function of the second kind and of zero order.

---

† Modified Bessel functions are Bessel functions of imaginary argument:

$$I_0(x) = J_0(ix)$$

$$K_0(x) = i \frac{\pi}{2} [J_0(ix) + i Y_0(ix)]$$

where $J_0(x)$ and $Y_0(x)$ are the zero order Bessel functions of the first and second kind respectively. $I_0(x)$ and $K_0(x)$ are real.

The constants B_1 and B_2 follow from the boundary conditions at the outer and inner rims of the annular frame, say at $r = r_2$ and $r = r_1$. When external heat transfer on the surfaces of the shell occurs by heat radiation or free convection, numerical methods must be used.

5.5 Boundary conditions in one-dimensional heat flow

It was previously assumed that the temperatures are known at the boundaries. In general this is not the case and, instead, a relation is given between the rate of heat flow and the temperature differences depending on the mode of the external heat transfer. If this relation is linear, as for instance for heat transfer by forced convection, one obtains:

$$q_{w,j} = \frac{T_{f,j} - T_{w,j}}{R_{f,j}} \cdots j = 1 \text{ or } 2 \qquad (5.5.1)$$

where T_f and R_f are respectively reference temperatures and resistances in external heat transfer; the subscripts 1 and 2 refer to the external media and the wall temperatures at the ends of the body. For instance in the case of heat flow in a slab and in a direction normal to its surface one obtains $R_f = 1/h$ where h is a heat transfer coefficient.

By adding the resistances of the external heat transfer to the resistance of the body R_{12}, the total resistance is obtained for the heat flow between the temperature levels of the two external media. The rate or intensity of heat flow is equal to $(T_{f,1} - T_{f,2})/(R_{f,1} + R_{12} + R_{f,2})$ and if it is known, the temperature distributions follow as previously.

If external heat transfer occurs by free convection or heat radiation, the above method cannot be used for explicitly calculating temperature distributions. Even if a relation for heat transfer of the form of Eq. (3.1.6) is used, h and the corresponding value of R_f would depend on the surface temperatures. This dependence is small for free convection (see Section 3.5) and hence for that mode of heat transfer the previous method modified to an iterative form is practical. First a value of h is estimated and with its help a temperature distribution is calculated, which is used to improve h and so on till the final solution is obtained. In general this method converges rather rapidly.

If heat radiation is involved in the external heat transfer another method is necessary. We assume simultaneous heat transfer by forced convection and heat radiation, a case which is important for aeronautical applications. Further the treatment is general and even applicable to radial heat flow. The solid body and the external heat transfer conditions are replaced by the circuit of Fig. 5.1. In it the temperatures T_1, $T_{0,1}$, and $T_{0,2}$, the conductivities $K_{w,1}$ and $K_{0,w}$ and the radiation coefficient $C_{R,1}$ are given, and T_w is unknown. A straight line between two points in the figure indicates there is a linear relation between the rate of heat flow and the

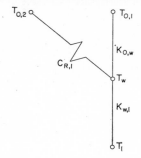

FIG. 5.1. Circuit for treatment of heat flow in a solid with heat transfer by forced convection and heat radiation at the surface.

temperatures and a zig-zag sign denotes radiative heat flow. The circuit of Fig. 5.1 covers, for instance, heat flow in a body with a surface exposed to heat transfer by forced convection (coefficient $K_{0,w}$ and reference temperature $T_{0,1}$) and thermal radiation (radiation coefficient $C_{R,1}$ and reference temperature $T_{0,2}$). If applied to a shell exposed to aerodynamic heating $T_{0,1}$ would be the adiabatic wall temperature T_{aw} of the boundary layer flow, and $T_{0,2}$ the ambient air temperature T_∞. The balance of heat flow for the "surface point" including the law for radiative heat flow (Section 3.6) yields,

$$K_{w,1}(T_w-T_1) = K_{0,w}(T_{0,1}-T_w)+C_{R,1}[T_{0,2}^4-T_w^4] \qquad (5.5.2)$$

Here conductivities instead of resistances $(K=1/R)$ have been used. The solution of this fourth degree equation is facilitated by introducing two parameters

$$T_c^* = (K_{w,1}+K_{0,w})^{-1}(K_{w,1}T_1+K_{0,w}T_{0,1}+C_{R,1}T_{0,2}^4) \qquad (5.5.3)$$

and

$$P^* = C_{R,1}(K_{w,1}+K_{0,w})^{-1}T_c^{*3} \qquad (5.5.4)$$

Both T_c^* and P^* can be calculated from given values. Then Eq. (5.5.2) can be expressed in the following general form:

$$P^*\left(\frac{T_w}{T_c^*}\right)^4+\frac{T_w}{T_c^*}-1=0 \qquad (5.5.5)$$

Eq. (5.5.5) is the same as (2.9.4) except that in the latter equation T_g/T_c replaces T_w/T_c^*. Hence solutions of Eq. (5.5.5) can be found from the nomogram given in Fig. 2.21.

5.6 Variable thermal properties

For most materials the thermal properties vary with temperature. If the temperature differences are moderate, suitable mean values can be used. For large variations in k, functions of the variables x or r and T respectively are collected on the left and right hand sides of Eqs. (5.2.1), (5.2.5) and (5.3.1). By integrating on both sides as previously one again obtains Eqs. (5.2.2), (5.2.3), (5.2.6), (5.2.7), (5.2.8), (5.3.2), (5.3.3), (5.3.4), (5.3.5), and (5.4.1), if in these equations k is replaced by the integrated mean value:

$$k_m = \frac{1}{T_{w,1}-T_{w,2}} \int_{T_{w,2}}^{T_{w,1}} k \, \mathrm{d}T \qquad (5.6.1)$$

Except for particular cases in which $T_{w,1}$ and $T_{w,2}$, the temperatures at surfaces or interfaces, are known, rates of heat flow and temperature distributions can not be calculated explicitly. To find them, either the analytical solutions of the preceding sections are used in an iterative procedure, or numerical methods are employed. In the first method temperature distributions are estimated in order to calculate values of k_m which in turn are used to improve the temperature distribution and so on. In most cases this procedure converges rapidly.

5.7 General remarks on two-dimensional heat flow

Two-dimensional heat flow is not treated here in detail because this case is less important for structures than the one-dimensional case. In the absence of internal heat sources and for constant thermal conductivity, temperature distributions are to be found from Laplace's partial differential equation, which has been extensively treated in the literature for bodies with boundaries of simple form (Ref. 3.1.1). However, for all but the simplest boundaries and boundary conditions, analytical methods become too laborious or difficult and numerical methods or analogues are then preferable (see Chapters 6 and 10).

References

5.1   VODICKA, V., Steady temperature in an infinite multilayer plate, ZAMM **40**, 4, 161–165 (1960).

5.2   VODICKA, V., Stationary temperature fields in multilayer cylindrical tubes, ZAMM **40**, 4, 165–170. (1960).

CHAPTER 6

STEADY HEAT FLOW II: NUMERICAL METHODS

6.1 Introduction

In certain cases of one-dimensional heat flow in solid bodies it is most convenient to use analytical methods, if the following conditions are satisfied: (a) the thermal conductivities in the bodies are constant, and (b) in the case of heat sources or sinks, (ba) the amount of heat developed or lost is constant or a function of the distance only, (bb) the amount of heat developed or lost is linearly dependent on temperature, but independent of the distance and (bc) boundary conditions of the non-linear type are excluded at surfaces and end-faces. The terms sources and sinks are used here in a mathematical meaning; for instance in slabs they correspond only to real sources inside the solid, but in shells with constant temperatures throughout the thickness they correspond to the rate of external heat transfer on the surfaces. A shell with surface heat transfer by free convection or by thermal radiation cannot be treated by the simple analytical methods of Chapter 5 because of the condition (bb). The analysis becomes simple in the case of linear heat flow (equidistant flow lines) and radial heat flow in bodies with cylindrical and spherical surfaces. These types of heat flow have been treated in the previous chapter. In the case of two-dimensional heat flow one encounters additional difficulties, due to the form of the boundary, for all but the simplest cases such as squares, rectangles, circles and so on.

Therefore approximate methods must be used in many cases. Only numerical methods are treated here and among them only those based on a finite difference form of the equation of heat conduction. This also affords a convenient opportunity for a general introduction to finite difference methods which are particularly important for transient heat flow.

The finite difference method is first explained in some detail for the case of one-dimensional heat flow and then extended to the two-dimensional case in which not many new points arise. First, a method is presented for explicitly solving systems of finite difference equations provided that these are linear in the temperatures. These restrictions can be dropped in the other two methods treated: the methods of successive approximations and of relaxation. In particular, the section on truncation errors is relevant to all the finite difference methods. For the sake of convenience these methods are explained mainly for equations which are linear in the temperatures, but extensions to non-linear cases can easily be made.

6.2 A finite difference equation for one-dimensional heat flow

Finite difference methods are explained in the case of a shell of constant thickness with constant temperature throughout the thickness. Heat transfer by forced convection is assumed on one surface while the other is thermally insulated (Fig. 6.1 (a)). The temperatures at the end-faces are given. This model may, for instance, correspond to an integral fuel

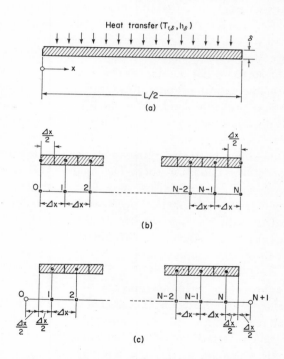

Fig. 6.1. A shell with external heat transfer on one surface only, and with constant temperature throughout the thickness. Heat flow within the shell directed parallel to its surface. (a) Sketch of shell, (b) and (c) division into sections for difference calculations. (b) Boundaries coinciding with temperature points in the finite difference method. (c) Boundaries each midway between a temperature point and an auxiliary point outside the shell for satisfying boundary conditions.

tank in an aircraft with separate compartments of length L (Fig. 6.2). One compartment is assumed empty and located between two full compartments. The rate of heat transfer from the inside of the skin to the liquid fuel

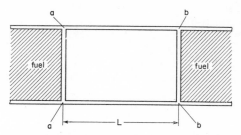

FIG. 6.2. Example of a structural element for the model of Fig. 6.1. A wing with integral tanks with one empty compartment between two full compartments.

is assumed so high that the skin has approximately the temperature of the fuel at the points a and b. The heat capacity of the fuel in the tank is sufficiently large so that the fuel temperature can be assumed constant during a certain time of flight.

For the model of Fig 6.1(a) the equation of heat conduction parallel to the surface in direction x is

$$k\delta\frac{\mathrm{d}^2 T}{\mathrm{d}x^2} = h_\delta(T - T_{f,\delta}) \qquad (6.2.1)$$

where T and $T_{f,\delta}$ are the temperatures of the shell and of the external medium respectively, k is the thermal conductivity in the shell and h_δ, the external heat transfer coefficient. In the illustrative example of Fig. 6.2 the temperatures at the end faces of the shell are given as mentioned before, and are equal to each other. Hence the temperature distribution is symmetrical with respect to the midpoint of the shell and only one half of it need be considered; the boundary condition of the midpoint $x = L/2$ is $(\mathrm{d}T/\mathrm{d}x) = 0$. In the finite difference method the range of the variable x is divided into equal sections of length Δx (Fig. 6.1(b) and (c)). The temperatures in the middle of each section are the unknown quantities occurring in the finite difference calculations. The sections and temperature points are successively numbered by subscript n. Expanding the temperatures at the points $n+1$ and $n-1$ in a Taylor series at the point n we obtain

$$T_{n\pm1} = T_n \pm \Delta x \left(\frac{\mathrm{d}T}{\mathrm{d}x}\right)_n + \frac{(\Delta x)^2}{2}\left(\frac{\mathrm{d}^2 T}{\mathrm{d}x^2}\right)_n \pm \frac{(\Delta x)^3}{6}\left(\frac{\mathrm{d}^3 T}{\mathrm{d}x^3}\right)_n + O[(\Delta x)^4]$$

$$(6.2.2)$$

The sum of the terms neglected in the series expansion is the truncation error and its order of magnitude is given between the brackets after the sign O in the above equation. Adding the two expressions for T_{n+1} and T_{n-1} yields

$$(\Delta x)^2 \left(\frac{d^2 T}{d x^2}\right)_n = T_{n+1} + T_{n-1} - 2 T_n + O[(\Delta x)^4] \tag{6.2.3}$$

Using Eq. (6.2.3), the finite difference form of Eq. (6.2.1), for a point n in the interior of the range of the variable x, reads,

$$p(T_{n+1} + T_{n-1}) - (1+2p) T_n + T_{f,\delta} = 0 \tag{6.2.4}$$

with

$$p = \frac{k\delta}{h_\delta (\Delta x)^2} \tag{6.2.5}$$

Equation (6.2.4) is valid at each interior point. In addition, there is a particular equation for the first and the last temperature points along the x-axis which follows from the boundary conditions. The sections of the x-axis can be arranged with respect to the boundaries in two ways: the boundaries either coincide with temperature points (Fig. 6.1(b)) or they lie midway between two such points (Fig. 6.1(c)). In the second case auxiliary points (0 and $N+1$ in Fig. 6.1(c)) are used outside the range of the independent variable x at a distance $\Delta x/2$ from the boundaries.

For boundary conditions in general, finite difference expressions are needed for T_b and $(dT/dx)_b$ (the index b indicating values at the boundary). These have been calculated, together with their truncation errors, from Eq. (6.2.2). The results are presented in Fig. 6.3 for the two positions of the boundaries relative to the temperature points shown in Figs. 6.1(b) and (c). If the temperatures at the boundary are given, the obvious course is to let the boundaries coincide with temperature points as in Fig. 6.1(b). If both temperatures and their gradients occur in the boundary conditions, their truncation errors are, in general, of the same order of magnitude as the largest of the individual errors. Hence, comparing expressions for T_b and $\left(\dfrac{dT}{dx}\right)_b$ in Fig. 6.3, the truncation errors are, in general, smaller for a position of the boundary as shown in Fig. 6.1(c) than in Fig. 6.1(b). Even when they are least, the truncation errors are still of $O[(\Delta x)^2]$ and therefore much larger than for interior points, where they are of $O[(\Delta x)^4]$ for the type of finite difference equation used here as follows from Eqs. (6.2.3) and (6.2.4), provided p is of $O(1)$.

Formulas are first given for the temperatures at an auxiliary point with subscript 0 for some simple boundary conditions. The boundary lies midway between the auxiliary point and the first temperature point inside

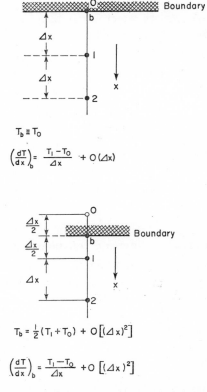

$$T_b \equiv T_0$$

$$\left(\frac{dT}{dx}\right)_b = \frac{T_1 - T_0}{\Delta x} + O\,(\Delta x)$$

$$T_b = \tfrac{1}{2}(T_1 + T_0) + O\left[(\Delta x)^2\right]$$

$$\left(\frac{dT}{dx}\right)_b = \frac{T_1 - T_0}{\Delta x} + O\left[(\Delta x)^2\right]$$

FIG. 6.3. Finite difference expressions for the temperature and its gradient at the boundary, and order of magnitude of respective truncation errors.

the shell $(n = 1)$, see Fig. 6.1(c). The following boundary conditions are important:

Case 1: Temperature T_b at the boundary given:

$$T_0 = -\,T_1 + 2T_b \tag{6.2.6}$$

Case 2: Heat flow at the boundary given:

$$T_0 = T_1 + q_w \frac{\Delta x}{k} \tag{6.2.7}$$

q_w is the rate of heat flow at the end face directed towards the inside of the body.

Case 3: Heat transfer by a linear relation between the rate of heat flow and the temperature difference

$$-k\left(\frac{\partial T}{\partial x}\right)_b = h(T_f - T_b) \tag{6.2.8a}$$

with h and T_f as parameters which differ in general from h_δ and $T_{f,\delta}$ used previously. When Eq. (6.2.8a) is re-written in a finite difference form, one obtains for T_0:

$$T_0 = \frac{1-s}{1+s} T_1 + \frac{2s}{1+s} T_f \tag{6.2.8b}$$

$$s = \frac{h\Delta x}{2k} \tag{6.2.8c}$$

For the auxiliary point T_{N+1} at the boundary, the subscripts 0 and 1 in the above equations are to be replaced by $N+1$ and N respectively. N is the number of sections into which the whole range of the variable x is divided.

6.3 Direct solutions of finite difference equations

Assuming the shell to be divided into N sections and the two boundary conditions to be of the form of Eq. (6.2.8a), then the system of resulting equations can be arranged as follows:

$$T_0 = \frac{1-s_0}{1+s_0} T_1 + \frac{2s_0}{1+s_0} T_{f,0} \tag{6.3.1a}$$

$$pT_{n+1} - (1+2p)T_n + pT_{n-1} = -T_{f,\delta}, \qquad n = 1,2,...,N \tag{6.3.1b}$$

$$T_{N+1} = \frac{1-s_N}{1+s_N} T_N + \frac{2s_N}{1+s_N} T_{f,N} \tag{6.3.1c}$$

Since the first and the last of these equations contain two unknowns each and the other equations three unknowns each, the system of $N+2$ equations for the $N+2$ unknown temperatures can be solved by a stepwise procedure. Use Eq. (6.3.1a) to eliminate T_0 from Eq. (6.3.1b) as written for $n = 1$; this yields a linear relation between T_1 and T_2. With the help of this relation, T_1 is eliminated from the next equation (i.e. Eq. (6.3.1b) for $n = 2$) and so on until finally two equations for T_N and T_{N+1} are obtained which are easily solved. These calculations can be simplified† if

---

† According to Richtmyer it is difficult to say who first introduced the method; a number of relevant references are given in Richtmyer's book (Ref. 8.1).

Eqs. (6.3.1a) and (6.3.1b) are re-written in the following general form,

$$T_0 = D_0^{(1)} T_1 + D_0^{(2)} \tag{6.3.2a}$$

$$-A_{n,n-1} T_{n-1} + A_{n,n} T_n - A_{n,n+1} T_{n+1} = B_n , \quad n = 1,2,...,N \tag{6.3.2b}$$

The coefficients $D_0^{(1)}$, $D_0^{(2)}$, $A_{n,n-1}$, $A_{n,n}$ and $A_{n,n+1}$ follow by direct comparison with Eq. (6.3.1). When the unknown temperatures in the system of equations (6.3.1) are eliminated step by step, one obtains equations of the following form:

$$T_{n-1} = D_{n-1}^{(1)} T_n + D_{n-1}^{(2)} , \quad n = 1,2,3,...,N+1 \tag{6.3.3}$$

The coefficients $D_{n-1}^{(1)}$ and $D_{n-1}^{(2)}$ for $n \geqslant 2$ are found in the following way. Eliminate T_{n-1} in Eq. (6.3.2b) with the help of Eq. (6.3.3) and solve for T_n; one obtains

$$T_n = \frac{A_{n,n+1}}{A_{n,n} - A_{n,n-1} D_{n-1}^{(1)}} T_{n+1} + \frac{B_n + A_{n,n-1} D_{n-1}^{(2)}}{A_{n,n} - A_{n,n-1} D_{n-1}^{(1)}} \tag{6.3.4}$$

Comparison of this equation with (6.3.3) yields the following recurrence formulas for $D^{(1)}$ and $D^{(2)}$:

$$D_n^{(1)} = \frac{A_{n,n+1}}{A_{n,n} - A_{n,n-1} D_{n-1}^{(1)}} , \quad D_n^{(2)} = \frac{B_n + A_{n,n-1} D_{n-1}^{(2)}}{A_{n,n} - A_{n,n-1} D_{n-1}^{(1)}} \tag{6.3.5}$$

Since all the coefficients A and B as well as $D_0^{(1)}$ and $D_0^{(2)}$ are known, $D_n^{(1)}$ and $D_n^{(2)}$ can be calculated recurrently in order of increasing index n. When all the D's are known, calculation of the temperatures proceeds by finding T_N and T_{N+1} from Eq. (6.3.1c), and using Eq. (6.3.3) in which $n = N+1$. Finally the temperatures T_n are calculated recurrently from Eq. (6.3.3) in order of decreasing index n, starting with the temperature T_N already known.

Since in the general treatment above the coefficients A and B may change from point to point, the method is applicable to general cases, for instance, with varying heat transfer conditions along the surface and varying thickness of the shell. However, linear relations between the temperatures are still necessary and cases with external heat transfer by heat radiation or free convection cannot be treated directly. The latter of these two cases can be solved by the above method, if used iteratively, because in the case of free convection the heat transfer coefficient h_δ depends only to a moderate degree on the temperatures. First, a temperature distribution in the body is calculated with an estimated value of h_δ; the wall temperature thus obtained is used to improve h_δ and then the calculations are repeated and so on. This procedure converges, in general, very rapidly.

6.4 A method of iteration for solving finite difference equations

In comparison with the previous method, iteration as well as relaxation, which is treated later, are less direct, but more flexible. Again, the simple "linear case" of Section 6.2 is treated first. Suppose in Eq. (6.2.4) the temperatures T_{n+1} and T_{n-1} to be known to a certain degree of accuracy and solving the equation for T_n, one obtains

$$T_n^{(m+1)} = \frac{1}{1+2p} T_{f,\delta} + \frac{p}{1+2p} (T_{n+1}^{(m)} + T_{n-1}^{(m)}) \qquad (6.4.1)$$

In the iteration procedure the superscripts denote two successive steps, i.e. the superscripts m and $m+1$ refer to the originally known and the calculated temperatures respectively. The temperatures at the ends of the series of points follow from the boundary conditions. If one or both of these are of a non-linear type, one unknown temperature is solved from a non-linear equation at a time; this can be done with the help of general curves. Initially a temperature distribution for the whole region is assumed by guessing. These temperatures are improved with the help of Eq. (6.4.1) and this is repeated again and again until the temperatures do not change any more. The rate of convergence depends on how good the initial guesses were.

6.5 The method of relaxation

Starting from an assumed temperature distribution as in the previous section, the error in the temperatures at each point is estimated and used to improve the temperatures according to certain rules. These can either be applied rigidly, which is usually done when an automatic computing machine is used, or flexibly so as to reduce most effectively the computational work in every particular case. The latter procedure is best suited for an experienced computer operator with insight into the particular problem under consideration.

The initial guesses for the temperatures do not, in general, satisfy Eq. (6.2.4) and hence the right-hand side of that equation is not zero, but its magnitude q_n is a measure of the size of the error:

$$q_n = p(T_{n+1} + T_{n-1}) - (1+2p) T_n + T_{f,\delta} \qquad (6.5.1)$$

q_n can be interpreted as a heat sink or source and is called the residual of the point n. All residuals are to be "relaxed" to zero by suitably changing the temperatures step by step. The following procedures have been developed in order to keep the amount of computational work to a minimum.

First, a useful aid is the relation between changes in the temperatures and the residuals. It is obtained from the difference form of Eq. (6.5.1) and

$$\Delta q_n = p(\Delta T_{n+1} + \Delta T_{n-1}) - (1+2p)\Delta T_n \qquad (6.5.2)$$

It connects the temperature changes at three neighbouring points with a change of the residual at the midpoint.

Starting from an initial "guess" for the temperatures, all residuals q_n are calculated. Suppose the largest of these is q_k. Assume there is no relation between adjacent temperature points, as might follow from certain boundary conditions for points near the boundaries; then q_k is made zero by changing the temperature T_k by an amount

$$\Delta T_k = \frac{1}{1+2p} q_k \qquad (6.5.3)$$

while all other temperatures are left unchanged. This expression follows from Eq. (6.5.2) by putting $n = k$ and then $\Delta T_{k+1} = \Delta T_{k-1} = 0$. If there is a relation between, say, T_{k+1} and T_k, then $\Delta T_{k+1} = f(\Delta T_k)$; the residual is now made zero by first eliminating ΔT_{k+1} from Eq. (6.5.2) while $\Delta T_{k-1} = 0$ and $\Delta q_k = -q_k$ as previously. As a consequence of the temperature change ΔT_k, the residuals in the two adjacent points change by an amount

$$\Delta q_{k\pm1} = p\Delta T_k \qquad (6.5.4)$$

Thus q_k has been made zero and, at the same time, changes in T_k, q_{k-1} and q_{k+1} have occurred. Then the largest of the remaining residuals is identified and the whole process is repeated again and again. Residuals which have been made zero at one time do not remain zero later on if residuals in adjacent points have also to be adjusted, as is often the case. In general the process converges, although not uniformly at any particular point, and ultimately all residuals disappear. Obviously in this simple relaxation procedure one uses a working formula which is equivalent to Eq. (6.4.1). However, as compared with the iteration procedure of Section 6.4, in relaxation the temperature is changed at only one point in any step and hence in future steps one may benefit from improvements already made. Further, instead of treating the points one by one according to a rigid pattern, the point with the largest residual is dealt with in each relaxation step.

In most cases the relaxation process can be considerably accelerated if, instead of relaxing residuals to zero at each point at a time, one or more of the following methods are used (Refs. 6.1 and 6.2):

(1) under- or over-relaxation,
(2) block relaxation,
(3) group relaxation,
(4) the use of multiplying factors.

With under- or over-relaxation, temperature changes are made which are smaller or larger than necessary to make the residuals at a point zero in order to anticipate changes due to adjustments in adjacent points. The amount of over- or under-relaxation is generally found by trial and error. In block relaxation, temperature changes of the same amount are made simultaneously at a number of connected points. In group relaxation, the changes differ in amount from point to point according to a certain pattern. Both block and group relaxation can be used to reduce to zero the sum of all residuals in a region and this is particularly useful if the residuals are large. When, during relaxation, the residuals at any time are found to be in the same ratio to each other as they were for another approximation, then the final solution can be found immediately by using a multiplying factor. If the residuals are only approximately in the same ratio to each other, the same device may still be used and leads at least to a substantial improvement in the approximation. The relaxation devices are best explained by means of a numerical example and this is done in the next section.

6.6 The iteration and relaxation method illustrated by an example

Consider a shell with constant temperature throughout its thickness and external heat transfer by forced convection, as introduced in Section 6.2. The differential equation is given by Eq. (6.2.1) and the boundary conditions considered here are:

$$x = 0, \quad T = 0 \text{ and } x = \frac{L}{2}, \quad \frac{dT}{dx} = 0 \qquad (6.6.1)$$

The non-dimensional quantities

$$\xi = \frac{x}{L} \qquad (6.6.2)$$

and

$$\varphi^2 = \frac{h_\delta L^2}{k\delta} \qquad (6.6.3)$$

are introduced into Eq. (6.2.1) and one obtains:

$$\frac{d^2 T}{d\xi^2} = \varphi^2 (T - T_{f,\delta}) \qquad (6.6.4)$$

Further $\varphi = 4$ and $T_{f,8} = 100$ is chosen in the present example. The finite difference form of Eq. (6.6.4) is given by Eq. (6.2.4), if there

$$p = \frac{1}{\varphi^2 (\Delta \xi)^2} \qquad (6.6.5)$$

and $\Delta \xi = (\Delta x)/L$ is the non-dimensional section length. The finite difference form of the boundary condition Eq. (6.6.1) becomes

$$T_0 = -T_1 \text{ and } T_N = T_{N+1} \qquad (6.6.6)$$

with T_0 and T_{N+1} as the temperatures of the auxiliary points (see Fig. 6.1(c)) and N as the number of sections in the finite difference calculations.

The purpose of this section is to illustrate the method of iteration and relaxation by a simple example. Hence the interval $\xi = 0$ to $\xi = 1/2$ is divided for the difference calculation into 2 or 4 sections at most. The exact solution of the finite difference equations could be found immediately in the case of 2 sections; for 4 sections the methods of Section 6.3 would then be better and they are also fairly fast. As a point of interest the exact solutions of the differential and finite difference equations are compared in Table 6.1. Considering the small number of sections, the

TABLE 6.1. Comparison of exact solutions

Solution	N = 2		N = 4			
	T_1	T_2	T_1	T_2	T_3	T_4
Analytical	37·5	70·0	21·2	49·8	65·6	72·6
Finite difference	42·9	71·4	23·4	50·9	66·1	72·9

result of the finite difference calculations is surprisingly good, a fact that is further pursued in Section 6.7.

First the simple method of successive approximations is used. The number of sections is assumed $N = 2$. From Eq. (6.6.5) and $\Delta \xi = \frac{1}{4}$ it follows that $p = 1$. In this case Eq. (6.4.1) becomes:

$$T_n^{(m+1)} = 33 \cdot 3 + 0 \cdot 333 (T_{n+1}^{(m)} + T_{n-1}^{(m)}) \qquad (6.6.7)$$

As an initial guess for the temperature distribution it is assumed that:

$$T_1 = 50 \text{ and } T_2 = 100 \qquad (6.6.8)$$

After the 7th step (see Table 6.2), the approximations to T differ from the exact solutions of the difference equation by only one figure after the decimal point and a higher accuracy would be pointless in view of the small number of sections in the present example.

TABLES 6.2–6. Application of finite difference methods to the example in Section 6.6. Range of variable x divided into two sections. ESD = exact solution of the difference equation. m = number of relaxation step

TABLE 6.2. Successive approximations

m	T_0	T_1	T_2	T_3
0	−50·0	50·0	100·0	100·0
1	−50·0	50·0	83·3	83·3
2	−44·4	44·4	77·8	77·8
3	−44·4	44·4	74·1	74·1
4	−43·2	43·2	72·8	72·8
5	−43·2	43·2	72·0	72·0
6	−42·9	42·9	71·7	71·7
7	−42·9	42·9	71·5	71·5
8	−42·9	42·9	71·5	71·5
ESD	—	42·86	71·43	—

Next a division into 4 sections is used. $\Delta \xi$ is now half as large as previously and hence $p = 4$ according to Eq. (6.6.5). The finite difference equation becomes

$$T_n^{(m+1)} = 11 \cdot 11 + 0 \cdot 444 \, (T_{n+1}^{(m)} + T_{n-1}^{(m)}) \tag{6.6.9}$$

The initial guess for the temperature distribution is assumed as: $T_1 = 50$, $T_2 = T_3 = T_4 = T_5 = 100$. The calculations are not given here, but 27 steps are now necessary before the approximations for the T_ns differ not more from the exact solutions of the finite difference equations than was the case previously for two sections. However, agreement with the exact solutions of the differential equations would now, of course, be better. The improvement in accuracy obtained by doubling the number of sections can be seen from Table 6.1; however the computational work for four sections is 8 times as much as for two sections. It is therefore more practical to obtain first solutions with a division into only a few sections and to use the results as a starting point for further calculations with a finer sectional division.

Next, the relaxation method is applied to the same example with two sections only. With this number of sections, the expression for the residual is

$$q_n = T_{n+1} + T_{n-1} - 3T_n + 100 \tag{6.6.10}$$

Starting with the initial guess for the temperature distribution in Eq. (6.6.8), a solution is obtained by reducing to zero the largest residual in each approximation. Since the temperature pairs: T_1 and T_0, T_2 and

T_3 are connected by the boundary conditions of Eq. (6.6.6) where now $N = 2$, Eq. (6.5.3) cannot be used for relaxing the residuals q_1 and q_2 to zero. Instead the temperature change ΔT_1 which makes the residual q_1 zero for $\Delta T_2 = 0$ is $\Delta T_1 = \frac{1}{4} q_1$, being obtained from Eq. (6.5.2) and from the boundary condition $T_0 = T_1$. Similarly $\Delta T_2 = \frac{1}{2} q_2$, if $\Delta T_1 = 0$ and if one uses the boundary condition $T_2 = T_3$. The same degree of accuracy in the results (Table 6.3) is obtained in about the same number of steps as was used previously by successive approximations. However,

TABLE 6.3 Relaxing largest residual at a time

m	T_0	T_1	q_1	T_2	q_2	T_3
0	−50·0	50·0	0	100·0	−50·0	100·0
1	−50·0	50·0	−25·0	75·0	0	75·0
2	−43·75	43·75	0	75·0	− 6·25	75·0
3	−43·75	43·75	− 3·12	71·88	0	71·88
4	−42·97	42·97	0	71·88	− 0·79	71·88
5	−42·97	42·97	− 0·39	71·49	− 0·01	71·49
6	−42·87	42·87	0·01	71·49	− 0·11	71·49
7	−42·87	42·87	− 0·04	71·44	− 0·01	71·44
ESD	—	42·86	—	71·43	—	—

it is to be noted that the advantages of the relaxation method as compared with the iteration method are to a large degree lost when only two sections are used.

Next under- and over-relaxation is tried. First a few steps were tried with an increase of 50 per cent in the temperature changes necessary to make the residuals zero. This was excessive, but 20 per cent over-relaxation was found to be satisfactory and with it the final solution (see Table 6.4) is reached more rapidly than before.

TABLE 6.4. Over-relaxing by 20 per cent of the temperature changes necessary to reduce residuals to zero

m	T_0	T_1	q_1	T_2	q_2	T_3
0	−50·0	50·0	0	100·0	−50·0	100·0
1	−50·0	50·0	−30·0	70·0	10·0	70·0
2	−41·0	41·0	6	70·0	1·0	70·0
3	−42·8	42·8	−1·2	70·0	2·8	70·0
4	−42·8	42·8	0·5	71·7	− 0·6	71·7
5	−42·8	42·8	0·2	71·4	0	71·4
ESD	—	42·86	—	71·43	—	—

The second device, block relaxation, cannot be expected to be very effective when the number of divisions is only 2. With a temperature change of the amount ΔT in T_1 and T_2, the sum of residuals q_1 and q_2 was changed by an amount

$$\Delta q_1 + \Delta q_2 = -4\Delta T \qquad (6.6.11)$$

For the initial guess it follows that $\Delta q_1 + \Delta q_2 = -50$, and the sum of the residuals would become zero if $\Delta T = -12\cdot5$ according to Eq. (6.6.11). Changing the temperatures by that amount, the individual residuals become $37\cdot5$ and $-37\cdot5$, respectively (Table 6.5). With this step the possibilities of block relaxation are exhausted in the present example.

TABLE 6.5. Block relaxation

m	T_0	T_1	q_1	T_2	q_2	T_3
0	$-50\cdot0$	$50\cdot0$	0	$100\cdot0$	$-50\cdot0$	$100\cdot0$
1	$-37\cdot5$	$37\cdot5$	$37\cdot5$	$87\cdot5$	$-37\cdot5$	$87\cdot5$
ESD	—	$42\cdot86$	—	$71\cdot43$	—	—

Applying group relaxation, we find it useful after some trials to change T_2 by an amount $5\Delta T$ and T_1 by ΔT. The sum of the residuals changes in one step by an amount

$$\Delta q_1 + \Delta q_2 = -8\Delta T \qquad (6.6.12)$$

Initially the sum of the residuals is -50 and it is made zero by $\Delta T = -6\cdot25$ according to Eq. (6.6.12); this yields $T_1 = 43\cdot75$ and $T_2 = 68\cdot75$ (Table 6.6). Thus one comes comparatively close to the final result with only one step.

TABLE 6.6. Group relaxation

m	T_0	T_1	q_1	T_2	q_2	T_3
0	$-50\cdot0$	$50\cdot0$	0	$100\cdot0$	$-50\cdot0$	$100\cdot0$
1	$-43\cdot75$	$43\cdot75$	$-6\cdot25$	$68\cdot75$	$6\cdot25$	$68\cdot75$
ESD	—	$42\cdot86$	—	$71\cdot43$	—	—

Next, the use of multiplying factors is discussed. Suppose that the ratio m of the residuals for two different temperature distributions is the same at all points n:

$$m = \frac{q_n^*}{q_n^{**}} \qquad (6.6.13)$$

Superscripts of one and two stars refer to the first and second temperature distribution respectively. If T_n is the final solution, ΔT_n^* and ΔT_n^{**} are respectively defined by the following equations:

$$T_n^* = T_n + \Delta T_n^* \qquad (6.6.14)$$

$$T_n^{**} = T_n + \Delta T_n^{**} \qquad (6.6.15)$$

We obtain from Eqs. (6.6.13) and (6.5.1)

$$m = \frac{p(T_{n-1} + \Delta T_{n-1}^* + T_{n+1} + \Delta T_{n+1}^*) - (1+2p)(T_n + \Delta T_n^*) + T_{f,\delta}}{p(T_{n-1} + \Delta T_{n-1}^{**} + T_{n+1} + \Delta T_{n+1}^{**}) - (1+2p)(T_n + \Delta T_n^{**}) + T_{f,\delta}} \qquad (6.6.16)$$

Since the residuals of the final solution are zero, all non-starred values can be cancelled in Eq. (6.6.16) because of Eq. (6.2.4). The remaining equation is satisfied for all values of n, only if

$$m = \frac{\Delta T_{n-1}^*}{\Delta T_{n-1}^{**}} = \frac{\Delta T_{n+1}^*}{\Delta T_{n+1}^{**}} = \frac{\Delta T_n^*}{\Delta T_n^{**}} \qquad (6.6.17)$$

Elimination of ΔT_n^* from Eq. (6.6.14) with the help of Eq. (6.6.17) yields:

$$T_n^* = T_n + m \Delta T_n^{**} \qquad (6.6.18)$$

Equations (6.6.15) and (6.6.18) are 2 equations for the unknowns T_n and ΔT_n^{**}. Solving for T_n yields finally:

$$T_n = -\frac{m}{1-m} T_n^{**} + \frac{1}{1-m} T_n^* \qquad (6.6.19)$$

The residuals in Table 6.5, line $m = 1$ (assumed as the one-starred values) and corresponding values in Table 6.6 line $m = 1$ (two-starred values) are in the same ratio and hence from Eq. (6.6.13) it follows that $m = -6$. From Eq. (6.6.19) and the corresponding values in the tables one obtains the final solution: $T_1 = 42 \cdot 9$ and $T_2 = 71 \cdot 4$, which is equal to the exact solution of the finite difference equation.

In order to show how the different relaxation procedures can be combined to obtain solutions as rapidly as possible, the previous example is treated again, but with the range of the variable x divided into 4 sections. Hence $N = 4$ and $p = 4$. The initial guess was purposely made rather poor as shown in Table 6.7. An inspection of the residuals in the first line of that table suggests that large adjustments will be necessary at T_2. First a group relaxation is made with $\Delta T_2 = 2\Delta T$ and $\Delta T_n = \Delta T$ valid for all $n \neq 0$ or 2; from the boundary condition, Eq. (6.6.6), it follows that $\Delta T_0 = -\Delta T$. As a result the sum of the residuals changes by $-13\Delta T$ as follows with the help of Eq. (6.5.2). Now the sum of the initial residuals which is -350 can be relaxed to zero by choosing $\Delta T = -26 \cdot 9$; this was

TABLE 6.7. Applying different relaxation procedures (see text) in order to obtain solutions as quickly as possible. Range of variable x divided into 4 sections. ESD = exact solutions of the difference equation. m = number of relaxation step

m	T_0	T_1	q_1	T_2	q_2	T_3	q_3	T_4	q_4	T_5
0	−50·0	50·0	−150·0	100·0	−200·0	100·0	0	100·0	0	100·0
1	−23·1	23·1	− 15·4	46·2	69·2	73·1	−80·8	73·1	26·9	73·1
2	−23·1	23·1	7·7	51·9	−5·8	67·3	− 5·8	73·1	3·8	73·1
3	−23·7	23·7	0	51·9	−3·5	67·3	− 2·7	73·9	0	73·9
4	−23·3	23·3	0	50·8	0·7	66·2	− 0·7	73·0	0	73·0
ESD	−23·4	23·4	0	50·9	0·1	66·1	− 0·1	72·9	0	72·9

done and results in the temperatures in the second line ($m = 1$) in Table 6.7. The residuals q_2 and q_3 are largest in absolute values, but of opposite sign. For improvement put in a group relaxation, first $\Delta T_2 = \Delta T$, $\Delta T_3 = -\Delta T$ and otherwise $\Delta T_n = 0$; then $q_2 - q_3$ is made zero, if $\Delta T = \frac{1}{26}(q_2 - q_3)$ as follows with the help of Eq. (6.5.2). This yields the values in the third line, where q_1 and q_4 are positive, and q_2 and q_3 are negative, their absolute values being of the same order of magnitude. Hence relaxing to zero the residuals at $n = 1$ and at $n = 4$ is a plausible step. Then all temperatures differ at most by 1·2 units from the exact solution of the finite difference equation. Further improvements are possible; in the next step the residuals q_1 and q_4 are to remain zero and, because they differ little from each other, T_2 and T_3 were each changed by an amount $-\Delta T$. Observing that $\Delta T_0 = -\Delta T_1$ and $\Delta T_4 = \Delta T_5$ as follows from Eq. (6.6.6) with $N = 4$, the requirement $\Delta q_1 = \Delta q_4 = 0$ yields with the help of Eq. (6.5.2) the result that $\Delta T_1 = -\frac{4}{13}\Delta T$ and $\Delta T_4 = -\frac{4}{5}\Delta T$. If $q_2 + q_3$ are to be zero, it follows that $\Delta T = -1·1$. As a result the temperatures differed by only 0·1 units from the exact finite difference solutions. Thus only four steps were necessary in comparison with about 15 to 20 steps when relaxing to zero only one residual at a time. This example clearly shows the advantage of using the more advanced relaxation devices.

6.7 Accuracy of the finite difference solutions

Is the surprisingly good agreement between the exact solutions of the finite difference equation and the differential equation in Table 6.1 fortuitous, or is it to be expected in general? In order to answer the question for a more general case the example dealt with in Section 6.6 was treated analytically (Ref. 6.3) and solutions for a wide range of the parameter φ are compared with those of the finite difference method. The boundary conditions Eq.(6.6.1) read in non-dimensional form:

$$\xi = 0, \quad T = T_b \text{ and } \xi = \frac{1}{2}, \quad \frac{dT}{d\xi} = 0 \qquad (6.7.1)$$

A solution of Eq. (6.6.4) satisfying these boundary conditions is

$$\frac{T - T_{f,\delta}}{T_b - T_{f,\delta}} = \frac{\cosh\left[\varphi\left(\frac{1}{2} - \xi\right)\right]}{\cosh(\varphi/2)} \qquad (6.7.2)$$

The exact and the finite difference solutions are compared in Fig. 6.4 for $\varphi = 1, 2, 3, 4, 6$ and 8. In the finite difference calculations the boundaries were made to coincide with temperature points as indicated in Fig. 6.1(b). The boundary condition of zero heat transfer at the mid-point of the shell was satisfied by assuming the temperature distribution to be symmetrical

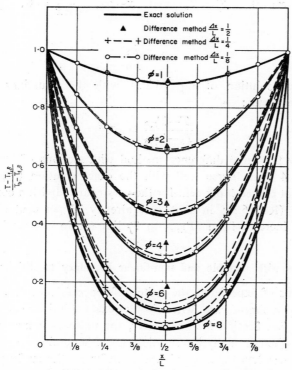

FIG. 6.4. Comparison between the exact solutions of the differential Eq. (6.2.1) and the finite difference Eq. (6.2.4) for the shell in Fig. 6.1(a) with boundary conditions as in Section 6.6 and values of $\varphi = \sqrt{\left(\dfrac{h_\delta L^2}{k\delta}\right)} = 1, 2, 3, 4, 6$ and 8. The whole length of the shell is divided into 2, 4 and 8 finite difference sections.

about that point which is at $x = N\Delta x$: hence $T_{N-1} = T_{N+1}$ with T_{N+1} as the temperature of the auxiliary point $N+1$ which is placed at a distance Δx from the boundary; with the boundary conditions of the present case solutions would not differ significantly, whichever of the two arrangements is used for the temperature points relative to the boundaries as shown in Figs. 6.1(b) and (c). Again, the solutions obtained with the finite difference method are surprisingly good for all values of φ. Even when only two divisions are used, the error is not more than 3 per cent of the maximum temperature difference $T_f - (T)_{x=0}$ occurring in the problem. For φ larger than 8 the shell reaches the temperature of the surrounding medium T_f and then solutions closely approach those for $\varphi \to \infty$, which corresponds to a shell being unlimited in one direction. In this case the boundary conditions are replaced by

$$x = 0, \quad T = T_b \quad \text{and} \quad x \to \infty, \quad \frac{\mathrm{d}T}{\mathrm{d}x} = 0. \tag{6.7.3}$$

Putting

$$\alpha^2 = \frac{h_\delta}{k\delta} \tag{6.7.4}$$

the [analytical solution of Eq. (6.2.1) with the boundary conditions, Eq. (6.7.3) becomes:

$$\frac{T - T_{f,\delta}}{T_b - T_{f,\delta}} = \mathrm{e}^{-\alpha x} \tag{6.7.5}$$

Solutions by the finite difference method with sections of length $\alpha\Delta x = = 1$, 2 and 4 again agree well with the exact solution (Fig. 6.5). The error does not exceed 3 per cent for the very coarse division corresponding to $\alpha\Delta x = 2$ (Ref. 6.3); in that case already 83 per cent of the entire temperature increase from $(T)_{x=0}$ to T_f lies within one section.

6.8 Problems with variable and non-linear boundary conditions

For reasons of expediency the finite difference method has so far been explained for a simple case, where in fact exact solutions can be obtained more easily (see Section 5.2). However, the finite difference method can also be used when the analytical solutions are either difficult or not available, as for instance when the external heat transfer on the surface of shells is (a) of non-linear type (free convection or heat radiation) or (b) when its parameters vary with x. For problems of type (a) the relaxation method would be most suitable. Then the relation between adjustments in temperatures and changes in residuals also contains the unknown temperatures themselves. For these, some approximate values would have to be used and hence residuals could not be reduced exactly to zero at once. This would not make much difference in practice, since a number of adjust-

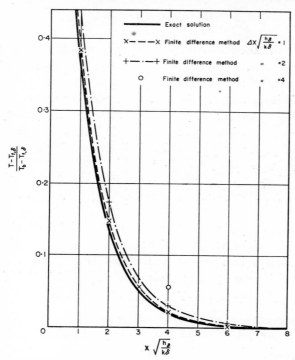

FIG. 6.5. Comparison as in Fig. 6.4, but for a shell extending to infinity.

ments are usually necessary until the residuals are everywhere zero. If in problems of type (b) the heat transfer conditions change rapidly with x, smaller sections must be used.

6.9 Two-dimensional heat flow. Numerical and graphical methods

The two-dimensional case is essentially an extension of the one-dimensional case and hence it can be treated in less detail, especially since the two-dimensional case is, in general, less important for heat transfer in structures.

The equation of steady heat flow in two dimensions with constant thermal conductivity k and with heat sources of strength S is

$$\frac{\partial^2 T}{\partial x^2} + \frac{\partial^2 T}{\partial y^2} = \frac{S}{k} \qquad (6.9.1)$$

$S = 0$ for heat flow in a solid structure where, in general, heat sources are absent. In a thin plate with constant temperature across the section one has

$$S = \frac{q}{\delta_\bullet} \qquad (6.9.2)$$

where δ is the thickness of the plate and q is the external heat flow rate per unit surface area depending on the surface temperature of the plate and on the mode of the external heat transfer.

Suppose $T_{n,l}$ is the temperature at a point with the coordinates $x = n\Delta$ and $y = l\Delta$, where $\Delta = \Delta x = \Delta y$ is the mesh size of a square grid. If the finite difference expression for the second derivative of the temperature in the x-direction, Eq. (6.2.3), and a similar expression for the derivative in the y-direction are added one obtains

$$\frac{\partial^2 T}{\partial x^2} + \frac{\partial^2 T}{\partial y^2} = \frac{1}{\Delta^2}(T_{n+1,l} + T_{n-1,l} + T_{n,l+1} + T_{n,l-1} - 4T_{n,l}) + O(\Delta^2) \quad (6.9.3)$$

where, as before, O means the order of magnitude of the neglected higher terms in the finite difference expressions.

First the heat flow in a solid without heat sources ($S = 0$) is considered and the finite difference equation reads, from Eqs. (6.9.1) and (6.9.2),

$$T_{n+1,l} + T_{n-1,l} + T_{n,l+1} + T_{n,l-1} - 4T_{n,l} = 0 \qquad (6.9.4)$$

As in the one-dimensional case, the truncation error is of the order of magnitude Δ^4. The temperatures at the grid points can be obtained directly from a system of equations for the unknown temperatures. Of these, the equations in which the pair of numbers n and l refer to interior points are of the form of Eq. (6.9.4), and the rest follow from the boundary conditions. However, this appears practical only if the number of grid points is not too high or where electronic computing machines are available. In many cases, solutions obtained with a rather coarse grid are of the desired degree of accuracy or can be used as a starting point for one of the following methods.

Next we discuss the method of successive iterations (see also Section 6.4) or Liebmann's method, as it is frequently called. Liebmann was the first to introduce it and to prove its convergence (Ref. 6.4). Eq. (6.9.4) is solved for $T_{n,l}$ and yields

$$T_{n,l}^{(m+1)} = \tfrac{1}{4}(T_{n+1,l}^{(m)} + T_{n-1,l}^{(m)} + T_{n,l+1}^{(m)} + T_{n,l-1}^{(m)}) \qquad (6.9.5)$$

Again, the superscripts m and $m+1$ indicate two successive approximations. Starting with an assumed initial temperature distribution, improved values are calculated at each point from the surrounding 4 points with the help of Eq. (6.9.5) until the temperatures no longer change.

In the relaxation method the residual is defined by

$$q_{n,l} = T_{n+1,l} + T_{n-1,l} + T_{n,l+1} + T_{n,l-1} - 4T_{n,l} \qquad (6.9.6)$$

The temperatures at each point are changed until the residuals become zero to the desired degree of accuracy by essentially the same procedures as in the one-dimensional case (Ref. 6.5, 6.6).

In the two-dimensional case it is often convenient to express Eq. (6.9.6) by a relaxation pattern (Fig. 6.6) in which the changes of the residuals are given at the centre and at the four surrounding points of a square grid

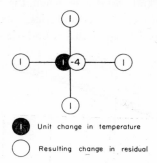

FIG. 6.6. Relaxation pattern for Eq. (6.9.1) with $S = 0$ and for a square grid in the interior of a region.

according to a unit change in the temperature at the centre. As an example of block relaxation, a pattern for a unit change in the temperatures at 4 adjacent points is shown in Fig. 6.7. Other block or group relaxation patterns can easily be derived from Eq. (6.9.6) (Ref. 6.1, 6.2). Over-relaxation

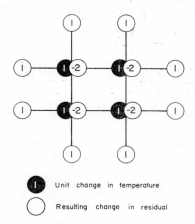

FIG. 6.7. Pattern for a block relaxation at four adjacent points of a square grid in the interior of a region. Otherwise as in Fig. 6.6.

has been found to be particularly suited to machine calculation (Ref. 6.7 and 6.8).

If the boundaries are straight lines and fit a grid with square meshes, they can be made to coincide with grid lines along their entire length. In that case the boundary conditions can be expressed directly by the relevant quantities lying on the boundaries; however, the truncation error in the finite difference expression for the temperature gradient at the boundary may then become large (see Section 6.2 and Fig. 6.3). In cases when this is important and otherwise when the boundaries do not fit the grid, particularly with curved boundaries, auxiliary points are again used for extending the grid beyond the boundaries, as shown in Fig. 6.8.

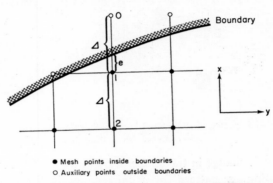

● Mesh points inside boundaries
O Auxiliary points outside boundaries

FIG. 6.8 Satisfying boundary conditions for a square grid by using auxiliary points outside the boundaries.

In that figure the temperature and the component in the x-direction of the temperature gradient at a boundary (subscript b) are:

$$\left.\begin{aligned} T_b &= \frac{e}{\Delta} T_0 + \left(1 - \frac{e}{\Delta}\right) T_1 \\ \left(\frac{\partial T}{\partial x}\right)_b &= \frac{1}{\Delta}\left[\left(\frac{e}{\Delta} - \frac{1}{2}\right) T_2 + \left(\frac{e}{\Delta} + \frac{1}{2}\right) T_0 - \frac{2e}{\Delta} T_1\right] \end{aligned}\right\} \quad (6.9.7)$$

where subscripts 0, 1 and 2 refer to values lying on grid lines parallel to the x-axis; similar expressions are valid on grid lines parallel to the y-axis.

Graphical methods can also be used (Ref. 6.9). They are based on the fact that isothermals and heat flow lines yield a system of orthogonal curves. This follows from a fundamental property of Laplace's differential equation. In order to facilitate the mapping of the heat flow field, the distance between the curves of each kind is chosen so that in a sufficiently small division the curves form squares. This condition, however, can only approximately be fulfilled, since for practical reasons the distances between the curves must not be too small. The condition takes the form that the sum of the lengths of opposite sides in the quasi-squares are equal to each other, or that the distances between opposite sides measured from mid-point to mid-point are equal to each other. It is recommended as being more accurate, that the diagonals in the quasi-squares should be made equal to each other (Ref. 6.10). The method becomes easier if the boundaries are isothermals. For details of construction, particularly for non-isothermal boundaries, see Ref. 6.11. Essentially one proceeds by trial and error. Starting with a free-hand sketch of the isothermals and heat-flow lines, improvements are made with regard to orthogonality of the curves and this is simplified by the additional requirement that the curves form quasi-squares. With some training and experience, the graphical method can give useful results for many engineering purposes.

References

6.1   SOUTHWELL, R. V., *Relaxation Methods in Engineering Science*, Oxford University Press, Oxford (1940).

6.2   ALLEN, D. N. DE G., *Relaxation Methods*, McGraw-Hill, New York (1954).

6.3   SCHUH, H., Differenzenverfahren zum Berechnen von Temperatur-Ausgleichs-vorgängen bei eindimensionaler Wärmeströmung in einfachen und zusammen-gesetzen Körpern, *VDI-Forschungsheft* 459 (1957).

6.4   LIEBMANN, H., Die angenäherte Ermittelung harmonischer Funktionen und konformer Abbildungen, *Sitzungsber. Kgl. Bayr. Akad. d. Wiss., Math.-Phys. Kl.*, 385–416 (1918).

6.4a   WOLF, F., Über die angenäherte numerische Berechnung harmonischer und biharmonischer Funktionen, *Z. Angew. Math. Mech.* **6**, 118–150 (1926).

6.5   EMMONS, H. W., The numerical solution of heat conduction problems. *Trans. A.S.M.E.* **65**, 6, 607–612 (1943).

6.6   DUSINBERRE, G. M., *Heat-transfer calculations by finite differences*, McGraw-Hill, New York (1961).

6.7   FRANKEL, S. P., Convergence rates of iterative treatments of partial differential equations, *Mathematical Tables and Other Aids to Computation*, Vol. 4, 65–75 (1950).

6.8   YOUNG, D., Iterative methods for solving partial difference equations of elliptic type, *Trans. Amer. Math. Soc.* **76**, 92–111 (1954).

6.9   SCHNEIDER, P. J., *Conduction Heat Transfer*, Addison-Wesley, Cambridge, Mass. (1955).

6.10   BETZ, A., *Konforme Abbildung*, Springer, Berlin (1948).

6.11   LUTZ, O., Graphical determination of wall temperatures for heat transfers through walls of arbitrary shape (Trans. from German), NACA TM No. 1280. Washington 1950.

CHAPTER 7

TRANSIENT HEAT FLOW I: ANALYTICAL METHODS

7.1 General

In analytical methods extensive use is made of the principle of super-position of solutions. This is possible only if the differential equation and the boundary conditions are linear in temperature and if the thermal properties ρ, c and k are independent of temperature. The simplest way to deal with non-linear boundary conditions, as, for instance, heat transfer by free convection or thermal radiation, is to replace them by approximate linear expressions (see Section 3.1.3), but the accuracy of the resulting solutions is of course limited. Exact solutions for boundary conditions of this type can be obtained by integral equations. These in turn can be solved by methods of iteration with any desired degree of accuracy or by step-wise procedures (semi-analytical methods) with a limited accuracy which is, however, sufficient for most practical purposes.

7.2 A survey of important analytical methods

The following methods are considered here: (1) Separation of variables. (2) Laplace transformation, (3) the use of sources and sinks, (4) satisfying boundary conditions by images and (5) Duhamel's method and integral equations. These methods are briefly outlined here for one-dimensional heat flow, extensions to two- and three-dimensional heat flow can be made in most cases, although solutions become more complicated (see Ref. 3.1.1).

The starting point for the first method is a particular solution which is the product of two functions of one variable each:

$$T_p = X_1(t) \cdot X_2(x) \qquad (7.2.1)$$

t is the time and x the space variable. Introducing T_p as given by Eq. (7.2.1) into Eq. (3.1.16) and collecting functions of t on one side and functions of x on the other, one obtains

$$\frac{1}{\varkappa X_1(t)} \frac{dX_1(t)}{dt} = \frac{1}{X_2(x)} \frac{d^2 X_2(x)}{dx^2} = -\lambda^2 \qquad (7.2.2)$$

Because in Eq. (7.2.2) a function of x only is equal to a function of t only, both must be equal to a constant which is here taken as $-\lambda^2$. Solutions of the double equation are

$$X_1(t) = e^{-\lambda^2 \varkappa t} \quad \text{and} \quad X_2(x) = \begin{cases} \cos \lambda x \\ \sin \lambda x \end{cases} \tag{7.2.3}$$

For a certain value of λ the particular solution T_p is

$$T_p = [A(\lambda) \cos \lambda x + B(\lambda) \sin \lambda x] e^{-\lambda^2 \varkappa t} \tag{7.2.4}$$

where A and B are functions of λ. By a suitable choice of values for λ it is possible to satisfy boundary conditions if they are homogeneous and if the region of the variable x is finite. The most important homogeneous boundary conditions are of the form $\vartheta = 0$, $\dfrac{\partial \vartheta}{\partial x} = 0$ or $\vartheta + B \dfrac{\partial \vartheta}{\partial x} = 0$, where ϑ is a temperature or a temperature difference and B a constant. By suitably shifting the zero point of the temperature, such that $\vartheta = T - T_r$ where T_r is a constant reference temperature, it is often possible to make boundary conditions homogeneous. For example, assume $T = T_w = \text{const.}$ at a boundary; if $\vartheta = T - T_w$ is used instead of T, the boundary condition becomes homogeneous, i.e. $\vartheta = 0$. By suitably choosing values of $A(\lambda)$ and $B(\lambda)$ and by superposing solutions of all possible values of λ, the initial conditions for the temperature can also be satisfied.

In the second method a functional transformation, the Laplace transformation (Refs. 3.1.1 and 7.2.1) is used; it is denoted by the symbol $\mathcal{L}\{\ \}$ and defined by

$$\overline{T}(x,p) = \mathcal{L}\{T\} = \int_0^\infty e^{-pt} T(x,t) \, dt \tag{7.2.5}$$

$\overline{T}$ is called the Laplace transform of T and p is a number whose real part is positive. An important relation for the time derivative of the temperature can be found from Eq. (7.2.5) and with the help of a partial integration:

$$\mathcal{L}\left\{\frac{\partial T}{\partial t}\right\} = p\overline{T} - T_i(x) \tag{7.2.6}$$

$T_i(x)$ is the initial temperature distribution. The derivatives of T with respect to the space variable become by the Laplace transformation:

$$\mathcal{L}\left\{\frac{\partial^n T}{\partial x^n}\right\} = \frac{\partial^n \overline{T}}{\partial x^n} \tag{7.2.7}$$

If the Laplace transformation is applied to both sides of Eq. (3.1.16), one obtains with the help of Eqs. (7.2.6) and (7.2.7):

$$\varkappa \frac{\mathrm{d}^2 \overline{T}}{\mathrm{d}x^2} - p\,\overline{T} + T_i(x) = 0 \tag{7.2.8}$$

TABLE 7.1. Table of Laplace transforms

No.	$\overline{T} = \mathcal{L}\{T\}$	$T = \mathcal{L}^{-1}\{\overline{T}\}$	
(1)	$\dfrac{1}{p}$	1	
(2)	$\dfrac{1}{p^{\alpha+1}} \quad \alpha > -1$	$\dfrac{t^\alpha}{\Gamma(\alpha+1)}$	
(3)	$\dfrac{1}{p+\alpha}$	$\exp\{-\alpha t\}$	
(4)	$\dfrac{e^{-x\sqrt{p}}}{p}$	$\mathrm{erfc}\left(\dfrac{x}{2\sqrt{t}}\right)$	a
(5)	$\dfrac{e^{-x\sqrt{p}}}{p^{1+\frac{n}{2}}}, \quad n = 0,1,2,\ldots$	$(4t)^{\frac{n}{2}}\, i^n\, \mathrm{erfc}\left(\dfrac{x}{2\sqrt{t}}\right)$	b
(6)	$\dfrac{e^{-x\sqrt{p}}}{(\sqrt{p}+\alpha)\,p^{1+\frac{n}{2}}}$	$\dfrac{1}{(-\alpha)^{n+1}}[\exp\{\alpha x + t\alpha^2\}]\mathrm{erfc}\left(\dfrac{x}{2\sqrt{t}}+\alpha\sqrt{t}\right) - $ $- \dfrac{1}{(-\alpha)^{n+1}}\displaystyle\sum_{j=0}^{n}(-2\alpha\sqrt{t})^j\, i^j\, \mathrm{erfc}\left(\dfrac{x}{2\sqrt{t}}\right)$	

[a] The function $\mathrm{erfc}(x)$ is defined by Eq. (7.4.3).
[b] The function $i^n\,\mathrm{erfc}(x)$ is defined by Eq. (7.4.12).

The boundary conditions for $\overline{T}$ are obtained in a similar way. As a consequence of the transformation the partial differential equation for T is replaced by an ordinary differential equation for $\overline{T}$ which in general is easier to solve. By applying a Laplace transformation to a partial differential equation, the number of independent variables can be reduced by one and this is the main advantage of the method. After the solution for $\overline{T}$, which satisfies the corresponding boundary conditions, has been found, it is re-transformed by an inverse Laplace transformation and thus the solution of the original variable T is obtained. The transformations are simplified by a number of theorems and further help is given by tables between functions of the original and the transformed variables, see Ref. 3.1.1 and Table 7.1. If the solutions for $\overline{T}$ do not lead to functions contained in tables of Laplace transforms, re-transforming to the original variable T is in general the more difficult part of the method.

Thirdly, the method of sources and sinks is based on particular solutions which correspond to instantaneous or continuous heat sources at a certain point. With their help it is possible to solve initial value problems by integration. Assuming one-dimensional linear heat flow in an infinite body, the solution for an instantaneous plane source is (Ref. 3.1.1):

$$T_p = \frac{S}{2\sqrt{(\pi k \rho c t)}}\exp\left\{-\frac{(x-x')^2}{4\varkappa t}\right\} \qquad (7.2.9)$$

S is the amount of heat per unit area concentrated in the plane x' at the time $t = 0$. It can be easily verified that T_p is a solution of Eq. (3.1.16).

Fourthly, boundary conditions can be satisfied by placing outside the region of the space variable a finite or infinite number of sources in an arrangement similar to the images produced by mirrors. In simple cases the boundary conditions are satisfied by reasons of symmetry. Take for instance an instantaneous plane source at $x' = a$ in a semi-infinite region $x > 0$ with zero heat flow as the boundary condition at the plane $x = 0$. This condition is simply satisfied by placing an instantaneous plane source of equal intensity at $x' = -a$. If a plane source is in the middle of a slab of width $2a$, with zero heat flow at the boundaries $x = 0$ and $x = 2a$, these conditions are satisfied by an infinite number of sources of equal intensities at $x' = -a, \pm 3a, \pm 5a, \pm 7a, \ldots$. If the plane source is not in the middle of the slab, but, say, at $x' = b \neq a$, images and repeated images have to be arranged by mirroring the original source at $x = 0$ and $x = 2a$. As a result the images are at $x' = -b, \pm(4a-b), \pm(4a+b), \pm(8a-b), \pm(8a+b), \ldots$

For other boundary conditions and for composite bodies this method can be generalized by assuming that the strength of the images differs from that of the original source. Then it is of advantage to interpret the method of images as reflections and transmissions of "waves" emanating from the original source (see Section 7.5.5).

Fifthly, Duhamel's method and related integral equations (Ref. 3.1.1) are considered. These methods are useful for satisfying certain time-dependent and even non-linear boundary conditions. Suppose that $\vartheta_{p,1}$ is the particular solution for the temperature in a body with zero initial temperature and with the temperature unity at the surface for $t > 0$. If the surface temperature T_r is given as a function of time and if the initial temperature T_i is uniformly distributed in the body, the solution is (Ref. 3.1.1)

$$T(x,t) - T_i = \int_0^t [T_r(t') - T_i]\frac{\partial \vartheta_{p,1}(x,t-t')}{\partial t}\,dt' \qquad (7.2.10)$$

TABLE 7.2(a). Thermal properties of some materials of interest in aeronautics (Metric units). Because the thermal properties, particularly for heat conduction, often depend on the precise chemical composition, the given values are only approximate

	T °C	ρ kg/m³	T °C	k kcal/(ms°C)	T °C	c kcal/(kg°C)	Melting point °C	ρc kcal/(m³°C)
Metals:								
Magnesium	20	1740	20	0·035	20	0·245	650	430
Beryllium	20	1840	20–250	0·036–0·031	20–250	0·42–0·59	1280	770–1080
	800	1840	800	0·021	800	0·74		1362
Aluminium	20	2700	20	0·057	800	0·211	660	570
Titanium	20	4510	20	0·0041	0–220	0·129	1660	580
			600	0·0037				
Nickel	20	8900	20–250	0·017–0·011	20–250	0·11–0·12	1460	980–1070
	800	8900	800	0·014	800	0·13		1160
Copper	20	8940	20	0·092	20	0·093	1084	830
	1000	8360						
Molybdenum	20	10200	20–250	0·032–0·030	20–250	0·061–0·063	2600	620–640
	800	10100	800	0·028	800	0·070		710
Tungsten	18	19300	20	0·040	20–100	0·032	3380	620
Alloys:								
Magnesium HK31A	20	1800	20	0·025	20	0·25	590–640	450
Aluminium 2024	20	2770	25	0·029	20	0·22	500–640	610
			200	0·039	200	0·23		
Steel (carbon)	20	7840	100–300	0·012	100–300	0·12–0·13	1170–1480	930–1000
			600	0·009	600	0·18		
Steel, stainless 17-7PH	20	7650	150	0·004	20–250	0·12	1370–1480	920

Material								
Nimonic 80A	20	8200	100	0·0029	20–100	0·103	1360–1390	845
			900	0·0066	20–900	0·128		
Refractory materials								
Alumina (Al₂O₃) (sintered)	20	3689	20–250	0·012–0·0040	20–250	0·195–0·225	2020	720–830
			800	0·0017	800	0·250		
Titanium carbide	20	4900	20	0·0041			3250	310
Graphite	20	1700	20	0·045	38	0·18	3590ᵃ	480
	250	1659	250	0·030	250	0·291		680
	800	1579	800	0·015	800	0·432		
Transparent materials								
Silica glass (96% silica)	20	2210	100	3·4 × 10⁻⁴	20	0·18	1540ᵇ	400
			600	5·0 × 10⁻⁴	500	0·29		
			1200	7·3 × 10⁻⁴				
Sodalime glass	20	2490	100	2·2 × 10⁻⁴	20	0·200		500
Acrylics (transparencies)	20	1200	20	4–6 × 10⁻⁵	20	0·30	720ᵇ	360
Plastics								
Plastics (Polyester reinforced by glass fibres)	20	1700	20	6 × 10⁻⁵	40	0·25		425
					205	0·31		
Insulating materials								
Glass wool (approx.)	20	96	93	1 × 10⁻⁵	20	0·2		20
			200	1·5 × 10⁻⁵	20–1000	0·26		
			320	2 × 10⁻⁵				
			540	3·7 × 10⁻⁵				

ᵃ Sublimation point at atmospheric pressure.
ᵇ Softening point.

TABLE 7.2(b). Thermal properties of some materials of interest in aeronautics (British units.) Because the thermal properties, particularly for heat conduction, often depend on the precise chemical composition, the given values are only approximate

	T °F	ρ lb/ft³	ρ lb/in³	T °F	k Btu/(ft h°F)	T °F	c Btu/(lb°F)	Melting point °F	ρc Btu/(ft³ °F)
Metals:									
Magnesium	70	109	0·0630	70	84·6	70	0·245	1202	27
Beryllium	70	115	0·0666	70–480	87–75	70–480	0·42–0·59	2340	48–68
	1470	115	0·0666	1470	51	1470	0·74		85
Aluminium	70	168	0·0978	70	138	70	0·211	1220	35
Titanium	70	281	0·163	70	99	32–430	0·129	3020	36
				1110	89				
Nickel	70	555	0·322	68–480	53–39	70–480	0·11–0·12	2660	61–66
	1470	555	0·322	1470	43·5	1470	0·13		72
Copper	70	558	0·323	70	222	70	0·093	1980	52
	1832	522	0·303						
Molybdenum	70	636	0·369	70–480	77–73	70–480	0·061–0·063	4710	39–40
	1832	630	0·365	1470	68	1470	0·070		44
Tungsten	70	1200	0·697	64	97	70–212	0·032	6120	38
Alloys:									
Magnesium HK31A	70	112	0·0650	70	60·5	70	0·25	1090–1190	28
Aluminium 2024	70	173	0·100	77	70	70	0·22	935–1180	38
				392	94·3	390	0·23		
Steel (carbon)	70	490	0·284	212–570	30	212–570	0·12–0·13	2100–2700	59–64
				1110	22	1110	0·18		

Material									
Steel, stainless 17-7PH	70	477	0·276	302	9·7	70-480	0·12	2500-2700	57
Nimonic 80A	70	511	0·296	212	7·0	70-212	0·103	2480-2530	53
				1650	16·0	70-1650	0·128		
Refractory materials									
Alumina (Al_2O_3) (sintered)	70	230	0·133	70-480	29-9·7	70-482	0·195-0·225	3670	45-52
				1470	4·1	1470	0·250		
Titanium carbide	70	306	0·177	70	9·9	100	0·18	5880	19
Graphite	70	106	0·0615	70	109	482	0·291	6500[a]	30
	480	104	0·0600	482	73	1472	0·432		43
	1470	98·5	0·0570	1470	36				
Transparent materials									
Silica glass (96% silica)	70	138	0·08	212	0·82	70	0·18	2800[b]	25
				1110	1·21	930	0·29		
				2190	1·77				
Sodalime glass	70	155	0·09	212	0·53	70	0·200	1330[b]	31
Acrylics (transparencies)	70	75	0·043	70	0·1-0·15	70	0·30		23
Plastics									
Plastics (Polyester reinforced by glass fibres)	70	106	0·061	70	0·15	104	0·25		27
						401	0·31		
Insulating materials									
Glass wool (approx.)	70	6	0·0035	200	0·025	70	0·2		1·2
				400	0·037	70-1830	0·26		
				600	0·049				
				1000	0·089				

[a] Sublimation point at atmospheric pressure
[b] Softening point

Equation (7.2.10) is also valid in cases of external heat transfer by forced convection, (see Eq. (3.1.7)), if $T_r(t)$ is the reference temperature of the external medium and $\vartheta_{p,1}$ is the solution for the temperature T_r equal to unity. However, the heat transfer coefficient must then remain constant and this is a severe limitation in aeronautical applications because both the reference temperature and the coefficient of external heat transfer change in general with speed and altitude.

Because of these difficulties one is also interested in solutions for which the rate of heat flow at the surface is given. This type of solution also permits extensions to non-linear boundary conditions. Assume $\vartheta_{p,2}$ to be a particular solution for the temperature in a body with zero initial temperature and with a constant rate of heat flow of unit intensity at the surface. By a reasoning similar to that which yields Eq. (7.2.10), the solution for an arbitrary rate of heat flow $q_w(t)$ at the surface of the body is (Ref. 3.1.1)

$$T(x,t)-T_i = \int_0^t q_w(t') \frac{\partial \vartheta_{p,2}(x,t-t')}{\partial t} \, dt' \qquad (7.2.11)$$

The above integral may be used to satisfy general boundary conditions of the form

$$q_w(t) = F[T(0,t),t] \qquad (7.2.12)$$

where F is an arbitrary function of the surface temperature $T(0,t)$ and the time t. If Eq. (7.2.11) is taken at the wall ($x=0$) and if $q_w(t')$ in Eq. (7.2.11) is eliminated with the help of Eq. (7.2.12) the following integral equation is obtained

$$T(0,t)-T_i = \int_0^t F[T(0,t'),t'] \frac{\partial}{\partial t}[\vartheta_{p,2}(0,t-t')] \, dt' \qquad (7.2.13)$$

for the unknown wall temperature $T(0,t)$. The integral equation is non-linear for non-linear boundary conditions. Once the wall temperature is known, the temperature inside the body can be found by standard analytical methods (see Ref.3.1.1).

An important property of the solutions can be directly read from Eqs. (7.2.10) and (7.2.11). Suppose either the temperature at the surface T_w ($=T_r$ in Eq. 7.2.10) or the rate of heat flow at the wall $q_w(t)$ is the sum of a number of components

$$T_w(t) = T_{w1}(t)+T_{w2}(t)+\dots \qquad (7.2.14)$$

or

$$q_w(t) = q_{w1}(t)+q_{w2}(t)+\dots \qquad (7.2.15)$$

respectively. If $\vartheta_1(x,t)$, $\vartheta_2(x,t),\dots$ are solutions which are initially zero and which correspond to the respective surface temperatures $T_{w1}(t)-T_i$,

$T_{w2}(t)$, $T_{w3}(t)$, or to the respective heat flow rates $q_{w1}(t)$, $q_{w2}(t)$,..., then the solution for zero initial temperature and for a given $T_w(t)$ or $q_w(t)$ is the sum of the component solutions:

$$T(x,t)-T_i = \vartheta_1(x,t)+\vartheta_2(x,t)+... \qquad (7.2.16)$$

7.3 Heating of shells with uniformly distributed temperatures

A simple, but important structural element is a shell heated from one side. Uniform temperature is assumed throughout the thickness of the shell and this is true under the conditions stated in Section 3.2. The assumption is in general valid for thin metal shells exposed to heating of moderate intensity. The rate of surface heat flow q_w is assumed to be uniformly distributed. The temperature of the shell with thickness δ can be calculated from

$$\rho_M c_M \delta \frac{dT_w}{dt} = q_w \qquad (7.3.1)$$

The subscript M refers to the material of the shell and q_w depends in general on T_w (see Section 3.1.3). If q_w is a function of only one of the two variables T_w or t, Eq. (7.3.1) can be integrated directly, although in the first case the solution is obtained in implicit form, that is, t is a function of T_w. If q_w is an arbitrary function of both T_w and t, the solution can be obtained by standard approximate methods (see for instance, Ref. 7.3.1). If q_w is due to heat transfer by forced convection as in Eq. (3.1.7), with the heat transfer coefficient h and the external medium temperature T_f both varying with time only, a general solution of Eq. (7.3.1) is

$$T_w(t^*) = \left[\exp\left\{-\int_0^{t^*} h\,dt^*\right\}\right]\left[T_w(0)+\int_0^{t^*} hT_f\left(\exp\left\{\int_0^{t^*} h\,dt^*\right\}\right)dt^*\right] \qquad (7.3.2)$$

where

$$t^* = \frac{t}{\rho_M c_M \delta}$$

The numerical evaluation of the expression on the right-hand side of Eq. (7.3.2) is often inconvenient, because $\exp\left\{-\int_0^{t^*} h\,dt^*\right\}$ may become small and $\exp\left\{\int_0^{t^*} h\,dt^*\right\}$ large. Then it is often more practical to find solutions by the finite difference method of Section 8.4.

If both h and T_f are constants, Eq. (7.3.2) simplifies to

$$T_w(t) = T_f+(T_w(0)-T_f)\exp\left\{-\frac{th}{\rho_M c_M \delta}\right\}. \qquad (7.3.3)$$

Obviously $(\rho_M c_M \delta)/h$ can be considered as a time constant which may be useful for estimating the effectiveness of a shell as a heat sink. For values of h in high speed flight see Chapter 2. Solutions of Eq. (7.3.2) can be given in closed form for particular cases. One solution of this type is given in Ref. 7.3.2 for constant h, but variable T_f. This quantity was assumed to depend on the Mach number as follows: $M = M_i + B_1 t + B_2 t^2$ ($M_i =$ = initial Mach number, B_1 and B_2 constants).

Suppose heat transfer on the surface of the shell occurs both by forced convection and by thermal radiation. Then, with C_R as the radiation coefficient and T_∞ as the ambient air temperature, Eq. (7.3.1) becomes

$$\rho_M c_M \delta \frac{\mathrm{d}T_w}{\mathrm{d}t} = h(T_f - T_w) - C_R(T_w^4 - T_\infty^4) \tag{7.3.4}$$

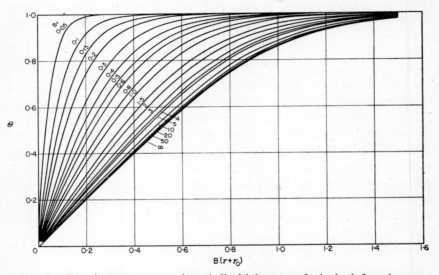

FIG. 7.1. Transient temperatures in a shell with heat transfer by both forced convection and heat radiation at one surface and zero heat flow at the other surface. Uniform temperature distribution in the shell. For Θ, τ, B and τ_0 see Eqs. (7.3.5) and (7.3.8).

Next, the equilibrium temperature T_g is introduced as defined in Section 2.9† in which a method is also given for calculating T_g. Further, on introducing the non-dimensional quantities

$$\Theta = \frac{T_w}{T_g}, \quad B = \frac{C_R T_g^3}{h} \quad \text{and} \quad \tau = \frac{ht}{\rho_M c_M \delta} \tag{7.3.5}$$

Equation (7.3.4) becomes

$$\frac{\mathrm{d}\Theta}{\mathrm{d}\tau} = 1 - \Theta + B(1 - \Theta^4) \tag{7.3.6}$$

---

† T_f and C_R correspond to T_{aw} and εC_σ respectively in Section 2.9.

If all the quantities except T_w and t are constant, a solution for Θ in a closed, but inverse form is

$$\tau = \int_{\Theta_i}^{\Theta} \frac{d\Theta}{1-\Theta+B(1-\Theta^4)} \tag{7.3.7}$$

where $\Theta_i = T_{w,i}/T_g$ with $T_{w,i}$ as the initial temperature of the shell at $\tau = 0$. In aeronautics this solution corresponds to an instantaneous change of speed with constant heat transfer parameters. Equation (7.3.7) has been solved on a digital computer and results are presented in Fig. 7.1 in the form of curves for $\Theta = F[B(\tau+\tau_0)]$ with B as the parameter. τ_0 is found from the initial temperature Θ_i as

$$\tau_0 = \int_0^{\Theta_i} \frac{d\Theta}{1-\Theta+B(1-\Theta^4)} \tag{7.3.8}$$

and $B\tau_0$ can be read directly from Fig. 7.1.

7.4 Initial phase of heat penetration into solid bodies. Thermal shock

In many cases the early phases of heat transfer are of particular interest. In slabs the heat flow is assumed to be directed normal to the surfaces and in shells parallel to them, see Fig. 3.3. Heat transfer on one boundary often dominates in intensity and then, for simplicity, zero heat transfer is assumed at the other surface. During the initial phase of transient heat flow the effects of temperature changes on the heated surface do not penetrate to the other surface. During this period the thickness of the shell has no influence and the temperature distribution is the same as in a semi-infinite body of the same material, and with the same boundary condition. If the method of images (see Section 7.5.5) is applicable, solutions of this type in suitable combinations can even be used in a later phase when the finite size of the body must be considered.

Consider a semi-infinite body in the region $x \geqslant 0$ with a uniform initial temperature T_i and with external heat transfer by forced convection at the surface $x = 0$. At infinity $(x \to \infty)$ the temperature gradient is to vanish. T_f is the external reference temperature and h the heat transfer coefficient. According to standard text-books (Ref. 3.1.1) the solution for one-dimensional heat flow is:

$$\Theta_{\text{si}}^{(1)}(\xi, Y) = \frac{T-T_i}{T_f-T_i} = \text{erfc}(\xi) - [\exp\{2\xi Y+Y^2\}]\,\text{erfc}\,(\xi+Y) \tag{7.4.1}$$

The non-dimensional quantities in the equation are

$$\xi = \frac{x}{2\sqrt{(\varkappa t)}} \quad \text{and} \quad Y = \frac{h}{k}\sqrt{(\varkappa t)} \tag{7.4.2}$$

and the function occurring in Eq. (7.4.1) is defined by

$$\mathrm{erfc}\,(x) = 1 - \frac{2}{\sqrt{\pi}} \int_0^x e^{-\eta^2} d\eta \qquad (7.4.3)$$

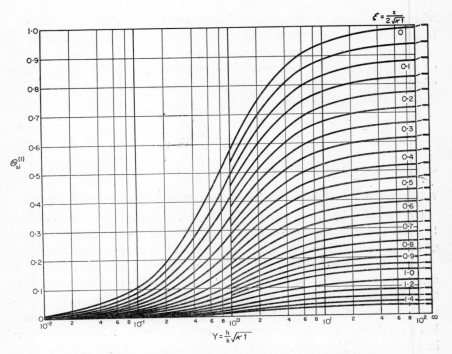

FIG. 7.2. Transient temperature distribution in a semi-infinite body due to forced convection at the surface. Also applicable to the "early" phase of heat flow in a slab. Uniformly distributed initial temperatures at $t = 0$ and constant parameters for the external heat transfer. For $\Theta_{si}^{(1)}$ see Eq. (7.4.1).

The second term on the right-hand side of Eq. (7.4.3) is generally known as the error function. A useful expansion of erfc(x) valid for large values of x is

$$\mathrm{erfc}\,(x) = \frac{1}{\sqrt{\pi}} e^{-x^2} \left(\frac{1}{x} - \frac{1}{2x^3} + \frac{1.3}{2^2 x^5} - \frac{1.3.5}{2^3 x^7} + \ldots \right) \qquad (7.4.4)$$

The series converges asymptotically for $x \to \infty$, if a finite number of terms is taken (semi-convergent series). Short tables for the error function are given in most text books on heat conduction, for instance in Ref. 3.1.1, and a more extensive table is given in Ref. 7.4.1. For large values of the time t, or for medium values of the time but large values of h, Eq. (7.4.1) reduces to

$$\frac{T-T_i}{T_f-T_i} = \text{erfc}\,(\xi) \tag{7.4.5}$$

and this is also the solution if the surface temperature $T_w = T_f$ is given. Figure 7.2 contains a general chart for the solution of Eq. (7.4.1). The surface temperature is obtained by putting $\xi = 0$ in Eq. (7.4.1)

$$\frac{T_w-T_i}{T_f-T_i} = 1-[\exp\{Y^2\}]\text{erfc}\,(Y) \tag{7.4.6}$$

This expression corresponds to the uppermost curve in Fig. 7.2.

In a number of aeronautical applications, particularly for a severe rate of heating, the difference between the reference temperature of the external medium and the wall temperature is so large that the changes in the latter quantity have no practical influence on the heat transfer. In that case it suffices to assume that the rate of heat flow is known on the surface. Frequently the initial temperature T_i at $t = 0$ is constant and in the simplest case the intensity of heat flow q_w is also constant for $t \geqslant 0$. The solution is (Ref. 3.1.1)

$$T-T_i = \frac{2q_w}{k}\,V(\varkappa t)\,\text{ierfc}\left(\frac{x}{2\,V(\varkappa t)}\right) \tag{7.4.7}$$

where ierfc is a function defined later on by Eq. (7.4.14).

Next, the rate of heat flow at the surface is of a more general form:

$$q_w = -k\left(\frac{\partial T}{\partial x}\right)_{x=0} = Dt^{n/2} \tag{7.4.8}$$

for $t \geqslant 0$. n is an integer. Applying the second Laplace transform of Table 7.1 to the boundary condition. Eq. (7.4.8), yields

$$-k\left(\frac{\partial \bar{T}}{\partial x}\right)_{x=0} = D\,\frac{\Gamma\left(1+\dfrac{n}{2}\right)}{p^{1+(n/2)}} \tag{7.4.9}$$

where $\Gamma\left(1+\dfrac{n}{2}\right)$ is the gamma function of the argument $1+\dfrac{n}{2}$. With this boundary condition, a constant initial temperature T_i and a vanishing temperature gradient at $x \to \infty$, the solution of Eq. (7.2.8) becomes:

$$\bar{T}-\frac{T_i}{p} = \frac{D}{V(\varrho ck)}\,\frac{\Gamma\left(1+\dfrac{n}{2}\right)}{p^{(3+n)/2}}\exp\left\{-x\,\Bigg/\left(\frac{p}{\varkappa}\right)\right\} \tag{7.4.10}$$

Re-transforming with the help of the fifth transform of Table 7.1 yields the final solution for the temperature distribution:

$$T - T_i = \frac{D}{V(\rho c k)}\left[\Gamma\left(1 + \frac{n}{2}\right)\right](4t)^{(n+1)/2}i^{n+1}\mathrm{erfc}\left(\frac{x}{2\sqrt{(\varkappa t)}}\right) \quad (7.4.11)$$

$i^n\mathrm{erfc}(x)$ is a repeated integral of the error function as defined by

$$i^n\mathrm{erfc}(x) = \int_x^\infty i^{n-1}\mathrm{erfc}(\eta)\,d\eta, \quad n = 1, 2, 3 \ldots \quad (7.4.12)$$

with

$$i^0\mathrm{erfc}(x) = \mathrm{erfc}(x) \quad (7.4.13)$$

x in Eqs. (7.4.12) to (7.4.15) is an arbitrary variable. For the particular case $n = 1$ one obtains from Eqs. (7.4.12) and (7.4.13)

$$\mathrm{ierfc}(x) = \frac{1}{\sqrt{\pi}}e^{-x^2} - x\,\mathrm{erfc}(x) \quad (7.4.14)$$

Obviously, the right-hand side of Eq. (7.4.7) is most simply expressed with the help of the function ierfc. The repeated error function, which is important for heat conduction problems, is tabulated in Ref. 3.1.1 for $n = 1$ to 6, and for higher values of n it can be calculated with the help of a recurrence formula:

$$2n\,i^n\mathrm{erfc}(x) = i^{n-2}\mathrm{erfc}(x) - 2x\,i^{n-1}\mathrm{erfc}(x) \quad (7.4.15)$$

For a rate of heat flow at the surface as given by Eq. (7.4.8) the surface temperature is obtained from Eq. (7.4.11) by putting there $x = 0$:

$$T_w - T_i = \frac{\Gamma\left(1 + \dfrac{n}{2}\right)}{\Gamma\left(\dfrac{3+n}{2}\right)}\frac{q_w\sqrt{t}}{V(\rho c k)} \quad (7.4.16)$$

because

$$i^n\mathrm{erfc}(0) = \frac{1}{2^n\Gamma\left(1 + \dfrac{n}{2}\right)} \quad (7.4.17)$$

which follows from Eq. (7.4.15).

A further quantity of importance is the penetration depth b. For a uniform initial temperature it is defined as the distance from the heated surface where a certain temperature increase, say 5 per cent of the corresponding value at the surface, is already noticeable. From an inspection of Eqs. (7.4.5), (7.4.7) and (7.4.1) it follows, with the help of Table I in Appendix II of the 2nd ed. of Ref. 3.1.1 that the penetration depth is

$$b = a\sqrt{(\varkappa t)} \quad (7.4.18)$$

where the value of the quantity a depends on the surface conditions: $a = 2 \cdot 8$ for constant temperatures and $a = 2 \cdot 3$ for constant rates of heat flow. For forced convection with constant values for h and T_f, a varies from $a = 2 \cdot 3$ for $Y < 0 \cdot 1$ to $a = 2 \cdot 8$ for $Y > 10$.

Sudden exposure of a structure or a solid to high intensity heat transfer is often called a thermal shock. It occurs during flight in the dense parts of the Earth's atmosphere at the surface of a vehicle subject to high rates of acceleration, as for instance obtained by rocket propulsion, and during re-entry into the atmosphere. It also occurs at the walls of rocket nozzles where rates of heat transfer are high due to the flow of the exhaust gases.

If we disregard the possibilities of controlling the external heat transfer by fluid injection or otherwise there are two different ways to protect the structure against heating: by using (a) a heat sink consisting of a material of high thermal conductivity and high heat capacity or (b) a shield of a non-brittle material of poor conductivity. In the first case heat spreads quickly inside the material and thus excessive surface temperatures are avoided. In the second case only a thin surface layer is heated, but by far the major part of the structure remains unaffected; the surface layer may lose its strength, undergo chemical reactions or even become ablated, but the material must not be brittle in order to withstand the thermal stresses which are generally large. In case of liquefaction or evaporation at the surface, additional amounts of heat are absorbed and this contributes further to protecting the rest of the structure.

In a heat sink the heat capacity of the material is used to absorb the thermal shock. The penetration depth in a semi-infinite solid is a measure of the minimum thickness of a thermal shield in which the surface temperatures are a minimum. Suppose that the inside of a shield (a) is thermally well insulated against the rest of the structure and (b) may experience a substantial temperature increase. Then the thickness of the shield need only be a little more than half the penetration depth, in order to obtain minimum surface temperatures, because "heat waves" penetrating from the heated surface into the shield are "reflected" at the inside of the shield and return to its outer surface after covering a total distance twice the thickness of the shield (see also Section 7.5.5). A further increase in the thickness of the shield would not result in reduced surface temperatures. If, however, the temperature increase at the inside of the shield is to remain small, then the thickness of the shield must be equal to, or exceed the full penetration thickness.

The influence of the thermal properties of materials on the characteristic quantities of a thermal shock follows from Eqs. (7.4.6), (7.4.16) and (7.4.18) under the assumption of constant thermal properties. The surface temperature minus initial temperature decreases with increasing values of $\sqrt{(\rho ck)}$ and is inversely proportional to this quantity for the particular cases when the rate of heat flow at the surface is either constant or varies as in Eq. (7.4.8). The penetration thickness is proportional to $\sqrt{\varkappa}$. A summary of some materials of interest and their characteristic properties is given in Table 7.2; for more information see Ref. 7.4.2.

In the second method for protecting structures poor conductors are used and the "penetration" thickness as defined earlier is a measure of how far the heat spreads into the structure. It is also a measure for the thickness of that layer in the shield which in most cases cannot be used for bearing mechanical loads, either because of the reduced strength of the hot parts of the body or because of ablation. In the latter case the penetration thickness is, of course, strongly affected by the process of ablation itself.

7.5 One-dimensional linear heat flow in simple and composite bodies

7.5.1 *Homogeneous region*

In slabs the direction of heat flow is assumed to be normal to the surfaces and in shells to be parallel to the (assumed) insulated surfaces. The following analytical solution is in the form of a series which converges rapidly for large times. The initial temperature T_i at $t = 0$ is assumed constant and external heat transfer by forced convection, with constant coefficient h and from a medium of constant temperature T_f is to occur at $x = 0$ while the other surface at $x = \delta$ is thermally insulated. Non-dimensional quantities are introduced for the distance and for the time

$$\xi = \frac{x}{\delta} \quad \text{and} \quad \tau = \frac{\varkappa t}{\delta^2} \tag{7.5.1}$$

The Biot modulus is a non-dimensional expression for the heat transfer coefficient:

$$\text{Bi} = \frac{h\delta}{k} \tag{7.5.2}$$

A solution is obtained by superposing partial solutions of the type of Eq. (7.2.4) in such a way that the initial and boundary conditions are satisfied. The method used for this purpose is classical and can be found for instance in Ref. 3.1.1. Hence only the result is given here:

$$\Theta(\xi, \tau) = \frac{T-T_i}{T_f-T_i} = 1 - \sum_{j=1}^{\infty} \frac{2\,\text{Bi}\cos\beta_j(1-\xi)}{(\beta_j^2+\text{Bi}+\text{Bi}^2)\cos\beta_j}\,e^{-\beta_j^2\tau} \tag{7.5.3}$$

The eigenvalues β_j are defined as the positive roots of

$$\beta\tan\beta = \text{Bi} \tag{7.5.4}$$

and are for instance tabulated in Ref. 3.1.1.

If the heat transfer coefficient becomes very large ($h \to \infty$ and hence $\mathrm{Bi} \to \infty$) the surface temperature T_w becomes equal to the temperature T_f of the external medium and is then known. The corresponding solution becomes

$$\Theta(\xi, \tau) = \frac{T - T_i}{T_w - T_i} =$$

$$= 1 - \frac{4}{\pi} \sum_{j=0}^{\infty} \frac{(-1)^j}{2j+1} \cos\left[\frac{\pi}{2}(2j+1)(1-\xi)\right] \exp\left\{-(2j+1)^2 \frac{\pi^2}{4}\tau\right\} \quad (7.5.5)$$

For small values of τ the convergence of the series expansion in Eqs. (7.5.3) and (7.5.5) is slow and not suitable for numerical calculations. Alternative solutions which converge rapidly for small times can be obtained either with the help of the Laplace transformation (Ref. 3.1.1 or Table 7.1) or directly from the solution for a semi-infinite body and from the method of images as discussed in Section 7.5.5. Thus the solution for a given wall temperature is

$$\Theta = \frac{T - T_i}{T_w - T_i} = \sum_{j=0}^{\infty} (-1)^j \left\{ \mathrm{erfc}\left(\frac{2j\delta + x}{2\sqrt{\varkappa t}}\right) + \mathrm{erfc}\left(\frac{2\delta(j+1) - x}{2\sqrt{\varkappa t}}\right) \right\} \quad (7.5.6)$$

For the case of external heat transfer by forced convection only the first two terms of the series expansion for small times are simple and they are (Ref.3.1.1):

$$\Theta = \frac{T - T_i}{T_f - T_i} = \Theta_{\mathrm{si}}^{(1)}\left(\frac{x}{2\sqrt{\varkappa t}}, Y\right) + \Theta_{\mathrm{si}}^{(1)}\left(\frac{2\delta - x}{2\sqrt{\varkappa t}}, Y\right) \quad (7.5.7)$$

Where $\Theta_{\mathrm{si}}^{(1)}(\xi, Y)$ is defined by Eq. (7.4.1) and plotted in Fig. 7.2; Y is defined by Eq. (7.4.2).

Since the temperature distribution in a slab is important for many applications, general charts are useful and a number of them have been published (see for instance Refs. 7.5.1, 7.5.2, 7.5.3 and—for further references—3.1.1). According to Eq. (7.5.3), the temperature in a slab is a function of three variables (distance, time and heat transfer coefficient in non-dimensional form) and therefore care must be taken lest these charts become too voluminous. This can be avoided in the following way. For small times the temperature distribution in the slab is given by Eq. (7.5.7) and numerical values for each of the 2 terms on the right-hand side of that equation can be read directly from Fig. 7.2. The temperature $\Theta(1, \tau)$ at the adiabatic surface ($x = \delta$) is given in Figs. 7.3 and 7.4 for all times. The ranges of validity of the solutions for small times, Eq. (7.5.7), are indicated in the figures. There are large regions in which both types of solutions are equally accurate within certain

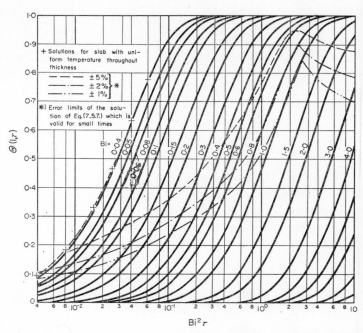

Fig. 7.3. Transient temperatures at the adiabatic surface of a slab whose other surface is heated by forced convection. Uniformly distributed initial temperatures and constant parameters for external heat transfer. For symbols see Eqs. (7.5.1)–(7.5.3).

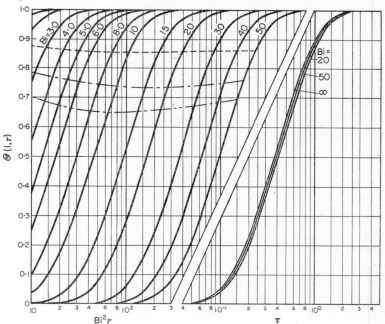

Fig. 7.4. Fig. 7.3 continued.

error limits. For large times the solution can be approximated by the first term in Eq. (7.5.3) and with the help of $\Theta(1, \tau)$, which can be taken from Figs. 7.3 and 7.4, the temperature distribution in the slab then becomes:

$$\frac{1-\Theta(\xi, \tau)}{1-\Theta(1, \tau)} = \cos \beta_1 (1-\xi) \tag{7.5.8}$$

The result can be read from Fig. 7.5 together with an approximate distribution of the truncation error as a percentage of $T_f - T_i$.

For "severe" heating the rate of heat flow at the surface q_w is approximately independent of the surface temperature; if, further, q_w is

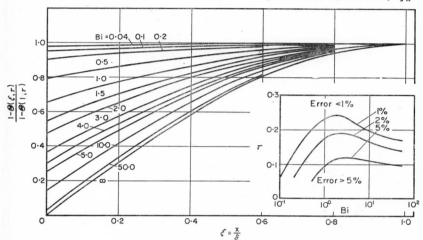

FIG. 7.5. Fig. 7.3. continued. Transient temperature distribution within the slab. Valid for comparatively large times with an error whose maximum value is given. Error in per cent of $T_f - T_i$.

constant, then the solution becomes:

$$T-T_i = \frac{q_w \delta}{k} \left\{ \tau + \frac{(1-\xi)^2}{2} - \frac{1}{6} - \frac{2}{\pi^2} \sum_{j=1}^{\infty} \frac{(-1)^j}{j^2} e^{-j^2\pi^2\tau} \cos[j\pi(1-\xi)] \right\}$$

$$\tag{7.5.9}$$

A solution for small times is obtained as previously:

$$T-T_i = \frac{2q_w \sqrt{t}}{\sqrt{(\rho c k)}} \sum_{j=0}^{\infty} \left[\text{ierfc} \left\{ \frac{2j\delta + x}{2\sqrt{(\varkappa t)}} \right\} + \text{ierfc} \left\{ \frac{2\delta(j+1) - x}{2\sqrt{(\varkappa t)}} \right\} \right] \tag{7.5.10}$$

The function ierfc(x) is defined in Eq. (7.4.14).

7.5.2 Two regions with different thermal properties. General solution for large times

In many applications, one-dimensional heat flow in composite regions is of interest. A composite slab with two different materials with perfect thermal contact has been treated by Mayer in Ref. 7.5.4. The equations of heat conduction for constant thermal properties are

$$\frac{\partial T_1}{\partial t} = \varkappa_1 \frac{\partial^2 T_1}{\partial x^2} \qquad 0 \leqslant x \leqslant \delta_1 \left.\begin{array}{c} \\ \\ \\ \\ \end{array}\right\}$$

$$\frac{\partial T_2}{\partial t} = \varkappa_2 \frac{\partial^2 T_2}{\partial x^2} \qquad \delta_1 \leqslant x \leqslant \delta_1 + \delta_2 \qquad (7.5.11)$$

Heat transfer by forced convection occurs at one surface, while the other is thermally insulated. The heat transfer coefficient h and the reference temperature of the external medium T_f are assumed constant. The boundary conditions thus become:

$$x = 0, \qquad -k_1 \frac{\partial T_1}{\partial x} = h(T_f - T_1)$$

$$x = \delta_1, \qquad T_1 = T_2, \; k_1 \frac{\partial T_1}{\partial x} = k_2 \frac{\partial T_2}{\partial x} \qquad (7.5.12)$$

$$x = \delta_1 + \delta_2, \qquad \frac{\partial T_2}{\partial x} = 0$$

A solution for $t \geqslant 0$ and of a type which converges rapidly for large times and which is similar to Eq. (7.5.3) is of the following form:

$$T_1 = T_f + \sum_{j=1}^{\infty} A_j \left(\cos\beta_{1j} \frac{x-\delta_1}{\delta_1} + \mu_{1j} \sin\beta_{1j} \frac{x-\delta_1}{\delta_1} \right) e^{-\alpha_j^2 t}, \quad 0 \leqslant x \leqslant \delta_1$$

$$T_2 = T_f + \sum_{j=1}^{\infty} A_j \left(\cos\beta_{2j} \frac{x-\delta_1}{\delta_2} + \mu_{2j} \sin\beta_{2j} \frac{x-\delta_1}{\delta_2} \right) e^{-\alpha_j^2 t}, \quad \delta_1 \leqslant x \leqslant \delta_1 + \delta_2$$

$$(7.5.13)$$

The eigenvalues β_{1j} follow from

$$\tan\left[\beta_1 + \tan^{-1}\frac{\beta_1}{\text{Bi}}\right] = \sigma \cot\eta\beta_1 \qquad (7.5.14)$$

where

$$\text{Bi} = \frac{h\delta_1}{k_1}; \qquad \sigma = \sqrt{\left(\frac{k_1\rho_1 c_1}{k_2\rho_2 c_2}\right)}; \qquad \eta = \frac{\delta_2}{\delta_1}\sqrt{\left(\frac{\varkappa_1}{\varkappa_2}\right)} \qquad (7.5.15)$$

When the eigenvalues β_{1j} are known, the following quantities can be obtained

$$\beta_{2j} = \eta\beta_{1j}; \qquad \alpha_j = \frac{\sqrt{\varkappa_1}}{\delta_1}\beta_{1j}$$

$$\mu_{1j} = \frac{\tan\beta_{2j}}{\sigma}; \qquad \mu_{2j} = \tan\beta_{2j} \qquad (7.5.16)$$

The first two eigenvalues β_{11} and β_{12} for a range of parameters

$$0.1 \leqslant \text{Bi} \leqslant 30, \qquad 0.1 \leqslant \eta \leqslant 10, \qquad 0.1 \leqslant \sigma \leqslant 1$$

are given in 5 diagrams in Ref. 7.5.4. If initially the temperature is uniformly distributed and equal to T_i, the coefficients A_j become

$$A_j = -(T_f - T_i) \frac{\rho_1 c_1 B_{1j} + \rho_2 c_2 B_{2j}}{\rho_1 c_1 D_{1j} + \rho_2 c_2 D_{2j}} \tag{7.5.17}$$

with

$$\left. \begin{aligned} B_{k,j} &= \frac{\delta_k}{\beta_{kj}} [\sin \beta_{kj} + (-1)^{k-1} \mu_{kj} (\cos \beta_{kj} - 1)] \\ D_{k,j} &= \frac{\delta_k}{2\beta_{kj}} [(1+\mu_{kj}^2)\beta_{kj} + (1-\mu_{kj}^2)\sin \beta_{kj} \cos \beta_{kj} + 2(-1)^k \mu_{kj} \sin^2 \beta_{kj}] \end{aligned} \right\}$$

$$\tag{7.5.18}$$

where $k = 1$ or 2.

7.5.3 Particular cases of composite slabs. Protection of structures by insulating layers

Consider a slab composed of two layers in perfect thermal contact and heated at one surface. Two cases are of particular interest: (a) the layer whose free surface is heated is thin and consists of an insulating material, (b) the layer whose free surface is adiabatic and consists of a metal slab of high conductivity.

The first case corresponds to a structure protected by a thin layer of insulation against aerodynamic heating. The heat capacity of the first layer can be neglected and the total effective resistance $1/h_{\text{eff}}$ is equal to the sum of the component resistances for the external heat transfer and for the resistance of the insulating layer:

$$\frac{1}{h_{\text{eff}}} = \frac{1}{h} + \frac{\delta_1}{k_1} \tag{7.5.19}$$

Under this assumption the temperature distribution in the second layer is the same as in Eqs. (7.5.3) and (7.5.7) for a simple slab with a heat transfer coefficient h_{eff} instead of h and with the thermal properties of the second layer. The temperature distribution in the first layer follows from quasi-steady heat flow conditions between the reference temperature T_f and the temperature at the interface of the two layers.

A thin protective coating can be effective only if δ_1/k_1 is of the same order of magnitude as, or larger than, $1/h$, provided, of course, that the time of exposure to heat is short. If h is large, as for instance at the walls of nozzles in rocket motors where the pressure and speed of the gas flow are high, a relatively thin coating may be effective. However a coating of the same thickness may not be effective at the surface of a vehicle in high speed flight at high altitudes because h is small due to the low densities at such altitudes.

The second case corresponds to a metal structure protected by a thick insulating layer with moderate rates of heat transfer at the surface. The temperature across the metal layer is constant. Hence the second equation of (7.5.11) is dropped and the second and third equations of (7.5.12) are replaced by a new boundary condition:

$$-k_1 \frac{\partial T}{\partial x} = \rho_2 c_2 \delta_2 \frac{\partial T}{\partial t}, \qquad x = \delta_1 \qquad (7.5.20)$$

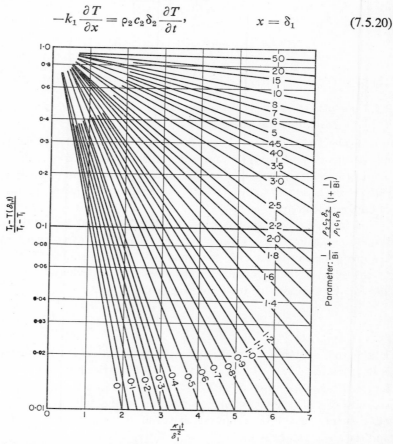

Fig. 7.6. Transient temperatures at the contact surface of a composite slab consisting of two layers with poor and with high conductivity (metal) respectively. Heat transfer by forced convection at the free surface of the first layer. No heat flow at the free surface of the second layer. Uniform temperature distribution initially in the whole slab and permanently in the second layer. Constant parameters for external heat transfer. Approximate results due to Grover and Holter (Ref. 7.5.5).

where now $T_1 \equiv T$. Equation (7.5.14) becomes

$$\tan\left[\beta_1 + \tan^{-1}\frac{\beta_1}{\mathrm{Bi}}\right] = \frac{1}{\beta_1}\frac{\rho_1 c_1 \delta_1}{\rho_2 c_2 \delta_2} \qquad (7.5.21)$$

β_{11} and β_{12} as functions of Bi and $(\rho_2 c_2 \delta_2)/(\rho_1 c_1 \delta_1)$ are given in Ref. 7.5.4.

This restricted problem has also been solved by Grover and Holter (Ref. 7.5.5) and their results are given in charts of $[T_f - T(\delta_1, t)]/(T_f - T_i)$ as a function of $(\varkappa_1 t)/\delta_1^2$ for values of $1/\mathrm{Bi} = k/h\,\delta_1$ and $(\rho_2 c_2 \delta_2)/(\rho_1 c_1 \delta_1)$ both equal to 0, 0·5, 1, 2 and 6. It was found possible to present all results approximately in one diagram (Fig. 7.6) in which the 2 previous parameters were replaced by a single parameter

$$\frac{1}{\mathrm{Bi}} + \frac{\rho_2 c_2 \delta_2}{\rho_1 c_1 \delta_1}\left(1 + \frac{1}{\mathrm{Bi}}\right)$$

7.5.4 Two regions with different thermal properties. Solutions for small times

In the following a composite slab is treated, but results would also be applicable to a composite shell with adiabatic surfaces. For small times, solutions similar to those for the initial phase in a slab are more convenient. They can be obtained with the help of the Laplace transformation by expanding the expressions for the temperature in the transformed domain for small values of $1/p$ where p is the Laplace transform variable. For a composite slab consisting of two finite layers the temperature distribution shortly after the start of the heat transfer is that for a semi-infinite body (see Section 7.4) and it is valid until the heat flow penetrates to the contact surface between the two layers at $x = \delta_1$. Thereafter one can use solutions for a region composed of a finite layer extending from $x = 0$ to $x = \delta_1$ and an adjacent infinite region; the materials of the two regions have different thermal properties and there is no thermal resistance at the interface. Such a solution has been given by Trimpi and Jones (Ref. 7.5.6):

$$
\begin{aligned}
T_1 - T_i = (T_f - T_i) \sum_{j=0}^{\infty} &\left\{\alpha^j G_j\left(2j + \frac{x}{\delta_1}, \sqrt{\tau}, \mathrm{Bi}\right)\right.\\
&\left. + \alpha^{j+1} G_j\left[2(j+1) - \frac{x}{\delta_1}, \sqrt{\tau}, \mathrm{Bi}\right]\right\}\\
T_2 - T_i = (T_f - T_i)(1+\alpha) \sum_{j=0}^{\infty} &\alpha^j G_j\left[2j + 1 + \frac{k_1}{k_2}\frac{1-\alpha}{1+\alpha}\left(\frac{x}{\delta_1} - 1\right), \sqrt{\tau}, \mathrm{Bi}\right]
\end{aligned}
$$

$$(7.5.22)$$

where

$$\alpha = \frac{1-\sigma}{1+\sigma} \qquad (7.5.23)$$

and

$$\tau = \frac{\varkappa_1 \tau}{\delta_1^2} \qquad (7.5.24)$$

σ and Bi are as defined in Eq. (7.5.15).

The first five functions G_j and their spatial derivatives are given in Ref. 7.5.6. For a finite composite slab the above solutions can be applied until the temperature increases in T_2 have penetrated to the inner (adiabatic) surface $x = \delta_1 + \delta_2$.

7.5.5 *Satisfying boundary conditions by the use of heat waves and images*

For composite regions and small to moderate times it is often convenient to use another method. It is based on the concept that heat flow occurs by "heat waves" which emanate from a "source" and are partly reflected and partly transmitted at interfaces separating regions with different thermal properties (Refs. 7.5.7, 7.5.8). The heat waves are in most cases not periodic, but are temperature changes which spread from a source. The thermal properties are assumed to be independent of temperature and the two regions considered are characterized by subscripts 1 and 2 respectively. The heat conduction equations and the range of the regions are:

$$\frac{\partial T_1}{\partial t} = \varkappa_1 \frac{\partial^2 T_1}{\partial x^2}, \qquad 0 \leqslant x \leqslant L_1, \qquad (7.5.25)$$

$$\frac{\partial T_2}{\partial t} = \varkappa_2 \frac{\partial^2 T_2}{\partial x^2}, \qquad L_1 \leqslant x < \infty \qquad (7.5.26)$$

The thermal contact at the interface is assumed perfect:

$$T_1 = T_2, \qquad x = L_1 \qquad (7.5.27)$$

$$k_1 \delta_1 \frac{\partial T_1}{\partial x} = k_2 \delta_2 \frac{\partial T_2}{\partial x}, \qquad x = L_1 \qquad (7.5.28)$$

The composite region considered here may be either a composite slab, or a composite shell with adiabatic surfaces but external heat transfer at the end faces. For a composite slab put $\delta_1 = \delta_2 = 1$ in the above equations while for a shell δ_1 and δ_2 are the wall thicknesses in the regions 1 and 2. The boundary condition at $x = 0$ corresponds to the "source", because heat penetrates from that surface into the body. Assume a solution for the temperature in a semi-infinite body $x \geqslant 0$, with diffusivity $\varkappa_1$, to be of the general form $\vartheta_{si}\left(\dfrac{x}{\sqrt{\varkappa_1}}, t\right) = BF\left(\dfrac{x}{\sqrt{\varkappa_1}}, t\right)$ where B may depend on a number of arbitrary parameters. Solutions for the temperatures T_1 and T_2 are assumed as:

$$T_1 - T_i = \vartheta_{si}\left(\frac{x}{\sqrt{\varkappa_1}}, t\right) + K_{12}^{(R)}\vartheta_{si}\left(\frac{2L_1 - x}{\sqrt{\varkappa_1}}, t\right), \quad 0 \leqslant x \leqslant L_1 \quad (7.5.29)$$

$$T_2 - T_i = K_{12}^{(S)}\vartheta_{si}\left(\frac{L_1 + (x - L_1)\sqrt{(\varkappa_1/\varkappa_2)}}{\sqrt{\varkappa_1}}, t\right), \quad L_1 \leqslant x < \infty \quad (7.5.30)$$

T_i is the constant initial temperature and $\vartheta_{si} = 0$ for $t = 0$. $K_{12}^{(R)}$ and $K_{12}^{(S)}$ are the reflection and transmission coefficients for a wave travelling in region 1 and arriving at the interface at $x = L_1$. T_1 and T_2 are valid for sufficiently small times, so that the contribution of the second term in Eq. (7.5.29) at $x = 0$ is negligible. These expressions for T_1 and T_2 satisfy the equations of heat conduction (7.5.25) and (7.5.26). They also fulfil the boundary conditions, at $x = L_1$, Eqs. (7.5.27) and (7.5.28), if

$$K_{12}^{(R)} = \frac{\sigma^* - 1}{\sigma^* + 1} \qquad\qquad (7.5.31)$$

$$K_{12}^{(S)} = \frac{2\sigma^*}{1 + \sigma^*} \qquad\qquad (7.5.32)$$

where

$$\sigma^* = \frac{\delta_1}{\delta_2}\sqrt{\left(\frac{k_1\rho_1 c_1}{k_2\rho_2 c_2}\right)} \qquad\qquad (7.5.33)$$

The second term on the right-hand side of Eq. (7.5.29) is due to an image of the source at $x' = 2L_1$ and the term on the right-hand side of Eq. (7.5.30) is due to an image at $x' = L_1(1 - \sqrt{(\varkappa_1/\varkappa_2)})$. All heat paths are referred to the first medium. The temperature in Eq. (7.5.29) can be interpreted as the sum of two waves: one which arrives directly from the source and the second which arrives after a reflection at the interface. The temperature in Eq. (7.5.30) is due to a wave transmitted through the interface.

For larger times, i.e. those for which $\vartheta_{si}\left(\dfrac{2L_1}{\sqrt{\varkappa_1}}, t\right) > 0$, the wave reflected at the plane $x = L_1$ reaches the boundary at $x = 0$ where it is again reflected. The wave reflected at $x = 0$ can be represented by an image of the original source at $x' = -2L_1$. The original boundary conditions must not be disturbed by wave reflections. If therefore the temperature is given at $x = 0$, the contribution due to an oncoming wave and the corresponding reflected wave must cancel each other; similarly, if the rate of heat flow is given at $x = 0$ the temperature gradient must not be changed there by the reflection of a wave. To meet these requirements the reflection factor must be -1, or $+1$, depending whether the temperature or the rate of heat flow respectively is given at the surface.

With increasing time one has to consider all the possible heat paths along which a heat wave emanating from a source can travel to a certain place x either directly or indirectly by simple and multiple reflections and transmissions.

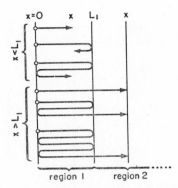

FIG. 7.7. A composite region with a finite and an infinite layer. Heat paths used in the method of heat waves and images.

We return to the example of a finite layer in perfect thermal contact with an infinite layer. The heat paths in the region 1 (see Fig. 7.7) are: x, $2L_1-x$, $2L_1+x$, $4L_1-x$, ... or generally $\Phi_{1j} = 2jL_1 - x$ for a wave travelling to the left and $\Phi_{1j} = 2(j-1)L_1 + x$ for a wave travelling to the right, with $j = 1,2,3...$ Corresponding values within the region 2 are: $L_1+(x-L_1)V(\varkappa_1/\varkappa_2)$, $3L_1+(x-L_1)V(\varkappa_1/\varkappa_2)$, $5L_1+(x-L_1)V(\varkappa_1/\varkappa_2)$ ... or generally $\Phi_{2j} = (2j-1)L_1+(x-L_1)V(\varkappa_1/\varkappa_2)$ and, because the region 2 is infinite, there are only waves travelling to the right. Corresponding to each heat path there is a contribution to the temperature from a heat wave. Each time a heat wave is reflected or transmitted its amplitude is changed by a factor $K^{(R)}$ or $K^{(S)}$ respectively.

If in the present example the rate of heat flow at the boundary $x = 0$ is given, the solution for the temperature in the region 1 is:

$$T_1 - T_i = \sum_{j=1}^{\infty} (K_{12}^{(R)})^{j-1} \left\{ K_{12}^{(R)} \vartheta_{\mathrm{s}i}\left(\frac{2jL_1 - x}{V\varkappa_1}, t \right) + \vartheta_{\mathrm{s}i}\left(\frac{2(j-1)L_1 + x}{V\varkappa_1}, t \right) \right\}$$

$$(7.5.34)$$

and in the region 2 it is:

$$T_2 - T_i = \sum_{j=1}^{\infty} K_{12}^{(S)} (K_{12}^{(R)})^{j-1} \; \vartheta_{\mathrm{si}} \left(\frac{(2j-1)L_1 + (x-L_1)V(\varkappa_1/\varkappa_2)}{V\varkappa_1}, t \right) \quad (7.5.35)$$

$\vartheta_{\mathrm{si}}(x, t) = T_{\mathrm{si}} - T_i$ is the solution for a semi-infinite region and for the respective boundary condition at $x = 0$. In most applications a few terms usually suffice and the contribution of the rest is negligible.

In a composite slab with several finite regions the procedure is similar, but it may become difficult to give a general expression for the solutions in the form of a sum with an infinite number of terms. This is usually no serious drawback, because a finite number of terms can always be given, which is sufficient for practical purposes. However, the method has another and more serious disadvantage; if it is extended to boundary conditions with heat transfer by forced convection or if there is a finite heat resistance at the interfaces between regions of different materials, the reflection and transmission coefficients become functions of time and the method becomes more difficult to handle: this is not dealt with here.

Next the method is extended to volume heat sources which are uniformly distributed in space, but may vary with time. The source is to be of strength $q_1(t)$ and is assumed to occur only in the region 1. The heat flow is to be zero at the boundary. Because of the source, a term $q_1/\rho_1 c_1 \delta_1$ is added on the right hand side of Eq. (7.5.25); in this term $\delta_1 = 1$ for a slab and for a shell δ_1 is equal to its thickness. For small times a solution in the first region is the sum of two terms, one due to the volume heat source and the other due to a wave reflected at the interface:

$$T_1 - T_i = \int_0^t \frac{q_1(t)\,\mathrm{d}t}{\rho_1 c_1 \delta_1} - \frac{1}{1+\sigma^*} \vartheta_{\mathrm{si}} \left(\frac{L_1 - x}{V\varkappa_1}, t \right) \quad (7.5.36)$$

In region 2 which was assumed to be free from heat sources, the solution due to the transmitted wave is:

$$T_2 - T_i = \frac{\sigma^*}{1+\sigma^*} \vartheta_{\mathrm{si}} \left(\frac{x-L_1}{V\varkappa_2}, t \right) \quad (7.5.37)$$

Again, the solution of Eq. (7.5.36) is valid during times for which the reflected wave, (i.e. the second term on the right-hand side of Eq. (7.5.36)), does not appreciably contribute to the temperature. Obviously, the first term on the right-hand side of Eq. (7.5.36) corresponds to an oncoming wave, the second term to a reflected wave and the term on the right-hand side of Eq. (7.5.37) to a transmitted wave.

156

The boundary condition (at $x' = 0$) for the solution $\vartheta_{si}(x', t)$ in the semi-infinite region follows from Eq. (7.5.27) as:

$$\vartheta_{si}(0, t) = \int\limits_0^t \frac{q_1(t)\,\mathrm{d}t}{\rho_1 c_1 \delta_1} \tag{7.5.38}$$

and the solution for $\vartheta_{si}(x', t)$ can be found from Ref. 3.1.1.

When reflected and transmitted waves reach a boundary, they are treated as previously.

7.6 One-dimensional heat flow in thin shells with heat transfer conditions varying along the surface

7.6.1 *Flat plate with heat transfer by forced convection*

As in Section 7.3 the temperature is assumed uniform throughout the thickness of the shell; the conditions for which this assumption is correct were given in Section 3.2. The following results are also valid for cylindrical shells if their thickness is small compared with the diameter of the cylinder.

During flight the heat transfer conditions vary in general with the distance x from the leading edge or nose and this has been dealt with in Chapter 2. For idealized flow along a flat plate with zero pressure gradient the heat transfer coefficient h decreases as $x^{-1/2}$ for laminar boundary layers and approximately as x^{-l} for turbulent boundary layers with l lying between $1/5$ and $1/10$. Similar conditions are also valid for slender bodies and wings, at some distance downstream of the stagnation point or line. Since the variation of the adiabatic wall temperature is generally small along the surface, variations in the rate of heat flow at the surface are largely due to variations in h.

Assume heat transfer by forced convection to occur at one surface of the shell while the other surface is thermally insulated. The temperature distribution in the shell is determined by Eq. (3.2.6), which reads

$$\rho_M c_M \delta \frac{\partial T_w}{\partial t} = \delta k_M \frac{\partial^2 T_w}{\partial x^2} + h(T_f - T_w) \tag{7.6.1}$$

and by suitable boundary and initial conditions. The subscript M in Eq. (7.6.1) refers to the shell of thickness δ, otherwise the notation is the same as in Section 3.2. T_f and T_w are the reference temperatures for the external heat transfer and the wall temperature respectively. If only heat transfer by forced convection is important, T_f is equal to T_{aw}. When other modes of heat transfer also contribute to the total heat flow, "linearized" laws can be used as approximations (see Section 3.1.3). Then a heat transfer coefficient $h + h_{eff}$ and an equilibrium temperature T_g have to be used instead of h and T_f respectively. For a uniformly distributed wall temperature the heat transfer coefficient, occurring in Eq. (7.6.1), for laminar and turbulent boundary layers in subsonic, supersonic and hypersonic flow, under the above conditions is:

$$h = B\rho_{a,e}c_{p,a,e}u_e \mathrm{Re}_x^{-l}, \qquad \mathrm{Re}_x = \frac{u_e x}{\nu_{a,e}} \qquad (7.6.2)$$

where ρ_a, $c_{p,a}$ and ν_a are respectively the density, specific heat at constant pressure and kinematic viscosity of the air. u is the air speed and x the distance from the leading edge. The subscript e refers to conditions at the outer edge of the boundary layer. B is a coefficient depending on the temperature ratio T_w/T_e as given in detail in Section 2.3.2. l is the exponent for the Reynolds number in the friction and heat transfer laws with values of $1/2$ for laminar and between $1/5$ and $1/10$ for turbulent boundary layers. The dependence of B on T_w/T_e is moderate for laminar, but large for turbulent flow; in many cases it can be taken into account by using suitable mean values. In cases of severe aerodynamic heating the changes in T_w are comparatively small, so that B would only change moderately even for turbulent boundary layers. Assuming an instantaneous change of speed followed by constant flight conditions, the following non-dimensional quantities are introduced for the distance from the leading edge and for the time:

$$\xi = \frac{x}{\delta}A \quad \text{and} \quad \tau = \frac{\varkappa_M t}{\delta^2}A^2 \qquad (7.6.3)$$

with

$$A = \left(\frac{u_e \delta}{\nu_{a,e}}\right)^{\frac{1-l}{2-l}}\left(\frac{k_{a,e}}{k_M}\mathrm{Pr}_e B\right)^{\frac{1}{2-l}} \qquad (7.6.4)$$

Pr is the Prandtl number of the air. Further, a non-dimensional temperature is introduced:

$$\Theta^* = \frac{T_w - T_f}{T_i - T_f} \qquad (7.6.5)$$

with T_i as the constant initial wall temperature. With the non-dimensional quantities defined by Eqs. (7.6.3) to (7.6.5) the equation of heat conduction becomes:

$$\frac{\partial \Theta^*}{\partial \tau} = \frac{\partial^2 \Theta^*}{\partial \xi^2} - \frac{\Theta^*}{\xi^l} \qquad (7.6.6)$$

The initial conditions are

$$\tau = 0; \quad \Theta^* = 1 \tag{7.6.7}$$

The shell is assumed semi-infinite with the boundary conditions

$$\xi = 0; \quad \frac{\partial \Theta^*}{\partial \xi} = 0 \tag{7.6.8a}$$

$$\xi \to \infty; \quad \frac{\partial \Theta^*}{\partial \xi} = 0 \tag{7.6.8b}$$

First, heat conduction is disregarded within the shell, i.e. the term $\frac{\partial^2 \Theta^*}{\partial \xi^2}$ in Eq. (7.6.6), is neglected. Then a solution is readily obtained as

$$\Theta^* = \exp\left\{-\frac{\tau}{\xi^l}\right\} \tag{7.6.9}$$

As an approximation to the solution of the full equation (7.6.6), the error is largest near the leading edge where $T_w = T_f$ as follows from Eq. (7.6.9).

A solution of Eq. (7.6.6) satisfying the boundary conditions (7.6.8) was obtained in the form of a series by Parker (Ref. 7.6.1) for laminar heat transfer ($l = 1/2$), but it yields useful numerical results only in a limited region. Also for laminar boundary layers, Tideman (Ref. 7.6.2) gives an approximate solution for which the error in Θ^* apparently does not exceed about 3 per cent of the initial value $\Theta^* = 1$, for all values of ξ and τ. For small to moderate values of the time τ this error could be improved by an iterative procedure which, however, will not be dealt with here. Following Tideman we put

$$\Theta^* = e^{-\Theta} \tag{7.6.10}$$

where Θ is a new non-dimensional temperature. Upon eliminating Θ^* from Eq. (7.6.6) with the help of Eq. (7.6.10) one obtains

$$\frac{\partial \Theta}{\partial \tau} = \frac{\partial^2 \Theta}{\partial \xi^2} + \frac{1}{\xi^l} - \left(\frac{\partial \Theta}{\partial \xi}\right)^2 \tag{7.6.11}$$

with the initial condition

$$\tau = 0; \quad \Theta = 0, \tag{7.6.12}$$

while the boundary conditions are the same for Θ as for Θ^* (see Eq. (7.6.8)). According to Tideman the last term $(\partial \Theta / \partial \xi)^2$ in Eq. (7.6.11) is neglected and then the equation corresponds to a given rate of heat flow at the surface of the shell and it can further be interpreted as an equation of heat conduction with internal heat sources depending on ξ only. In the case of turbulent heat transfer the errors in Θ^* due to the truncation of Eq. (7.6.11) would be smaller.

Of considerable interest in practice are shells which are long in comparison to their thickness. The temperature distributions in these shells do not differ from those in a semi-infinite shell except in the vicinity of the trailing edge. Hence the importance of semi-infinite shells: their solutions depend only on the time and on the distance from the leading edge, both in non-dimensional form, but do not depend on a further parameter as would be the case for a shell of finite length.

Heaps (Ref. 7.6.3) obtained analytical solutions in the form of a series for a shell of finite length L and for both laminar and turbulent boundary layers. However, rough approximations were used for the dependence of h on the distance from the leading edge and this resulted in errors in the vicinity of the leading edge. The same problem has also been treated by Johnson (Ref. 7.6.4) for a laminar boundary layer; an analytical method had been used and numerical results were given for the following value of the non-dimensional parameter containing the length:

$$\frac{B\,\rho_{a,e}\,c_{p,a,e}\,u_e\,L^2}{\mathrm{Re}_L^{1/2}\,\delta\,k_M} = 0\cdot2$$

Re_L follows from Eq. (7.6.2) with L instead of x; for laminar boundary layers $B = 0\cdot330/\mathrm{Pr}^{2/3}$.

7.6.2 Flat plate with a given rate of heat flow at the surface

For severe rates of heating the rate of heat flow at the surface is approximately independent of the surface temperature, and the equation of heat conduction would be:

$$\rho_M\,c_M\,\delta\frac{\partial T_w}{\partial t} = k_M\,\delta\frac{\partial^2 T_w}{\partial x^2} + q_w \tag{7.6.13}$$

Assuming q_w to vary with distance from the leading edge in a similar way as given by Eq. (7.6.2), i.e. inversely proportional to x^l, we put

$$q_w = D\left(\frac{x}{\delta}\right)^{-l} \tag{7.6.14}$$

where D is a constant. Introducing

$$\Theta = (T_w - T_i)\frac{k_M}{D\delta^{1-l}} \tag{7.6.15}$$

one obtains for the truncated Eq. (7.6.11)

$$\frac{\partial\Theta}{\partial\tau} = \frac{\partial^2\Theta}{\partial\xi^2} + \frac{1}{\xi^l} \tag{7.6.16}$$

if τ and ξ are again defined by Eq. (7.6.3) with $A = 1$. For severe rates of aerodynamic heating, i.e. if $T_f \gg T_w$, one has $q_w = hT_f$ and then one obtains from Eqs. (7.6.14) and (7.6.2)

$$D = B\rho_{a,e} c_{p,a,e} u_e \left(\frac{u_e \delta}{\nu_{a,e}}\right)^{-l} T_f \qquad (7.6.16a)$$

The initial condition for Θ is given by Eq. (7.6.12) and the boundary conditions by Eq. (7.6.8), if in the latter Θ^* is replaced by Θ. The solution of Eq. (7.6.16) is the sum of two components

$$\Theta(\xi, \tau) = \Theta^{(1)}(\xi) + \Theta^{(2)}(\xi, \tau) \qquad (7.6.17)$$

where $\Theta^{(1)}(\xi)$ is a partial solution of Eq. (7.6.16) which for $l \neq 1$ is:

$$\Theta^{(1)}(\xi) = -\int_0^\xi d\eta_2 \int_0^{\eta_2} \frac{d\eta_1}{\eta_1^l} = -\frac{\xi^{2-l}}{(1-l)(2-l)} \qquad (7.6.18)$$

with η_1 and η_2 as integration variables. $\Theta^{(1)}$ also fulfils the boundary condition at $\xi = 0$, Eq. (7.6.8a) if $l < 1$ which is the case for both turbulent and laminar boundary layers. It suffices to add to this solution a general solution $\Theta^{(2)}$ of the homogeneous part of Eq. (7.6.16) (i.e. without the last term on the right-hand side of the equation). The initial condition for $\Theta^{(2)}$ is

$$\tau = 0; \quad \Theta^{(2)}(\xi, 0) = -\Theta^{(1)}(\xi) \qquad (7.6.19)$$

so that $\Theta^{(1)}(\xi) + \Theta^{(2)}(\xi, \tau)$ satisfies Eq. (7.6.12). Because of Eq. (7.6.19) the boundary condition Eq. (7.6.8b) is also satisfied, since the initial temperatures prevail at very large distances ($\xi \to \infty$) for all finite times. Thus the solution of $\Theta^{(2)}$ is equal to the temperature in a semi-infinite body without internal heat sources and with initial temperature distribution of Eq. (7.6.18). A general solution of this problem is well known (Ref. 3.1.1) and reads in the present case:

$$\Theta^{(2)}(\xi, \tau) = \frac{1}{2(1-l)(2-l)\sqrt{(\pi\tau)}} \int_0^\infty \eta^{2-l} \left[\exp\left\{-\frac{(\xi-\eta)^2}{4\tau}\right\} + \exp\left\{-\frac{(\xi+\eta)^2}{4\tau}\right\}\right] d\eta \qquad (7.6.20)$$

Since l is 1/2 for laminar boundary layers and between 1/5 and 1/10 for turbulent flow, the integral can not be evaluated generally in a closed form. Introducing

$$z = \frac{\xi}{\sqrt{\tau}} \qquad (7.6.21)$$

and changing the variable of integration accordingly, one obtains for the complete solution with the help of Eqs. (7.6.17) and (7.6.20):

$$\Theta(\xi,\tau) = \Theta^{(1)}(\xi) + \Theta^{(2)}(\xi,\tau) = \frac{\tau^{\frac{2-l}{2}}}{(1-l)(2-l)\sqrt{\pi}}[F(z;l)-z^{2-l}\sqrt{\pi}] \qquad (7.6.22)$$

with

$$F(z;l) = \tfrac{1}{2}\int_0^\infty \eta_1^{2-l}[\exp\{-\tfrac{1}{4}(z-\eta_1)^2\}+\exp\{-\tfrac{1}{4}(z+\eta_1)^2\}]d\eta_1 \qquad (7.6.23)$$

However, for $z = 0$ the integral in Eq. (7.6.23) can be evaluated in a closed form as given in Ref. 7.6.5 and this yields

$$F(0;l) = \int_0^\infty \eta_1^{2-l}\exp\left\{-\frac{1}{4}\,\eta_1^2\right\}d\eta_1 = 2^{2-l}\Gamma\left(\frac{3-l}{2}\right) \qquad (7.6.23a)$$

With the help of Ref. 7.6.6 it follows that $F(0;\tfrac{1}{2}) = 2^{\frac{3}{2}}\Gamma(\tfrac{5}{4}) = 2{\cdot}564$ for laminar flow ($l = \tfrac{1}{2}$) and $F(0;\tfrac{1}{6}) = 2^{\frac{11}{6}}\Gamma(\tfrac{17}{12}) = 3{\cdot}159$ for turbulent flow with $l = \tfrac{1}{6}$. The integral in Eq. (7.6.23) can be expanded into a series converging for small values of z and into an asymptotic series for large values of z (see Ref. 7.6.2).

In Fig. 7.8 $\Theta/\tau^{\frac{2-l}{2}}$ vs. z is given for laminar heat transfer ($l = \tfrac{1}{2}$) and for turbulent heat transfer with $l = \tfrac{1}{6}$. According to Eq. (7.6.10) the same curves are also approximately applicable for surface heat transfer by forced convection, if the ordinate is $-\ln\Theta^*/\tau^{\frac{2-l}{2}}$ with Θ^* defined by Eq. (7.6.5). It should be observed that the results for very small values of x are not strictly realistic. If δ is finite, the leading edge is blunt, since δ was assumed constant. However, the heat transfer conditions of Eq. (7.6.2) refer to a sharp leading edge. If on the other hand $\delta \to 0$, the boundary layer equation would not hold for $x \sim \delta \to 0$. In reality the heat transfer coefficient would always be finite at $x = 0$, though large. So the present solution for $x = 0$ corresponds only approximately to real conditions for a solid leading edge.

7.6.3 *Extension to cylinders and wings*

The present method can easily be extended to cylinders or cylindrical wings placed normal, or at an angle of yaw, to the direction of the undisturbed flow. In that case q_w can be any function of x depending on the distribution of the rate of heat flow at the surface of the cylinder or wing. If the radius of curvature is finite at the leading edge, h remains finite even

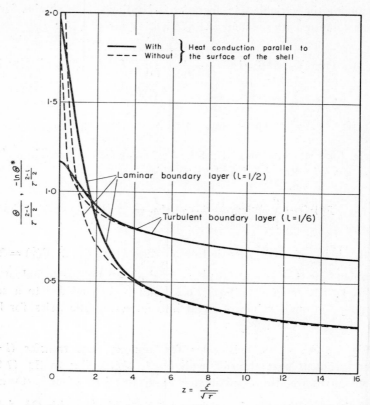

Fig. 7.8. Transient temperature distribution in a semi-infinite flat plate (shell) of uniform thickness and with uniform temperature throughout the thickness, due to Tideman (Ref. 7.6.2) and Schuh. Convective heat transfer at one surface through a laminar ($l = \frac{1}{2}$) or a turbulent boundary layer ($l = \frac{1}{6}$) with zero pressure gradient; no heat flow at the other surface. Effect of wall temperature and its gradient on heat transfer coefficient neglected. Constant initial temperature, sudden start of heat transfer (motion) with constant parameters (flight condition). Θ exact solutions for severe rates of heating; for symbols see Eq. (7.6.3) in which $A = 1$, further Eqs. (7.6.15) and (7.6.16a). $\Theta^* = (T_w - T_f)/(T_i - T_f)$ approximate solutions for any rates of heating; for symbols see Eqs. (7.6.3) and (7.6.4).

at the forward stagnation point. In a similar way as described previously, a partial solution is first obtained from the nonhomogeneous Eq. (7.6.13) by omitting the term $\rho_M c_M \delta\, \partial T_w/\partial t$. Then it suffices to omit q_w from Eq. (7.6.13) and to solve the remaining homogeneous equation for an initial temperature distribution equal to the negative value of the partial solution. Thus the problem has been reduced to finding the temperature in a slab for a given initial temperature distribution. General solutions for a slab are given in Ref. 3.1.1.

7.6.4 Errors due to using heat transfer coefficients calculated for uniform wall temperatures

So far the value of the heat transfer coefficient h has been assumed the same as for a uniformly distributed wall temperature although in the present case the wall temperature varies considerably along the surface and this fact must influence h (see Section 2.3.5). Bryson and Edwards Ref. 7.6.7 investigated the heating of shells with due regard to the non-uniformity of the wall temperature, but they neglected heat conduction in the direction parallel to the surfaces. Assuming a supersonic laminar boundary layer in which the viscosity v_a and the heat conductivity k_a of the air are proportional to the temperature and c_p is constant, the following approximate expression for q_w is used which is independent of the Mach number (see also Eq. (2.3.10)):

$$q_w = -0.332 \left(\frac{u_e}{v_{a,e}x}\right)^{1/2} \mathrm{Pr}^{1/3} k_{a,e} \left[\int_0^x \frac{dT_w}{d\eta} \frac{d\eta}{\left[1-\left(\frac{\eta}{x}\right)^{3/4}\right]^{1/3}} + T_{w,0} - T_f \right]$$

(7.6.24)

This expression is essentially due to Lighthill (Ref. 2.3.16). $T_{w,0}$ is the wall temperature at the leading edge. In the present case, where the heat conduction parallel to the surface of the shell is neglected, $T_{w,0} - T_f = 0$. The temperature distribution in the shell follows with the help of Eq. (7.3.1).

Introducing Eq. (7.6.24) into (7.3.1) the following solution is finally obtained (Ref. 7.6.7):

$$\Theta = \frac{T_w - T_i}{T_f - T_i} = \left[\Gamma\left(\frac{2}{3}\right) \right]^{-1} \Gamma\left\{\left[\tau \Gamma\left(\frac{5}{3}\right)\right]^{\frac{3}{2}}; \frac{2}{3}\right\}$$

(7.6.25)

where

$$\Gamma\{\alpha;\beta\} = \int_0^\alpha \exp(-\eta)\eta^{\beta-1} d\eta ;$$

(7.6.26)

$\Gamma(\alpha)$ and $\Gamma(\alpha;\beta)$ are the complete and incomplete gamma functions respectively. Further

$$\tau = \frac{th(x)}{\rho_M c_M \delta}$$

(7.6.27)

and $h(x)$ is the heat transfer coefficient for a uniformly distributed wall temperature as given by Eq. (7.6.2) with $B = 0.332 \mathrm{Pr}^{-2/3}$ and $l = \frac{1}{2}$. The temperature distribution according to Eq. (7.6.25) is compared in Fig. 7.9 with that obtained for heat transfer with the coefficient $h(x)$

for a uniformly distributed wall temperature. The difference between the two temperature distributions is moderate. This is also true for the rate of heat flow. However, heat transfer coefficients (not shown in Fig. 7.9)

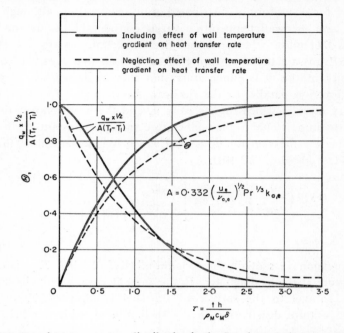

FIG. 7.9. Transient temperature distribution in the flat plate of Fig. 7.8 neglecting heat conduction in the shell parallel to the surface. Laminar boundary layer only. Comparison between solutions obtained with a heat transfer coefficient h for an assumed uniform and for the real non-uniform distribution of the wall temperature. From Ref. 7.6.7.

would differ appreciably (see Ref. 7.6.7) in the present laminar case. This is not important for structures, but would matter in a wind tunnel test intended for determining heat transfer coefficients.

Emmons (Ref. 7.6.8) has given a method of calculation which takes account of the heat conduction parallel to the surface of a shell of finite length and of the influence on h of a non-uniform wall temperature distribution. However, this method appears rather lengthy and the only example given is not very illuminating. Bryson and co-workers (Ref. 7.6.9) obtained solutions of Emmons' problem for a laminar boundary layer and for the leading edge ($x = 0$). Their result is compared in Fig. 7.10 with Tideman's approximate solution in which a value of h was used as for a uniform wall temperature distribution. The differences between the two solutions are very small and only noticeable for large times.

In Fig. 7.11 an example is given showing the temperature distribution in the skin of a thin wing with a sharp leading edge and zero angle of attack. The boundary layer on the surface of the wing is partly laminar

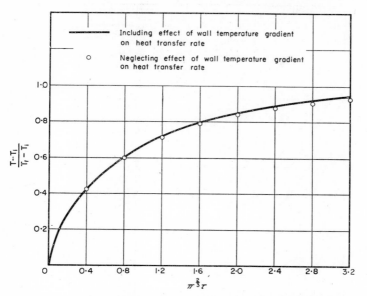

FIG. 7.10. Transient temperature in the leading edge of the flat plate of Fig. 7.8. Laminar boundary layer only. Comparison between solutions obtained with a heat transfer coefficient h for an assumed uniform distribution of the wall temperature and for the real non-uniform wall temperature. The first solution is approximate and taken from Fig. 7.8, the second exact and due to Bryson *et al.* (Ref. 7.6.9).

and partly turbulent with transition occurring at 50 per cent of the chord which is $L = 10$ ft long (Ref. 7.6.10). The skin is 0·39 in. thick and made of aluminium ($\rho = 178$ lb/ft³, $c = 0·21$ Btu/lb°F, $k = 90·8$ Btu/ft h°F). The temperature is uniform throughout the thickness of the skin. Initially the wing is in thermal equilibrium for a flight speed corresponding to $M = 0·9$ at an altitude of 65,000 ft. Then sudden acceleration to $M = 2·5$ in level flight occurs. T_{aw} and h were calculated from the formulas given in Chapter 2 and the influence on heat transfer of the pressure gradient in the air flow around the 5 per cent thick wing has been approximately taken into account, by using local values of ρ_e, u_e and ν_e in the formulae for the heat transfer coefficient at zero pressure gradient. The solutions are not accurate at the leading edge, because there the assumptions of a shell of constant thickness and a sharp leading edge cannot generally be reconciled with each other. The results were obtained by the finite difference method treated in the next chapter. Further calculations were made in Ref. 7.6.10 with heat transfer coefficients for both an assumed uniform distribution and the real non-uniform distribu-

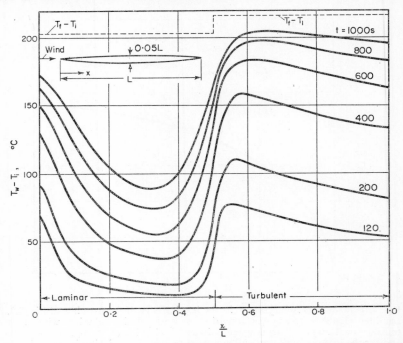

FIG. 7.11. Transient temperature distribution in a thin wing due to a boundary layer that is partly laminar and partly turbulent with transition occurring at 50 per cent of a chord of 3 m (ca. 10 ft) length. Thickness of aluminium skin 10 mm (0·4 in.), sudden acceleration from $M = 0·9$ to $M = 2·5$ at an altitude of 20 km (65,000 ft). Constant initial temperature corresponding to thermal equilibrium at initial flight conditions.

tion of the wall temperature. The differences in the corresponding solutions for the skin temperatures were found to be surprisingly small even in places with large local temperature gradients.

Schmidt and Hanawalt (Ref. 7.6.11) investigated skin temperature distributions of a form likely to be encountered in flight structures and concluded that in many cases the errors in heat flow rates would be below 10 or at most 20 per cent if heat transfer coefficients are used for uniform rather than for the real non-uniform distributions of the wall temperature.

A number of papers have reported strong influences on the laminar heat transfer coefficient of wall temperature variations in cases where the difference in temperature between the outer edge of the boundary layer and the wall increased with distance from the leading edge x according to $T_w - T_e = Cx^\gamma$ where in compressible flow T_e is to be replaced by T_{aw} (see also Section 2.3.5). However, in many applications which refer, of course, to compressible flow $T_w - T_{aw}$ is either finite at the leading edge or $T_w - T_{aw}$ is large compared with the variations of the wall temperature along the surface. Both facts would tend to diminish the influence of non-uniform distribution of the wall temperature on h. If this influence can be neglected, calculations are considerably simplified.

7.7 Heat flow with time-dependent boundary conditions of general form (semi-analytical methods)

The boundary conditions at the surfaces of structures and solids which have been treated so far have been mainly of two types, namely heat transfer by forced convection and a given rate of heat flow at the surface. In the first case constant heat transfer parameters have been assumed, while in the latter case the time dependence was of a particular form, e.g. $q_w = t^{\frac{n}{2}}$, (n an integer), which includes both constant ($n = 0$) and linearly varying ($n = 2$) rates of heat flow. Solutions of this type can be suitably combined to cover particular forms of the time dependence of the surface heat flow rates. However, in this chapter we deal with boundary conditions which depend on time in an arbitrary way.

With the help of Duhamel's integral (see Section 7.2) it is possible to calculate directly the temperature in a body with time dependent boundary conditions in the following cases: (a) given surface temperature, (b) given surface rate of heat flow, and (c) heat transfer at the surface by forced convection with variable reference temperature, but constant heat transfer coefficient. In other cases Duhamel's integral leads to integral equations. These are non-linear for non-linear boundary conditions and can then be solved by analytical methods with the help of a series of approximations converging to the exact solution, see for instance Ref. 7.7.1.

In the following semi-analytical methods solutions are obtained by a step-by-step procedure with the integrals replaced by sums. The basis of this method is Eq. (7.2.11) or a similar equation containing an integral of Duhamel's type. Dividing the time variable into equal intervals of size Δt and replacing the integration variable by a suitable sum, the following expression is obtained

$$T(x, m) - T_i = \sum_{j=0}^{m-1} \overline{q}_w\left(j + \frac{1}{2}\right) \vartheta'\left(x, m - j - \frac{1}{2}; \Delta t\right) \qquad m \geqslant 1 \qquad (7.7.1)$$

$T(x, m)$ is the temperature at the distance x and at the time $t = m\,\Delta t$ (where m is a whole number), and T_i is the constant initial temperature. $\vartheta'(x, l - \frac{1}{2}; \Delta t)$ is the temperature increase in the point x and at the time $l\,\Delta t$ (l a whole number) due to a unit rate of heat flow at the surface, prevailing from the time zero to Δt; afterwards the heat flow at the surface is again zero (Fig. 7.12(a)). $\bar{q}_w(l + \frac{1}{2})$ is a suitable mean value for

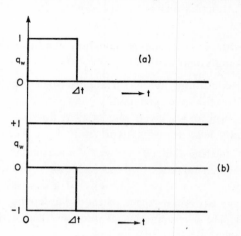

Fig. 7.12. (a) Heat input q_w at a surface. (b) The heat input of (a) obtained by superposing two step functions.

the rate of heat flow at the surface during the interval extending from $l\,\Delta t$ to $(l+1)\,\Delta t$. A rough estimate of the accuracy of the method can be obtained from the quantity ε in the following equation

$$Q(m) = \sum_{j=0}^{m-1} \bar{q}_w\left(j + \frac{1}{2}\right)\Delta t + \varepsilon \qquad (7.7.2)$$

where $Q(m)$ is the total amount of heat flow gained or lost by the body from $t = 0$ till the time $t = m\,\Delta t$ and ε is the summation error which depends on the size of Δt. The surface temperature follows from Eq. (7.7.1) by putting $x = 0$. Re-writing this equation one obtains

$$T(0, m) - T_i = \sum_{j=0}^{m-2} \bar{q}_w\left(j + \frac{1}{2}\right)\vartheta'\left(0, m - j - \frac{1}{2}; \Delta t\right) +$$

$$+ \bar{q}_w\left(m - \frac{1}{2}\right)\vartheta'\left(0, \frac{1}{2}; \Delta t\right) \qquad (7.7.3)$$

The boundary conditions at the surface at any time $l\Delta t$ are of the general form:

$$q_w(l) = F[T(0, l)] \tag{7.7.4}$$

A corresponding relation exists for mean values during the time interval extending from $l\,\Delta t$ to $t = (l + 1)\,\Delta t$:

$$\bar{q}_w\left(l+\frac{1}{2}\right) = \bar{F}\left[T\left(0, l+\frac{1}{2}\right)\right] \tag{7.7.5}$$

Assume that the calculations have already proceeded to the time $(m-1)\,\Delta t$; then all values of $\bar{q}_w\,(j+\frac{1}{2})$ from $j = 0$ to $m-2$ are known as well as the sum on the right-hand side of Eq. (7.7.3). Hence the two unknowns $T(0, m)$ and $\bar{q}_w(m - \frac{1}{2})$ follow from Eqs. (7.7.3) and (7.7.5) if, in the latter, $l = m-1$. Starting with an initial value, the temperature and the rate of heat flow at the surface can be calculated step by step. Then the temperature distribution can be obtained from Eq. (7.7.1).

Since the form of the boundary condition, Eq. (7.7.4), is quite general this method is applicable for all modes of heat transfer and for arbitrary time variations of the heat transfer parameters. It suffices to calculate once and for all $\vartheta'(x, l; \Delta t)$ for selected values of x, l and Δt; solutions can then be obtained by the present method for any boundary conditions and for any form of their time dependence.

The considerations governing the choice of the size of Δt are similar to those in the finite difference method of Chapter 8: in order to keep the computational work as small as possible, one has to choose Δt as large as possible with regard to the accuracy of the solutions.

So far the general outline of the method has been presented and now a convenient calculating scheme is developed. It appears useful, particularly for boundary conditions as in Eq. (7.7.4), to express $\bar{q}_w$ in Eq. (7.7.1) by the values of q_w at multiples of Δt. Thus one obtains:

$$\bar{q}_w(j+\tfrac{1}{2}) = \tfrac{1}{2}\,[q_w(j)+q_w(j+1)] \tag{7.7.6}$$

provided q_w is a continuous function of t. Suppose the temperature $\vartheta(x, l)$ — where l stands for $t = l\Delta t$ — is initially, at $l=0$, zero and is a solution for a unit rate of heat flow at the surface starting at $l = 0$. Then the temperature increase $\vartheta'\,(x, m - j - \frac{1}{2}; \Delta t)$ due to the heat input of Fig. 7.12(a) is assumed as

$$\vartheta'(x, m-j-\tfrac{1}{2}; \Delta t) = \vartheta(x, m-j)-\vartheta(x, m-j-1) \tag{7.7.7}$$

and it is obviously equal to the difference between two temperatures each due to a heat input at the surface in form of a step function, but with the discontinuities being a time interval Δt apart (see Figs. 7.12(a) and (b)).

By our choice all q_w's and ϑ's are taken at times which are multiples of Δt; this appears convenient, but need not necessarily be so. Introducing the expressions of Eqs. (7.7.6) and (7.7.7) into (7.7.1) and re-arranging terms behind the summation sign one finally obtains:

$$T(x, m) - T_i = \sum_{j=0}^{m} q_w(j)\vartheta''(x, m, j; \Delta t) \tag{7.7.8}$$

where

$$\vartheta''(x, m, j; \Delta t) = \begin{cases} \vartheta_{m,0}(x) = \tfrac{1}{2}[\vartheta(x, m) - \vartheta(x, m-1)], & j = 0 \\ \vartheta_{m,j}(x) = \tfrac{1}{2}[\vartheta(x, m-j+1) - \vartheta(x, m-j-1)], \\ \qquad\qquad\qquad\qquad\qquad 1 \leqslant j \leqslant m-1 \\ \vartheta_{m,m}(x) = \tfrac{1}{2}[\vartheta(x, 1) - \vartheta(x, 0)], & j = m \end{cases} \tag{7.7.9}$$

In order to interpret Eq. (7.7.8) replace $q_w(t)$ by a sequence of steps (Fig. 7.13) with jumps occurring at $m+\tfrac{1}{2}$, ($m = 0, 1, 2, ...$) and multiply each value of $q_w(m)$ by an influence function $\vartheta''(x, m, j; \Delta t)$. On inspecting

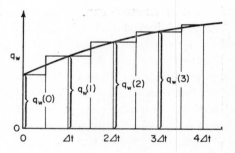

FIG. 7.13. Replacing $q_w(t)$ by a sequence of steps.

Eq. (7.7.9) and remembering the definition of $\vartheta(x, l)$ one finds that $\vartheta_{m,j}(x)$ should be equal to $\vartheta(x, m-j+\tfrac{1}{2}) - \vartheta(x, m-j-\tfrac{1}{2})$ rather than to the corresponding expression in Eq. (7.7.9) which was obtained as a consequence of the assumptions leading to Eq. (7.7.7). Similar considerations apply to $\vartheta_{m,0}(x)$ and $\vartheta_{m,m}(x)$. Therefore more accurate expressions for the $\vartheta_{m,j}$'s are:

$$\begin{aligned} \vartheta_{m,0}(x) &= \vartheta(x, m) - \vartheta(x, m-\tfrac{1}{2}), & j &= 0 \\ \vartheta_{m,j}(x) &= \vartheta(x, m-j+\tfrac{1}{2}) - \vartheta(x, m-j-\tfrac{1}{2}), & 1 &\leqslant j \leqslant m-1 \\ \vartheta_{m,m}(x) &= \vartheta(x, \tfrac{1}{2}) - \vartheta(x, 0), & j &= m \end{aligned} \tag{7.7.9a}$$

In calculating these expressions $\vartheta(x, l)$ has to be found for $l = m$ and $l = m+\tfrac{1}{2}$ instead of for only $l = m$ as in Eq. (7.7.9). For thick bodies the time-derivative of the surface temperature $\vartheta(0, t)$ is infinitely large at $t = 0$, hence $\vartheta_{m,m}(0)$ as calculated from Eq. (7.7.9) would become rather inaccurate and so also would $T(m, 0)$, particularly for small values of m. In order to save time when calculating $\vartheta_{m,0}(x)$ it is often sufficient to use $\vartheta_{m,0}(x) = \frac{1}{2} [\vartheta(x, m+\frac{1}{2}) - \vartheta(x, m-\frac{1}{2})]$ instead of the corresponding expression in Eq. (7.7.9a).

Equation (7.7.8) can be written in the form of a matrix equation†

$$
\begin{bmatrix} T(x, 1)-T_i \\ T(x, 2)-T_i \\ \cdot \\ \cdot \\ \cdot \\ T(x, m)-T_i \end{bmatrix} = \begin{bmatrix} \vartheta_{1,0}(x), & \vartheta_{1,1}(x), & 0, & 0, & \cdot & \cdot \\ \vartheta_{2,0}(x), & \vartheta_{2,1}(x), & \vartheta_{2,2}(x), & 0, & \cdot & \cdot \\ \cdot & \cdot & \cdot & \cdot & \cdot & \cdot \\ \cdot & \cdot & \cdot & \cdot & \cdot & \cdot \\ \cdot & \cdot & \cdot & \cdot & \cdot & \cdot \\ \vartheta_{m,0}(x), & \vartheta_{m,1}(x), & \cdot & \cdot & \cdot & \vartheta_{m,m}(x) \end{bmatrix} \begin{bmatrix} q_w(0) \\ q_w(1) \\ \cdot \\ \cdot \\ \cdot \\ q_w(m) \end{bmatrix} \qquad (7.7.10)
$$

which is easier to handle for both hand and machine calculations. If the q_w's are known, the calculations are straightforward and need only be made for those times $t = m \Delta t$ and those points x which are of interest. However, if the boundary conditions are of the form of Eq. (7.7.4) the surface temperature $(x = 0)$ must be calculated first. Then the matrix equation (7.7.10) must be solved line by line starting from the top, since the q_w's are not known *a piori*. One then proceeds as explained below. Assume all values of q_w for $t \leqslant (m-1) \Delta t$ are known; then Eq. (7.7.3) is obtained in the present notation by re-writing Eq. (7.7.8) as follows:

$$
T(0, m) - T_i = q_w(m)\vartheta_{m,m}(0) + P_{m-1} \qquad (7.7.11)
$$

where the sum on the right-hand side of Eq. (7.7.8) has been divided into two parts: the last term and

$$
P_{m-1} = \sum_{j=1}^{m-1} q_w(j)\vartheta_{m,j}(0) \qquad (7.7.12)
$$

Eliminating $q_w(m)$ from Eq. (7.7.11) with the help of Eq. (7.7.4) one obtains

$$
T(0, m) - \vartheta_{m,m}(0) F[T(0, m)] - T_i - P_{m-1} = 0, \qquad (7.7.13)
$$

an equation for the unknown $T(0, m)$. A solution of this equation can be given explicitly for a linear relation between q_w and $T(0, m)$ as would, for instance, correspond to the case of heat transfer by forced convection.

---

† In the first matrix on the right-hand side of Eq. (7.7.10) values are the same on diagonal lines falling from left to right except values in the first column, as follows from Eqs. (7.7.9) and (7.7.9a).

If $T(0, m)$ is known, $q_w(m)$ follows immediately from Eq. (7.7.4). Once the q_w's are known, the temperatures for interior points follow from Eq. (7.7.10) by a simple matrix multiplication on the right-hand side of that equation. If heat transfer by forced convection occurs at the surface with q_w as in Eq. (3.1.7) and with T_f as the temperature of the external medium and $T(0, m)$ as the wall temperature, an explicit solution for $T(0, m)$ is obtained from Eq. (7.7.13) in the following form

$$T(0, m) = \frac{1}{1+h\vartheta_{m,m}(0)}\{T_i + P_{m-1} + \vartheta_{m,m}(0)h\, T_f\} \qquad (7.7.14)$$

Even if the error is zero in the balance of the total amount of heat gained or lost by the body and that calculated by Eq. (7.7.2), there still remains an error in the temperatures due to the assumption of constant q_w during a time interval Δt. It is obvious that the contribution to this error differs for the different terms in the sum of, for instance, Eq. (7.7.8). If the time which has elapsed since a certain heat input was effective is much larger than the length of the time interval Δt during which the same heat input was operative, it will obviously not make much difference whether q_w is constant or not during that time interval. Hence appreciable errors will result only from the contributions of those time intervals immediately preceding the time for which the temperatures are sought. Since the amount of these contributions to the temperatures is small to moderate, depending on the size of Δt, the errors in the temperature will be small.

The method used in Hill's paper (Ref. 7.7.2) is similar in its main features, but somewhat more complex in approach and in details. The surface values of the rate of heat flow or the temperature are again determined first. A different form of Duhamel's integral is used as a starting point.

$$q_w(t) = \int_0^t q_{w,p}(t')\frac{\partial}{\partial t}\{T_w(t-t')\}\,\mathrm{d}t' \qquad (7.7.15)$$

$q_{w,p}(t)$ is the rate of heat flow at the heated surface due to a unit step in the surface temperature T_w at $t = 0$; $q_w(0) = 0$ for $t = 0$. The time is again divided into equal intervals Δt and the increase in surface temperature $T_w - T_i$ is replaced by a sequence of straight lines, for example $0 - a - b - c - d - e$ in Fig. 7.14. As can easily be shown this temperature history is equal to the total sum of the overlapping triangular temperature variations: 0–a–2, 1–b–3, 2–c–4, and so on. Further $q_{w,p}(t)$ in Eq. (7.7.15) is replaced by $q_{w\Delta}(l)$ and this quantity is the rate of heat flow at $t = l\,\Delta t$ due to a single triangular variation of $T_w - T_i$ which is for

$l \geqslant 2$, zero at $t = 0$, increases linearly to 1 at $t = \Delta t$ and then decreases linearly to zero at $t = 2\Delta t$ (0–a–c in Fig. 7.15); for $l = 1$ the triangle is 0–a–b in the same figure. In order to increase accuracy, $q_{w\Delta}(l)$ is re-

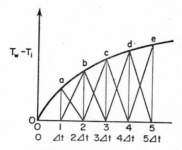

FIG. 7.14. Replacing the temperature increase at the surface by a sequence of straight lines (0—a—b—c—d—e) for which the total amount of heat gained from $t = 0$ to $t = 5\Delta t$ is equal to the sum of the triangles 0—a—2, 1—b—3, 2—c—4, 3—d—5 and 4—e—5.

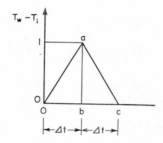

FIG. 7.15. A triangular variation of the increase in the surface temperature.

placed by $\bar{q}_{w\Delta}(l)$ which is obtained by integrating $q_{w\Delta}$ from $t = (l-1)\Delta t$ to $t = l\Delta t$ and dividing by Δt. Adding the contributions to q_w from all triangular temperature variations $T_w - T_i$ of Fig. 7.14, the integral on the right-hand side of Eq. (7.7.15) can be approximated by the sum

$$\sum_{j=1}^{m} \bar{q}_{w\Delta}(m-j+1)[T_w(j) - T_i] \text{ where } t = m\Delta t. \ \bar{q}_{w\Delta}(l) \text{ is found as follows. If}$$

$q_w^*(l)$ is the surface heat flow at $t = l\Delta t$ due to a surface temperature which is zero for $t \leqslant 0$ and at $t = 0$ starts to increase linearly by an amount 1 during every time interval Δt, then $\bar{q}_{w\Delta}(l) = \bar{q}_w^*(l) - 2\bar{q}_w^*(l-1) + \bar{q}_w^*(l-2)$. The bar above $\bar{q}_w^*(l)$ indicates a value averaged in the same way as $\bar{q}_{w\Delta}(l)$. For $l = 1$ the third term in the expression for $\bar{q}_{w\Delta}(l)$ is dropped and the second is zero at any rate. General heat transfer conditions at the surface can be satisfied by procedures similar to those given previously in this Section.

In some cases it may be more convenient to replace the rate of heat flow at the surface in Duhamel's integral Eq. (7.2.11) by a stepwise function as in Fig. 7.16 with unequal time intervals (Ref. 7.7.3). If, as intro-

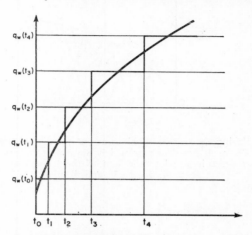

FIG. 7.16. Replacing the rate of surface heat flow by a stepwise function with equal increments in q_w.

duced earlier, $\vartheta(x, t)$ is then the solution for a unit rate of heat flow at the surface, the sum approximating Duhamel's integral becomes

$$T(x, t) - T_i = q_w(t_0)\vartheta(x, t-t_0) +$$

$$+ \sum_{j=1}^{m-1} [q_w(t_j) - q_w(t_j-1)]\vartheta(x, t-t_j), \quad t_{m-1} \leqslant t \leqslant t_m \qquad (7.7.16)$$

T_i is the assumed constant initial temperature at $t = t_0$. If q_w is known numerical calcul ationsbecome simpler if the increments in q_w are of equal size so that $q_w(t_j) - q_w(t_{j-1}) = \Delta q_w = $ const. This method is of advantage if the time-derivatives of q_w change quickly. The disadvantage is that numerical values of $\vartheta(x, t)$ must be available for all times. General boundary conditions can be satisfied in a similar way as given earlier.

The method explained at the beginning of this section is illustrated by an example which is treated in more detail later on in Section 9.1.2, viz. a skin reinforced by an integral stiffener (see Fig. 9.1). The temperature in the skin is assumed to be uniformly distributed; hence the simplified problem of Section 9.1.2 is treated here. The dimensions of the structure and the flight plan are given at the beginning of Section 9.3. The non-dimensional quantities given in Eqs. (9.1.6) to (9.1.8) are also used here. Although the skin temperature $\Theta_1(\tau)$ is readily found by simple analysis, see Eq. (9.1.9b), it is also calculated by the present method. For heat transfer by forced convection with constant h_f and T_f, Eq. (9.7.4) becomes (replacing $\tau = m\,\Delta\tau$ simply by m):

$$q_w(m) = h_f(T_f - T_i)[1 - \Theta_1(m)] \tag{7.7.17}$$

Next it is necessary to know the temperature increase of the skin, $\vartheta_1(\tau)$, due to a unit rate of heat input at the surface. Because the heat flow to the stiffener is neglected in the heat balance of the skin, one obtains

$$\frac{d\vartheta_1(\tau)}{d\tau} = \frac{1}{h_f} \tag{7.7.18}$$

where h_f is the external heat transfer coefficient. For $\vartheta_1(0) = 0$ the solution of Eq. (7.7.18) becomes $\vartheta_1(\tau) = \dfrac{\tau}{h_f}$. Then it follows from Eq. (7.7.9)†

$$\left.\begin{aligned}
\vartheta_{1;m,0} &= \vartheta_{1;m,m} = \frac{\Delta\tau}{2h_f} \\[2mm]
\vartheta_{1;m,j} &= \frac{\Delta\tau}{h_f}, \quad 1 \leqslant j \leqslant m-1
\end{aligned}\right\} \tag{7.7.19}$$

These values being known, one obtains from Eqs. (7.7.12), (7.7.14) and (7.7.17), with the definition of Θ_1 according to Eq. (9.1.6),

$$\Theta_1(m) = \frac{1}{2+\Delta\tau}\left\{\Delta\tau + 2h_f\sum_{j=0}^{m-1}[1 - \Theta_1(j)]\vartheta_{1;m,j}\right\} \tag{7.7.20}$$

With the help of this equation $\Theta_1(m)$ can be calculated step by step starting with $\Theta_1(0) = 0$.

In this particular case the expressions for $\vartheta_{1;m,j}$ are simpler than the corresponding quantities $\vartheta_{2;m,j}(\xi_2)$ inside the stiffener. There the temperatures due to a heat input to the skin in the form of a step function can be found from Eqs. (9.1.66) to (9.1.68) for small times, if in these equations we put $n = 0$ and $D = 1$. A solution for large times is given in Eq. (9.1.69), if $q_w = 1$ there. It suffices here to use the expression for small times in Eq. (9.1.68). Then $\vartheta_{2;m,j}(x)$ follows with the help of Eq. (7.7.9) and $\Theta_2(\xi_2, t)$‡ with the help of Eqs. (7.7.8) or (7.7.10), and (7.7.17). Omitting details, the results of the numerical calculations are shown in

---

† Because of the particular form of $\vartheta_1(\tau)$ Eqs. (7.7.9) and (7.7.9a) yield in this case the same results.

‡ $\Theta_2(\xi_2, t)$ is defined by Eq. (9.1.6).

Fig. 7.17. For $\Delta\tau = 0.2$, and at the places $x_2 = 0$ and $x_2 = L_2$ the errors are less than 0·1 per cent, even for $\Delta\tau$ as large as 0·6 the errors remain below 2 per cent. Because the amount of computational work is inversely

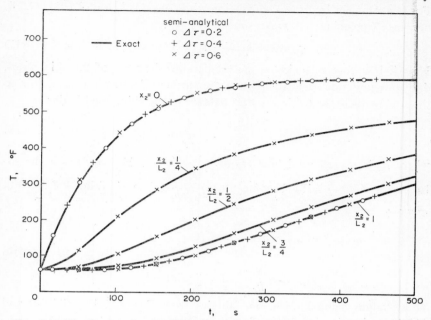

FIG. 7.17. The numerical example of Section 9.1.2 re-calculated by a method of Section 7.7. (See also Fig. 9.12.)

proportional to $(\Delta\tau)^2$ approximately, it is advantageous to use large time steps whenever this can be done without impairing the accuracy of the solution.

7.8 Heat conduction in a semi-infinite solid with melting or sublimation at the surface

Assuming constant thermal properties, the equation of heat conduction is given by Eq. (3.1.16). Initially the temperature is constant in the solid and equal to T_i; the surface is at $x = 0$ before melting or sublimation begins. Far away from the surface, at $x = \infty$, the temperature retains its initial value T_i. The melting temperature† is T_P and the specific heat of melting is S_P. The rate of heat flow at the surface is q_w and is assumed

---

† The following treatment is also valid for sublimation, if T_P and S_P are the sublimation temperature and the heat of evaporation respectively, but for simplicity we refer only to melting.

constant. As long as the surface temperature remains below the melting temperature T_P, the temperature distribution is given by Eq. (7.4.7). Hence, the time when melting starts at the surface $(x = 0)$ is:

$$t_P = \frac{\pi}{4} \frac{k \rho c}{q_w{}^2} (T_P - T_i)^2 \tag{7.8.1}$$

with k, ρ and c as the thermal properties of the solid. Thereafter the boundary condition at the surface becomes as in Eq. (3.4.1a) with corresponding changes in the subscripts:

$$q_w = -k \frac{\partial T}{\partial x} + \rho S_P \frac{\mathrm{d}s}{\mathrm{d}t} \tag{7.8.2a}$$

$$T = T_P \tag{7.8.2b}$$

where $s(t)$ is the distance of the melting surface from the initial surface before melting began. The liquid formed by melting is assumed to be immediately removed by the air forces acting on the surfaces. This assumption is approximately valid for materials with a low viscosity (molten metals), but would not be true for very viscous materials like glass. Thus the liquid boundary layer can be neglected and it suffices to consider only the penetration of heat inside the solid under the boundary conditions (7.8.2). A non-dimensional temperature is introduced

$$\Theta = \frac{T - T_i}{T_P - T_i} \tag{7.8.3}$$

and a non-dimensional distance and time by

$$\xi = \frac{x - s(t)}{[\varkappa t_P]^{1/2}} \tag{7.8.4}$$

and

$$\tau = \frac{t}{t_P} - 1 \tag{7.8.5}$$

respectively. For the following analysis it is convenient to introduce two further quantities

$$\Gamma = \frac{\rho S_P}{q_w} \frac{\mathrm{d}s}{\mathrm{d}t} \tag{7.8.6}$$

and

$$m_P = \frac{\pi^{1/2}}{2} \frac{c (T_P - T_i)}{S_P} \tag{7.8.7}$$

Re-writing Eq. (3.1.16) in the new variables Θ, τ and ξ, one obtains:

$$\frac{\partial \Theta}{\partial \tau} = \frac{\partial^2 \Theta}{\partial \xi^2} + m_P \Gamma(\tau) \frac{\partial \Theta}{\partial \xi} \tag{7.8.8}$$

At the beginning of melting, that is at $\tau = 0$, the temperature distribution is given by Eq. (7.4.7) in which one has to put $t = t_P$ with t_P given by Eq. (7.8.1); one obtains finally:

$$\Theta = \pi^{1/2} \text{ierfc} \left(\frac{\xi}{2} \right), \quad \text{at } \tau = 0 \tag{7.8.9}$$

where ierfc stands for the function defined by Eq. (7.4.14). The boundary conditions (7.8.2) for melting become

$$\text{at } \xi = 0 \quad \begin{cases} 1 = -\frac{2}{\pi^{1/2}} \left(\frac{\partial \Theta}{\partial \xi} \right)_{\xi=0} + \Gamma(\tau) & (7.8.10a) \\ \\ \Theta = 1 & (7.8.10b) \end{cases}$$

At infinity the initial temperature prevails for all finite times and this yields

$$\Theta = 0 \quad \text{for } \xi \to \infty \tag{7.8.11}$$

Summarizing, the temperature distribution during melting is determined by the differential equation (7.8.8), the boundary conditions (7.8.10) and (7.8.11), and the initial conditions (7.8.9).

Equation (7.8.8) is non-linear, as follows when $\Gamma(\tau)$ is eliminated from (7.8.8) with the help of (7.8.10a).

First a steady state solution is derived by putting $\frac{\partial}{\partial \tau} = 0$ in Eq. (7.8.8) and $\Gamma = \Gamma_{st} = \text{const.}$; one obtains:

$$\Theta = \exp\{-m_P \Gamma_{st} \xi\} \tag{7.8.12}$$

From Eq. (7.8.10a) it follows that

$$\Gamma_{st} = (1 + 2m_P \pi^{-1/2})^{-1} \tag{7.8.13}$$

Equation (7.8.12) can be re-written with the help of Eqs. (7.8.1), (7.8.4), (7.8.7) and (7.8.13) in a form which shows directly the physical variable

$$\Theta = \exp\left\{ -v_{ab} \frac{x - s(t)}{\varkappa} \right\} \tag{7.8.14}$$

where

$$v_{ab} = \frac{q_w}{\rho \left[S_P + c(T_P - T_i) \right]} \tag{7.8.15}$$

is the speed of ablation in the steady state. $s(t)$ is the thickness of the material lost since ablation began. During the early phase the speed of ablation differs from the above value, therefore the exact steady state expression for s can not be found directly. For sufficiently long times one may approximately put

$$s(t) \approx v_{ab}(t - t_P) \tag{7.8.16}$$

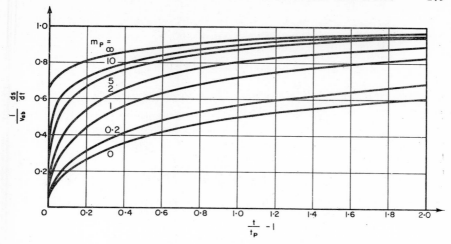

FIG. 7.18. Rate of melting in an ablating semi-infinite body. From Ref. 3.4.1.

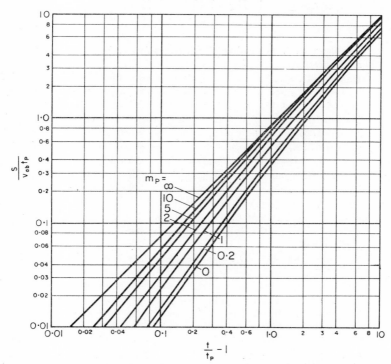

FIG. 7.19. Thickness of melted layer in an ablating semi-infinite body. From Ref. 3.4.1.

The exact expression can be found from the following balance of heat flow which in the present case (q_w = const. and T_i = const.) is:

$$q_w t = \rho c \int_{s(t)}^{\infty} [T(x, t) - T_i] \mathrm{d}x + \rho [S_P + c (T_P - T_i)] s(t) \qquad (7.8.17)$$

This equation states that the total amount of heat transferred to the body, in this case $q_w t$, is equal to the amount of the heat stored in the solid plus the amount of the heat required to raise the temperature to the melting point and to melt the ablated material. With the help of Eqs. (7.8.3) and (7.8.12) the integral on the right-hand side of Eq. (7.8.17) can be evaluated. Using Eq. (7.8.15) and solving Eq. (7.8.17) for $s(t)$ yields the exact steady state expression for $s(t)$

$$s(t) = v_{\mathrm{ab}} t - \frac{k}{q_w} (T_P - T_i) \qquad (7.8.18)$$

Solutions for the transient case have been obtained numerically by Landau (Ref. 3.4.1) and the results for the rate of melting and the thickness of the melted layer are given in Figs. 7.18 and 7.19.

References

7.2.1   CARSLAW, H. S. and JAEGER, J. C., *Operational Methods in Applied Mathematics*, Oxford University Press, Oxford (1941).

7.3.1   HARTREE, D. R., *Numerical Analysis*, Clarendon Press, Oxford (1952, 1955).

7.3.2   SAELMAN, B., Integration of some thermal differential equations, *J.Aero/Space Sci.* **26**, 11, 754–755 (1959).

7.4.1   *Tables of Probability Functions*, Vol. I. Federal Works Agency, Work Projects Administration for the City of New York (1941).

7.4.2   GOLDSMITH, A., WATERMAN, T. E. and HIRSCHHORN, H. J., *Handbook of thermophysical properties of solid materials*, Rev. ed., Macmillan, New York (1961).

7.5.1.   GURNEY, H. P. and LURIE, J., Charts for estimating temperature distributions in heating or cooling solid shapes, *Ind. and Eng. Chem.* **15**, 11, 1170 (1923).

7.5.2   HEISLER, M. P., Temperature charts for induction and constant-temperature heating, *Trans. A.S.M.E.* **69**, 3, 227–236 (1947).

7.5.3   BACHMANN, H., *Tafeln über Abkühlungsvorgänge einfacher Körper*, Springer, Berlin (1938).

7.5.4   MAYER, E., Heat flow in composite slabs, *J. Amer. Rocket Soc.* **22**, 3, 150–158 (1952).

7.5.5   GROVER, J. H. and HOLTER, W. H., Solution of the transient heat-conduction equation for an insulated, infinite metal slab, *Jet. Prop.* **27**, 12, 1249–1252 (1957).

7.5.6   TRIMPI, R. L. and JONES, R. A., Transient temperature distribution in a two-component semi-infinite composite slab of arbitrary · materials subjected to aerodynamic heating with a discontinuous change in equilibrium temperature or heat-transfer coefficient, NACA TN 4308 (1958).

7.5.7 (a)   CAMPBELL, W. F., A rapid analytical method for calculating the early transient temperature in a composite slab, Rep. No. MT-32, Division of Mech.

Engng., Nat. Res. Council, Ottawa, Canada, April 1956, see also Trans. of the Engng. Institute of Canada No. 1, 15, Sept. 1957.

(b) CAMPBELL, W. F., One-dimensional transient heat flow in a multi-layer slab, *J. Aero. Sci.* **25**, 5, 340–341 (1958).

7.5.8 FRITZ, R. J., Evaluation of transient temperatures and stresses, *Trans. A.S.M.E.* **76**, 913–921 (1954).

7.6.1 PARKER, H. M., Transient temperature distributions in simple conducting bodies steadily heated through a laminar boundary layer, NACA TN 3058 (1953).

7.6.2 TIDEMAN, M., On the temperature distribution in thin flat plates with laminar supersonic boundary layers, Svenska Aeroplan AB TN 39 (1958).

7.6.3 HEAPS, N. S., Transient thermal stress in a flat plate due to non-uniform heat transfer across one surface, *Aeronautical Research Council Current Paper* 299 (1956).

7.6.4 JOHNSON, C. H. J., On a method of determining the transient temperature distribution in a flat plate with non-uniform surface heating, Dept. of Supply, Australian Defence Scientific Service, Aeronautical Res. Lab., Mech. Engineering Note 237 (1959).

7.6.5 GRÖBNER, W. and HOFREITER, N., *Integraltafel, Zweiter Teil.* Springer, Wien (1961).

7.6.6 British Ass. Advancement of Science, Mathematical tables, Vol. I (1931).

7.6.7 BRYSON, A. E. and EDWARDS, R. H., The effect of non-uniform surface temperature on the transient aerodynamic heating of thin-skinned bodies, *IAS Preprint* No. 365 (1952).

7.6.8 EMMONS, H. W., The non-steady aerodynamic heating of a plate. "*50 Jahre Grenzschichtforschung*". *Eine Festschrift in Originalbeiträgen.* Herausgegeben von H. Görtler und W. Tollmien, Vieweg, Braunschweig (1955), S. 385–392.

7.6.9 BRYSON, A. E., BUDIANSKY, B. and CARRIER, G. F., Leading-edge temperature of a flat plate subjected to aerodynamic heating, *J.A.S.* **24**, 4, 311–312 (1957).

7.6.10 SCHUH, H., Zur Bestimmung der Temperaturverteilung in dünnen Platten mit anliegender Überschallgrenzschicht. *Grenzschichtforschung, Symposium Freiburg/Br.*, 26. bis 29. August 1957. Springer, Berlin (1958).

7.6.11 SCHMIDT, C. M. and HANAWALT, A. J., The effect of an arbitrary distribution of surface temperatures on heat transfer in the compressible laminar boundary layer, *J. Aero. Sci.* **24**, 1, 73 (1957).

7.7.1 ABARBANEL, S. S., On some problems in radiative heat transfer, O.S.R.U. S.A.F. Techn. Note No. 59–531 (1959).

7.7.2 HILL, P. R., A method of computing the transient temperature of thick walls from arbitrary variation of adiabatic wall-temperature and heat-transfer coefficient, NACA Rep. 1372 (1958).

7.7.3 TEARNEN, J. C., A method of determining the transient temperature distribution in an entry-vehicle heat sink, A.S.M.E. Paper 59-AV-31 (1959).

CHAPTER 8

TRANSIENT HEAT FLOW II: NUMERICAL METHODS

8.1 One-dimensional heat flow. General remarks on finite difference methods

8.1.1 *Considerations in choosing difference equations*

Finite difference methods were previously used in Chapter 6 in the case of steady heat flow, and in the transient case one proceeds in an analogous way. The space and time variables are divided into intervals Δx and Δt respectively, and the differential expressions in the equation of heat conduction are replaced by finite difference expressions. This can be done in various ways and the proper choice of a particular type of finite difference equation to approximate the differential equation depends on such considerations as (a) convergence, (b) stability, (c) accuracy, (d) amount of computational work and (e) regularity of the solutions. Convergent difference solutions approach the corresponding differential solutions to any desired degree of accuracy for $\Delta x \rightarrow 0$ and for $\Delta t \rightarrow 0$. Difference solutions are stable if computational errors do not grow as the calculations proceed in the direction of increasing time, and they are regular if oscillations and other physically impossible features do not occur. In order to secure the desired properties in the solutions it is not only necessary to choose the proper type of finite difference equation but certain conditions, regarding the relative magnitudes of Δx and Δt, have to be satisfied for a number of finite difference equations. These will be discussed later but, before proceeding, it is noted here that the amount of computational work involved in solving the finite difference equations becomes very large unless the finite differences are chosen as large as possible without impairing the desired accuracy and regularity of the solutions.

8.1.2 *Convergence and stability. Behaviour of solutions for large differences*

It is convenient at this stage to introduce the following definitions: T is an exact solution of the partial differential equation, $T_{n,m}$ and $Z_{n,m}$ are the exact and numerical solutions respectively of the partial finite difference equation. Further two errors are of interest: first, the truncation error $T_{n,m}-T$, which is the difference between the exact solutions of a finite difference equation and a differential equation, and secondly, the numerical error $Z_{n,m}-T_{n,m}$ which is the difference between the numerical and the exact solutions of a finite difference equation. The properties of solutions (a) and (b) in Section 8.1.1 can now be defined more exactly. Difference solutions are convergent, if and only if the truncation error $T_{n,m}-T \to 0$ for $\Delta x \to 0$ and $\Delta t \to 0$ in the whole domain of the space and time variables. The solutions are stable, if the numerical error $Z_{n,m}-T_{n,m}$ remains bounded for Δx and Δt both being fixed and finite.

Consider first the equation of heat conduction (3.1.16) with constant thermal properties and without heat sources; since it is linear and homogeneous, any numerical errors existing at a certain time propagate in exactly the same way as the temperatures themselves. Hence by an intuitive reasoning one would expect convergence and stability to be two equivalent properties of finite difference solutions. A rigorous mathematical proof of this equivalence has recently been given by Lax, see Ref. 8.1. The classical method of von Neumann for investigating convergence and stability is given briefly in Section 8.2.2.

For continuous initial temperature distributions and as $\Delta x \to 0$ and $\Delta t \to 0$, the conditions of convergence and stability would suffice for acceptable solutions in the whole region of the variables, since the truncation error would then tend to zero. Later on, however, it is proved that the amount of computational work for obtaining finite difference solutions in a widely used method of the so-called explicit type (see next section) is inversely proportional to $(\Delta x)^3$ and would therefore increase strongly when $\Delta x \to 0$. Hence one would be interested in the behaviour of finite difference solutions for relatively large values of Δx. The mere condition of boundedness would obviously not suffice for acceptable finite difference solutions. In fact it will be shown that stable and convergent solutions for large values of Δx can have features which are not permissible from a physical point of view. Hence in Sections 8.2.3 to 8.2.8 the behaviour of finite difference solutions for any values, however large, of Δx and Δt and at any time $t = m \Delta t$ will be investigated in some detail, thus providing a deeper insight into the properties of finite difference solutions.

8.2 One-dimensional heat flow. A simple explicit finite difference equation

8.2.1 *Derivation of the finite difference equation*

The finite difference equation which follows is one of the simplest and at the same time it is also widely used. Assume one-dimensional, linear heat flow in a continuous body with constant thermal properties; divide the coordinate x and the time t into equal intervals Δx and Δt respectively. The temperature at a certain point having the coordinate $x = n\,\Delta x$, and at a certain time $t = m\,\Delta t$, is $T_{n,m}$. The differential equation (3.1.16) is replaced by the following finite difference equation†

$$\frac{T_{n,m+1}-T_{n,m}}{\Delta t} = \varkappa \frac{T_{n-1,m}-2T_{n,m}+T_{n+1,m}}{(\Delta x)^2} \qquad (8.2.1)$$

The finite difference expression in T on the left-hand side of the equation is of first order with respect to time and that on the right-hand side is of second order with respect to x.

If both difference expressions in Eq. (8.2.1) are interpreted as being central with respect to the time and the space points used, they refer to the same place $x = n\,\Delta x$ but to two different times—on the left-hand side to $t = (m+\tfrac{1}{2})\Delta t$ and on the right-hand side to $t = m\,\Delta t$. There is therefore a time interval of $\tfrac{1}{2}\Delta t$ between the two difference expressions and it obviously introduces an error. Its existence can also be explained by interpreting Eq. (8.2.1) by physical concepts. On the left- and right-hand sides of that equation stand respectively the *mean value* of the temperature increase of a section with width Δx during a time interval of length Δt, and the balance of heat flow of the same section at the *beginning* of the time interval. Although it would be more correct to use a mean value also for the balance of heat flow during the time interval Δt, Eq. (8.2.1) has the advantage that it yields a simple explicit expression for the unknown temperature $T_{n,m+1}$, which is convenient for a step-by-step procedure. This is seen at once by solving Eq. (8.2.1) for $T_{n,m+1}$:

$$T_{n,m+1} = p(T_{n-1,m}+T_{n+1,m})+(1-2p)T_{n,m} \qquad (8.2.2)$$

where

$$p = \frac{\varkappa\,\Delta t}{(\Delta x)^2} \qquad (8.2.3)$$

If the temperatures at a point n and two adjacent points $n-1$ and $n+1$ are known at a time m, then the temperature at the point n and at the time $(m+1)$ can be calculated directly with the help of Eq. (8.2.2). A treatment of the finite difference method for transient heat flow from a general engineering point of view is given in Ref. 6.6 where many examples can be found.

---

† This equation and a graphical method for its solution are known from a classical paper by Schmidt (Ref. 8.3).

8.2.2 *Von Neumann's method for investigating stability*

Stability conditions have been treated extensively in the literature, although in most cases the numerical errors are unimportant in comparison with the truncation errors. However, such studies lead to important results because conditions for convergence and stability are equivalent (see Section 8.1.2). Von Neumann's method which was first published in Ref. 8.4 is probably the best known. Any arbitrary initial distribution for the numerical error $E_{n,0}$ can be written as a Fourier series for which it is convenient here to use the following form:

$$E_{n,0} = \sum_{j=-\infty}^{+\infty} A_j \exp\left\{i j n \Delta x \frac{\pi}{L}\right\} \qquad (8.2.4a)$$

The constants A_j and A_{-j} are complex conjugates, A_0 is real and $i = \sqrt{-1}$; then the right-hand side of the equation is also real. A finite body extending from $x = 0$ to $x = L$ is assumed. The development of E with time can be written, with ζ_j as a parameter as:

$$E_{n,m} = \sum_{j=-\infty}^{+\infty} A_j \, (\zeta_j)^m \exp\left\{i j n \Delta x \frac{\pi}{L}\right\} \qquad (8.2.4b)$$

Introducing Eq. (8.2.4b) in the difference equation (8.2.2), the relation

$$\zeta_j = 1 + 2p\left[\cos\left(j \Delta x \frac{\pi}{L}\right) - 1\right] \qquad (8.2.5)$$

must be satisfied for each component in the sum of (8.2.4b). Because $\cos\left(j \Delta x \frac{\pi}{L}\right)$ is bounded between -1 and $+1$, the following limits for ζ_j are obtained:

$$1 - 4p \leqslant \zeta_j \leqslant 1. \qquad (8.2.6)$$

According to Eq. (8.2.4b) the numerical error does not increase with time if $|\zeta_j| \leqslant 1$, and hence it is sufficient to limit p by

$$0 \leqslant p \leqslant \frac{1}{2} \qquad (8.2.7)$$

Because of the equivalence theorem this is also the condition for convergence of the difference equation (8.2.2). If oscillations in $E_{n,m}$ are to be avoided, ζ_j in Eq. (8.2.4b) must be positive, and from Eq. (8.2.6) it follows that $p \leqslant \frac{1}{4}$, which is equal to the condition for convergence of the fourth kind to be introduced later on. For more detailed mathematical investigations on stability and convergence, see Refs. 8.1, 8.2 and the extensive literature cited therein.

8.2.3 *Difference solutions for an instantaneous plane source*

Some idea of the properties of those solutions of Eq. (8.2.2) which are obtained with large differences Δx and Δt can easily be gained as follows. Assume an infinite body with constant thermal properties and without heat sources; the temperature is to be T_i everywhere except in one point characterized by the index $n = 0$ where it is $T_{0,0}$. Within the limited accuracy of the finite difference method this initial temperature distribution corresponds either to an instantaneous source (with finite heat content) or to a rectangular temperature distribution ($T = T_{0,0}$ for $-\frac{1}{2}\Delta x \leqslant x \leqslant +\frac{1}{2}\Delta x$, and $T = T_i \neq T_{0,0}$ elsewhere) as shown in Fig. 8.1. The exact solutions

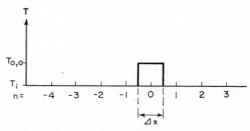

FIG. 8.1. Rectangular initial temperature distribution representing a source in the finite difference method. $T = T_{0,0}$ at $n = 0$ and $T = T_i \neq T_{0,0}$ at $n \neq 0$.

of the finite difference equation (8.2.2) for values of $p = 1, \frac{1}{2}, \frac{1}{3}, \frac{1}{4}$ are compared in Fig. 8.2 with the exact solution of the differential equation (3.1.16) for two initial temperature distributions, i.e. that of Fig. 8.1 and one corresponding to an instantaneous plane source at $n = 0$. As time increases the various solutions obtained with the finite difference method at the location of the initial singularity ($n = 0$) behave as follows: (a) for $p = 1$ they oscillate with rapidly increasing amplitudes (divergent solutions), (b) for $p = \frac{1}{2}$ they remain bounded, but oscillate with amplitudes of the same order of magnitude as the temperatures $T_{0,m} - T_i$ themselves, (c) for $p = \frac{1}{3}$ the oscillations are of rapidly decreasing amplitude and the truncation error is small when the oscillations have died out and (d) for $p = \frac{1}{4}$ there are no oscillations and agreement with the exact solution is good at all times. The spatial distributions in Fig. 8.3 show similar behaviour. It is important to note that the observed irregularities are not in any way connected with rounding-off errors. Experience shows that the truncation error by far exceeds the numerical errors, which therefore have no practical importance in most cases (Ref. 8.4). If one superposes three of these oscillating solutions which are identical, but whose midpoint is located at three adjacent points, say, $n = -1$,

0 and $+1$, the resulting temperatures oscillate less, both in time and space, than each single component alone. If therefore the initial temperature distribution is free from discontinuities and if the region where the initial

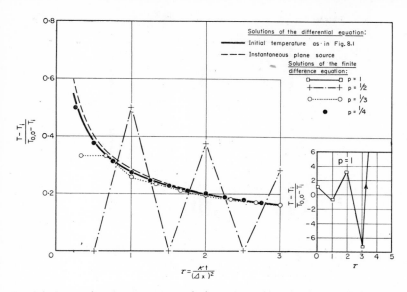

FIG. 8.2. Comparison between exact solutions of the differential and the finite difference equation (8.2.2) for an instantaneous plane source. Values of the finite difference parameter $p = 1$, 1/2, 1/3 and 1/4. The temperature at the location of the instantaneous source as a function of time.

temperature is different from zero is divided into a sufficiently large number of sections, solutions obtained with $p \leqslant \frac{1}{2}$ will be to a large extent free from oscillations. When discontinuities exist in the initial distribution, $p \leqslant \frac{1}{3}$ can be used, if oscillations are accepted in the first steps of the finite difference method, but $p \leqslant \frac{1}{4}$ must be used if oscillations are to be avoided.

8.2.4 Four different types of behaviour in difference solutions

The example of the previous section shows that solutions become more accurate and, in addition, physically erroneous features are eliminated if more severe conditions for the size of p are chosen than those which only prevent divergence of the solutions. A more detailed knowledge of the behaviour of the solutions is therefore desirable. In the following investigations an unlimited body is assumed and later on the influence of boundary conditions is investigated. It appears reasonable to define the first type of behaviour by such conditions as would prevent the solutions from increasing infinitely with time (divergent solutions). However, this alone is in general no guarantee for useful solutions. Consider finite difference solutions as shown in Fig. 8.4(a)† where times are characterized

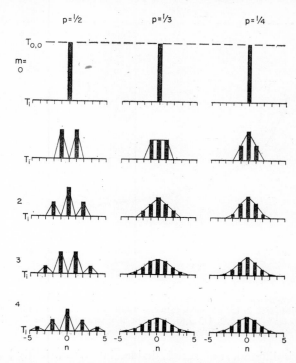

FIG. 8.3. Spatial distribution of the finite difference solutions for the source of Fig. 8.2 for $p = 1/2$, $1/3$ and $1/4$ at the beginning ($m = 0$) and at the end of the first 4 time steps ($m = 1$ to 4) which, however, differ in duration for different p.

by $m = 0$, 1, ... and refer to the initial ($m = 0$) and successive values $m\Delta t$. Obviously the solutions are bounded, but they would be rather useless because of the violent oscillations. Since the initial temperature distribution at the time $m = 0$ is nowhere negative and if the lowest temperature in the whole system is zero, then all negative temperatures occurring in the solutions are incompatible with the fundamental law of heat conduction and are therefore erroneous. In almost all cases elementary physical

---

† Since the behaviour of type 1 and 2 coincides for heat flow without internal heat sources, an example was taken from Section 8.4. The initial temperature distribution was as in Section 8.2.3; the difference equation was Eq. (8.4.1) with $p = \frac{1}{4}$ and $p_h = \frac{1}{2}$ in the case of Fig. 8.4(a) and $p = \frac{1}{4}$ and $p_h = \frac{1}{4}$ in the case of Fig. 8.4(b); $T_{n,m}^{(f)} = 0$ in both cases.

considerations are available for the upper and lower limits within which solutions for the temperatures must lie. These limits need only be fixed for the first time step, since one can always proceed step by step in an initial value problem such as heat conduction. The erroneous features of the solutions in Fig. 8.4(a) could be avoided by prescribing such limits for the temperatures. Thus the behaviour of the second type is characterized. Consider next any two successive temperature distributions as given in Fig. 8.4(b). Although these solutions satisfy the condition for the second type of behav-

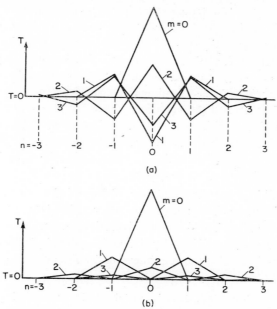

FIG. 8.4. Two examples for finite difference solutions with features incompatible with the fundamental law of heat conduction. These features are in (a) the occurrence of negative values and in (b) the sequence of temperatures at certain places, for instance at $n = 0$. (See text.) Temperature distributions as a sequence of straight lines through the temperature points used in the finite difference method.

iour, successive temperatures, as for instance those at the point $n = 0$ in Fig 8.4(b)†, would not be possible in reality, because they could occur only if heat had flowed, at times, in the direction of increasing temperature. This is, of course, physically impossible and the second and subsequent temperature distributions in Fig. 8.4(b) are erroneous in certain regions. Obviously, these errors can be avoided by making conditions which would preclude the possibility of temperature distributions, and the corresponding heat flows, which violate the fundamental law of heat conduction. Hence

† See footnote on page 188.

the finite difference gradient of the temperature must everywhere have a sign opposite to that of the local heat flow which follows from the local balance of heat flows; later on certain reservations are made for small temperature gradients. This is the condition for the third type of behaviour.

It is natural to require, as the condition coming next in increasing order of severity, that the finite difference form of the balance of heat flow for a section as calculated from the instantaneous distribution of the temperatures shall have the same sign as the finite difference form of the time derivative of the temperature in the same section. If the balance of heat flow is positive (i.e. the incoming amount of heat exceeds the outgoing amount) then the derivative of the temperature with respect to time must be positive, i.e. the temperature increases with time. Summarizing, it is required in the third and fourth types of behaviour that the finite difference form of the fundamental law of heat conduction (i.e. $q = -k\,\partial T/\partial x$) and of the equation of heat conduction (i.e. Eq. (3.1.16)) are both satisfied with respect to the sign at all times and places. The various finite difference expressions to be used are defined later on. It is to be noted that the particular finite difference equation (8.2.2) does not in general meet these requirements.

The conditions for the behaviour of finite difference solutions are now discussed in more detail; they are not restricted to a particular finite difference equation. The 4 types of behaviour are summarized in Table 8.1 where they are numbered in order of increasing severity in their requirements; each type satisfies also the requirements for the preceding types. The first

TABLE 8.1. Behaviour of finite difference solutions

Type	Limits for temperatures	Condition[a],[b]	
		$\sigma\left(\dfrac{\Delta T}{\Delta x}\right) = \sigma(-q)$	$\sigma\left(\dfrac{\Delta^2 T}{\Delta x^2}\right) = \sigma\left(\dfrac{\Delta T}{\Delta t}\right)$
I	$|T| \leqslant B$	may not be satisfied	may not be satisfied
II			
III	$B_{min} \leqslant T \leqslant B_{max}$	satisfied	
IV			satisfied

☐ Conditions defining behaviour.

[a] $\sigma(\ldots) = \text{sign. }(\ldots)$. Rate of heat flow q to be found from the distribution of the local balances of heat flow or finite difference quantities as defined in the text.

[b] Does not apply in places where derivatives are small.

type can be defined by a limit B for the absolute value of the temperatures and thus finite difference solutions remain bounded as the calculations proceed. The second type can be defined by an upper and lower limit for the solutions B_{max} and B_{min}. These quantities have to be chosen from physical considerations as mentioned earlier. For systems without internal heat sources $B = T_{i,max}$ can be chosen for the first type; for the second type, $B_{max} = T_{i,max}$ and $B_{min} = T_{i,min}$, because in an infinite body the temperatures can neither exceed the highest nor fall below the lowest level of the initial temperatures without violating the fundamental law of heat conduction. Further, for such systems the first and second types of behaviour can be made to coincide by shifting the zero point of temperature to $\frac{1}{2}(T_{i,max} + T_{i,min})$ and by choosing $B = \frac{1}{2}(T_{i,max} - T_{i,min})$. For the third type of behaviour $\Delta T / \Delta x \sim (T_{n+1,m} - T_{n,m})$ is required to be of opposite sign to the heat flow between the same points $n+1$ and n at the beginning and at the end of each time step except where both quantities are small. The heat flow between two points of the finite difference grid could be found from the distribution of the local balances of heat flow. In the cases investigated later, conditions which exclude heat flow in a prohibited direction can be easily and directly found. Thus compatibility with the fundamental law of heat conduction is obtained everywhere. If $\Delta T / \Delta x$ is of the same order of magnitude as the truncation error, deviations from the above requirement must obviously be allowed. For the fourth type of behaviour there is the additional requirement that the balance of heat flow $k \Delta^2 T / (\Delta x)^2$ shall have the same sign as the time derivative of the temperature at all places n and at all times m; more precisely $\Delta T / \Delta t \sim (T_{n,m+1} - T_{n,m})$ is to be of the same sign as $\Delta^2 T / (\Delta x)^2 \sim$ $\sim (T_{n+1,k} + T_{n-1,k} - 2T_{n,k})$ at the beginning $(k = m)$ and at the end $(k = m+1)$ of each time step, except where both quantities are small.

Before seeking, for the difference equation (8.2.2), the conditions corresponding to the 4 types of behaviour just defined, it is useful to continue the physical interpretation of that equation. It was found in Section 8.2.1 that the mean rate of increase in the temperature of a section *during a time interval* of length Δt is equal to the balance of heat flow of the same section at the *beginning of the time interval*. Hence if Δt is sufficiently large, more heat flows either to or from a section during a time interval Δt than would be necessary for equalizing the temperature difference between a section and its two neighbours (see for instance the case $p = \frac{1}{2}$ in Fig. 8.3). This yields successive temperature distributions which could only be explained by heat flowing at times from a cold to a hot place and this is, of course, in contradiction to the fundamental law of heat conduction. As a further consequence, the balance of heat flow changes sign at the beginning of each time step and, hence, at a fixed point there occur temperature oscillations of a type which was observed in the solutions for $p = \frac{1}{2}$ in Fig. 8.2. If Δt is increased still further, the temperature differences between two fixed places may become larger at the end of a time interval than they were at the beginning. If repeated many times, such solutions would clearly diverge, like those for $p = 1$ in Section 8.2.2.

When investigating the behaviour of the finite difference equation (8.2.2), only one time step need be considered, since the temperature distribution at the end of one time interval can be conceived as the initial temperature distribution for the next time interval. Because heat sources are absent, conditions for only one of the first two types of behaviour need to be investigated, as has been remarked previously, and of these the second type is chosen here. Since the temperature at any point n is determined from the temperatures at the points $n-1$, n and $n+1$ at one time step earlier, only the temperatures at these points need be considered. Because any linear combination of solutions of Eq. (8.2.1) is also a solution, it suffices to assume initial temperatures with the values 0 and 1. Further, because $T_{n+1,m}$ and $T_{n-1,m}$ can be exchanged in Eq. (8.2.2) without influencing the value of $T_{n,m+1}$, only the following distributions of the initial temperatures at the three adjacent points need be considered: 1,1,1; 1,0,1; 1,1,0; 1,0,0 and 0,1,0. If it is further observed that initial temperatures and solutions can be superposed, eventually only the solutions for: 1,0,0 and 0,1,0 need to be considered. The initial temperatures are bounded between 0 and $+1$ and hence the condition for the behaviour of the second type is that the temperatures after one or more steps be $0 \leqslant T \leqslant 1$. From that and Eq. (8.2.2) it follows for the above two initial distributions that $0 \leqslant p \leqslant 1$ and $0 \leqslant 1-2p \leqslant 1$, and these conditions are both satisfied if

$$0 \leqslant p \leqslant \frac{1}{2}. \tag{8.2.8}$$

These limits for p have already been obtained from von Neumann's investigation of the stability (see Section 8.2.2) and also in the case of an instantaneous plane source in Section 8.2.3.

Conditions for the third and fourth types of behaviour can be found by investigating the temperature distributions resulting from the initial distribution $T_{0,0} = 1$ and $T_{n,0} = 0$ with $n \neq 0$, which corresponds to the case of an instantaneous plane source. The results are also valid for any initial temperature distribution, because solutions can be superposed. From Eq. (8.2.2) it follows that after one time step the temperatures change in these points only: $n = -1$, 0 and $+1$. Because of the symmetry it suffices to consider $n \geqslant 0$. The third type of behaviour requires that the heat flow in the physical interpretation of the finite difference equations must not be in the direction of increasing temperatures. Thus, the temperature of the point $n = 1$ cannot become larger than that at $n = 0$, because the direction of heat flow in the present finite difference method is determined by the initial temperature distribution. This yields:

$$T_{1,1} - T_{0,1} \leqslant 0 \qquad (8.2.9)$$

The correct sign of the temperature gradient between the points $n = 1$ and $n = 2$ follows already from the condition for the second type of behaviour. For the present initial temperatures one has: $T_{1,1} = p$ and $T_{0,1} = 1-2p$. Introducing these values into Eq. (8.2.9) one obtains

$$0 \leqslant p \leqslant \frac{1}{3} \qquad (8.2.10)$$

because $p \geqslant 0$. For the fourth type of behaviour it is noted that in the present case the temperature diminishes at the point $n = 0$ during the time interval considered and therefore the time derivative is negative there. At $n = \pm 1$ the temperature increases during the same time interval and hence the time derivative is positive there. Because $\Delta^2 T/(\Delta x)^2$ must have the same sign at the end of the time interval as $\Delta T/\Delta t$ did during the time interval, then for the points $n = 0$ and $n = 1$:

$$\left. \begin{aligned} \left(\frac{\Delta^2 T}{\Delta x^2}\right)_{n=0} &= T_{1,1} - 2T_{0,1} + T_{-1,1} \leqslant 0 \\ \left(\frac{\Delta^2 T}{\Delta x^2}\right)_{n=1} &= T_{2,1} - 2T_{1,1} + T_{0,1} \geqslant 0 \end{aligned} \right\} \qquad (8.2.11)$$

Since $T_{-1,1} = T_{1,1}$, the first inequality in Eq. (8.2.11) again yields Eq. (8.2.10) and the second, with $T_{2,1} = 0$, $T_{1,1} = p$ and $T_{0,1} = 1-2p$; yields

$$0 \leqslant p \leqslant \frac{1}{4} \qquad (8.2.12)$$

The features of the finite difference solutions for the instantaneous heat source of Section 8.2.3 can now be understood in terms of the general properties of the finite difference solutions (see also Table 8.1).

8.2.5 The influence of boundary conditions on convergence. Boundaries coinciding with temperature points

It is assumed in this section that the spatial division into finite intervals is made so that the boundaries coincide with the temperature points which are used in the finite difference calculations (see Fig. 8.5). First, constant heat transfer conditions are assumed at the boundaries. The space variable is continued outside the body to infinity with such an initial temperature distribution as to satisfy the boundary conditions. Some analytical solu-

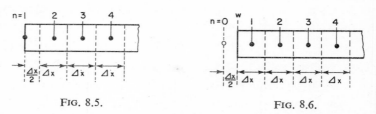

FIG. 8.5.   FIG. 8.6.

FIGS. 8.5. and 8.6. Division into sections for finite difference calculations. In Fig. 8.5 with a temperature point coinciding with boundaries and in Fig. 8.6. with an auxiliary temperature point ($n = 0$) for satisfying boundary conditions.

tions of Chapter 7 possess such properties and, for instance, a solution for the slab treated in Section 7.5.1 consists of component solutions of wave form in the space variable x which can be continued outside the body. Therefore the previous conditions for the behaviour of solutions are sufficient; but they could be relaxed for a finite body and a finite size of Δx by the following considerations. Solutions for an initial temperature distribution which is periodic in space can be found by suitably superposing plane source solutions treated in Section 8.2.3. These solutions had been found to oscillate both in space and time for $p > \frac{1}{2}$. Now, waves of constant, increasing or decreasing amplitude retain in general their character if two or more waves of the same type are superposed, but in particular cases waves may extinguish each other wholly or partly and two or more waves with increasing amplitudes may even result in a wave with constant or decreasing amplitude. Hence conditions for convergence may be less severe for finite bodies, provided that the boundaries coincide with temperature points. This can also be proved by von Neumann's method, see Ref. 8.4.

If the temperature at the boundary or, as in convective heat transfer, the temperature of the external medium, varies in time, but not the heat transfer coefficient, solutions can be constructed by suitably superposing functions of the type $F(x, t-t_p)$ which are valid for $t \geqslant t_p \geqslant 0$. $F(x,t)$ is a partial solution with constant heat transfer conditions at the boundaries and with an initial temperature distribution $F(x, 0)$. This method is known under Duhamel's name, see Section 7.2.   For variable h a mean value of h can be assumed during each time step of the finite difference method. The temperature distribution at the end of the time step is the initial distribution for the next step with a new value for h. Therefore in these cases the requirements for convergence are the same as for constant heat transfer conditions.

However, if a finite body is suddenly exposed to external heat transfer on one of its surfaces, as often occurs or is assumed, discontinuities exist in the surface temperature or its time derivative. On satisfying the boundary conditions by an extension of the solutions beyond the body's boundaries, it is seen that the discontinuities at the boundaries correspond to those in the extended initial temperature distribution. In reality, once heat flow starts, these discontinuities disappear; the conditions for avoiding them in finite difference solutions for $t > 0$ have already been mentioned in Section 8.2.3.

8.2.6 *Auxiliary points for satisfying boundary conditions*

The boundaries need not coincide with temperature points, but may lie between two temperature points of which the one lying outside the range of x is called an auxiliary point. It has already been introduced in Section 6.1.2. An important case occurs when the boundary lies midway between the auxiliary and the next interior point (Fig. 8.6). The temperature at the auxiliary point is expressed by boundary values and by the temperature of the adjacent interior point with the help of the finite difference expressions for T_b and $(\partial T/\partial x)_b$† given in Fig. 6.3. In Section 6.2 it was shown that the truncation error of the finite difference expressions for general boundary conditions is less in theory if an auxiliary point is used, than for boundaries and temperature points coinciding. In addition, another source of error may occur in transient heat flow. For boundaries coinciding with temperature points the heat capacity of a section of width $\Delta x/2$ adjacent to the boundary is neglected in the finite difference method.‡ This follows easily from Fig. 8.5 and from a physical interpretation of the finite difference Eq. (8.2.1) similar to that in Section 8.2.1. This neglect may cause considerable error if Δx is relatively large compared with the size of the

---

† For use in this section the total derivatives of the temperatures with respect to x in Fig. 6.3 are to be replaced by partial derivatives.

‡ From a mathematical point of view the difference between the two ways of satisfying boundary conditions is as follows: For N sections the heat conduction equation is satisfied at $N-1$ points when temperature points coincide with boundaries, but it is satisfied at N points when using auxiliary points; hence in the latter case more accurate results can be expected for the same number of sections, particularly if N is small. Thereby it is assumed that the truncation error of the finite difference approximation of the boundary condition is the same in both cases.

whole range of x. Large values of Δx are, however, necessary if the amount of computational work for solving the finite difference equations is to remain small. When auxiliary points are used, the heat capacity is neglected nowhere and therefore a possible source of inaccuracy is avoided.

In the finite difference expressions with an auxiliary point the temperature at the surface is expressed by

$$T_{w,m} = \frac{1}{2} (T_{0,m} + T_{1,m}) \tag{8.2.13}$$

and the rate of heat flow by

$$q_{w,m} = -k \left(\frac{\partial T}{\partial x}\right)_w = -k \frac{T_{1,m} - T_{0,m}}{\Delta x} \tag{8.2.14}$$

The indices w, 0 and 1 refer to values at the surface, the auxiliary point and the adjacent inside point respectively (Fig. 8.6).

If the wall temperature is given, the temperature of the auxiliary point $T_{0,m}$ is found from Eq. (8.2.13)

$$T_{0,m} = 2T_{w,m} - T_{1,m} \tag{8.2.15a}$$

and in the case of a given rate of heat flow from Eq. (8.2.14):

$$T_{0,m} = T_{1,m} + \frac{\Delta x}{k} q_{w,m} \tag{8.2.15b}$$

For convective heat transfer the temperature of the auxiliary point becomes, from Eq. (6.2.8b),

$$T_{0,m} = \frac{1-s_m}{1+s_m} T_{1,m} + \frac{2s_m}{1+s_m} T_{f,m} \tag{8.2.16}$$

with

$$s_m = \frac{h_m \Delta x}{2k} \tag{8.2.17}$$

The subscript m at T_w, q_w, T_f, h and s indicates that these quantities may change with time and, if they do so rapidly, it is useful to take mean values during the time interval Δt. It would be more consistent to proceed in this way not only for T_w and T_f, but also at the same time for T_0 and T_1. However, such a modification would lead to another type of finite difference equation which will be discussed later in Section 8.3. If the simple method hitherto used is to be retained, the above modifications for the values of T_w and T_f in the boundary conditions may be justified by noting that the external heat transfer conditions can change more quickly than the temperatures inside the solid are able to follow. The expressions modified for rapidly changing heat transfer conditions are therefore for given wall temperatures

$$T_{0,m} = T_{w,m} + T_{w,m+1} - T_{1,m} \qquad (8.2.18a)$$

for a given rate of heat flow at the surface:

$$T_{0,m} = T_{1,m} + \frac{\Delta x}{2k}(q_{w,m} + q_{w,m+1}) \qquad (8.\ 2.18b)$$

and for convective heat transfer at the surface:

$$T_{0,m} = \frac{1-s_m}{1+s_m} T_{1,m} + \frac{s_m}{1+s_m}(T_{f,m} + T_{f,m+1}) \qquad (8.2.19)$$

When auxiliary points are used, conditions for the behaviour of solutions for the temperature of the first point inside the body ($n = 1$ in Fig. 8.6) may differ from those of Section 8.2.4; because of the boundary condition, there is an additional relation between the temperatures at the auxiliary and at the interior point. This can be investigated by the same method used in Section 8.2.4. Suitable initial temperatures are assumed at the three adjacent points: $n = 0$ (auxiliary point), $n = 1$ (first inside point) and $n = 2$ (second inside point) and the temperature distribution resulting after one time interval is investigated. If the surface at the boundary is adiabatic, i.e. $T_{0,m} = T_{1,m}$, or if the temperature distribution is of the form: $T_{0,0} = T_{1,0} = 0$ and $T_{n,0} =$ = arbitrary for $n \geqslant 2$, conditions are the same as in Section 8.2.4. In the case of convective heat transfer, the zero point of temperature is first shifted so that $T_{f,m} + T_{f,m+1} = 0$. This operation does not change the character of the finite difference equation. Hence only the following initial temperature distribution need be investigated $T_{1,0} = 1$, $T_{n,0} = 0$ for $n \geqslant 2$; from the boundary condition (8.2.19) there follows:

$$T_{0,0} = \frac{1-s_m}{1+s_m} \qquad (8.2.20)$$

Thus the initial temperature is known for the auxiliary point and one obtains from Eq. (8.2.2) the following temperatures at the end of the first time interval:

$$T_{1,1} = 1 - \frac{1+3s_m}{1+s_m}\, p; \qquad T_{2,1} = p \qquad (8.2.21)$$

From these values $T_{0,1}$ can again be found from Eq. (8.2.19). As the temperature distribution $T_{0,1}$, $T_{1,1}$ and $T_{2,1}$ at the end of the first time interval is known, the conditions for the behaviour of the solutions at the point $n = 1$ are found by the same method as used in Section 8.2.3 and the results are given in Table 8.2. The conditions for a given wall temperature correspond to $s \to \infty$, as follows by comparing Eqs. (8.2.15a) and (8.2.16); those for a given rate of heat flow at the surface correspond to $s \to 0$ while

TABLE 8.2. Additional limitations on the magnitude of the finite difference parameter p in Eq. (8.2.2) when an auxiliary point is used for satisfying boundary conditions

Type of behaviour	Heat transfer by forced convection	Surface temperature given $(s \to \infty)$	Surface rate of heat flow given $(s \to 0)$
I and II	$p \leqslant \dfrac{1+s_m}{1+3s_m}$	$p \leqslant \dfrac{1}{3}$	$p \leqslant 1$
III	$p \leqslant \dfrac{1}{2}\dfrac{1+s_m}{1+2s_m}$	$p \leqslant \dfrac{1}{4}$	$p \leqslant \dfrac{1}{2}$
IV	$p \leqslant \dfrac{1}{3}\dfrac{1+s_m}{1+\frac{5}{3}s_m}$	$p \leqslant \dfrac{1}{5}$	$p \leqslant \dfrac{1}{3}$

$s_m T_{f,m}$ remains finite. Hence these two particular cases are limits of the forced convection case.

These conditions are additional to those valid for inside points in general as were given in Section 8.2.4. Thus there are now two conditions for each type of behaviour and the more severe of them is to be retained and the other dropped. For instance, in the case of a given wall temperature and for the first type of behaviour the resulting condition is

$$p \leqslant \frac{1}{3} \qquad (8.2.22)$$

similarly for external heat transfer

$$\left.\begin{array}{ll} p \leqslant \dfrac{1}{2}, & \text{for } s_m \leqslant 1 \\[2mm] p \leqslant \dfrac{1+s_m}{1+3s_m}, & \text{for } s_m \geqslant 1 \end{array}\right\} \qquad (8.2.23)$$

8.2.7 *Accuracy and amount of work in finite difference computations*

For engineering applications of the finite difference method the amount of computational work is important. This is perhaps not so serious for automatic computing machines, but if calculations are to be made by hand, even with the help of a desk calculator, efforts must be made to keep the numerical work as small as is compatible with the desired accuracy of solutions, if the amount of work is not to become excessive.

Suppose the temperature distribution in a slab is to be found by the finite difference method. The question arises, into how many sections the slab is to be divided. Very often a purely intuitive approach is used and 10 or 20 sections are chosen. It is then tacitly assumed that the size of the truncation error would approximately be of the same order of magnitude as the size of a section measured as a fraction of the thickness of the slab. With such a fine division a human computer would have to work many weeks in order to find the major part of the time history of the temperature in the slab in only one particular case. Later on it will be shown that a division into 10 to 20 sections is unnecessarily fine and that results sufficiently accurate for engineering purposes can be obtained with much coarser divisions and by an acceptable amount of computational work.

For a finite body and for one-dimensional heat flow the number of basic mathematical operations is inversely proportional to both the width of the section Δx and the time interval Δt. Because of the convergence condition the maximum size of p and hence also of Δt is limited. From Eq. (8.2.3) there follows

$$(\Delta t)_{max} = \frac{(\Delta x)^2}{\varkappa} p_{max} \tag{8.2.24}$$

If the largest possible time step is used, the minimum amount of computational work is inversely proportional to $(\Delta x)(\Delta t)_{max}$; for which quantity one obtains with the help of Eq. (8.2.24)

$$(\Delta x)(\Delta t)_{max} = \frac{p_{max}(\Delta x)^3}{\varkappa} \tag{8.2.25}$$

Because in any particular case $\varkappa$ and p_{max} are fixed, the minimum amount of computational effort is inversely proportional to the third power of Δx. If for instance the number of sections could be reduced by a half, $\frac{7}{8}$ of the original effort could be saved. If an unnecessary amount of effort is to be avoided, it is of paramount importance to choose the section width Δx as large as is possible with regard to accuracy. This can be done only if the truncation errors of the finite difference solutions are known. Order of magnitude estimates would obviously not be sufficient for these errors. Since no other suitable methods appear to be available at present, the magnitude of the truncation error is derived here from a few calculated fundamental cases and certain general considerations.

As a fundamental case consider a slab of thickness δ which has heat transfer by convection on one side and which is thermally insulated on the other side. Further assumptions are: constant initial temperature T_i at $t = 0$, external heat transfer with a constant coefficient h into a

TABLE 8.3. Truncation error of finite difference solutions of Eq. (8.2.2) for a slab heated at one surface, while at the other surface the heat flow is zero. N number of sections. Auxiliary points for satisfying boundary conditions

time $\tau = \dfrac{xt}{\delta^2}$	$\Theta^{a)}, q_w^{a)}$	Given wall temperature (Bi→∞) truncation error[b]					Bi = 2	truncation error[c]		
		exact	variant A N=2	variant A N=4	variant B N=2	variant B N=4	exact	N=2	N=4	N=8
$\frac{1}{16}$	Θ_w	—	—	—	—	—	0·6158	−0·025	−0·006	−0·001
	Θ_b	0·8426	−0·148	−0·028	−0·060	−0·014	0·9608	−0·035	−0·008	−0·003
	Θ_c	0·9907	0·009	0·009	0·009	0·009	0·9986	0·001	0·001	−0·001
	Θ_{mean}	0·7179	−0·072	−0·012	−0·006	−0·012	0·9101	−0·049	−0·004	−0·001
	q_w*	2·2560	−0·696	−0·182	0	−0·070	1·2316	−0·186	−0·012	−0·002
	q_w**	—	—	—	—	—	1·2316	−0·050	−0·012	−0·002
$\frac{1}{4}$	Θ_w	—	—	—	—	—	0·4256	−0·009	−0·001	0
	Θ_b	0·4870	−0·043	−0·011	−0·022	−0·006	0·7592	−0·009	0·001	0·002
	Θ_c	0·6855	−0·056	−0·013	−0·018	−0·007	0·8732	−0·002	−0·005	0·003
	Θ_{mean}	0·4377	−0·026	−0·006	−0·004	−0·002	0·7222	−0·024	−0·007	0
	q_w*	1·0870	−0·050	−0·013	−0·006	−0·002	0·8512	−0·018	−0·001	0
	q_w**	—	—	—	—	—	0·8512	−0·018	−0·001	0
$\frac{1}{2}$	Θ_w	—	—	—	—	—	0·3131	−0·003	0·001	0·001
	Θ_b	0·2621	−0·030	−0·008	−0·020	−0·005	0·5666	−0·011	0	0·002
	Θ_c	0·3708	−0·043	−0·011	−0·028	−0·007	0·6596	−0·014	0	0·002
	Θ_{mean}	0·2360	−0·021	−0·005	−0·011	−0·003	0·5396	−0·023	−0·003	−0·001
	q_w*	0·5820	−0·039	−0·009	−0·014	−0·003	0·6262	−0·006	−0·002	0·002
	q_w**	—	—	—	—	—	0·6262	−0·006	−0·002	0·002
$\frac{3}{4}$	Θ_w	—	—	—	—	—	0·2341	−0·004	0	−0·001
	Θ_b	0·1415	−0·021	−0·005	−0·015	−0·004	0·4240	−0·013	−0·001	−0·002
	Θ_c	0·2001	−0·029	−0·007	−0·021	−0·005	0·4938	−0·016	−0·001	−0·001
	Θ_{mean}	0·1274	−0·015	−0·004	−0·010	−0·003	0·4038	−0·021	−0·003	−0·001
	q_w*	0·3140	−0·031	−0·007	−0·018	−0·004	0·4682	−0·009	0	0·002
	q_w**	—	—	—	—	—	0·4682	−0·009	0	0·002

a) $\Theta = (T-T_f)/(T_i-T_f)$; $q_w* = q_w\delta/[k(T_f-T_i)]$; $q_w** = [h\delta(T_f-T_w)]/[k(T_f-T_i)]$ and the subscripts i, f, w, b, c and "mean" refer respectively to the initial conditions (uniform), the external medium, the wall, the midpoint of the slab, the adiabatic wall and the mean value for the whole slab. b) For $p_{max} = \frac{1}{3}$. c) For $p_{max} = \frac{1}{2}$.

medium with constant temperature T_f. Exact analytical solutions for this case were presented in Section 7.5. The exact and the finite difference solutions are compared in Table 8.3 for two particular cases, one with the non-dimensional heat transfer coefficient $Bi = (h\delta)/k = 2$ and the other with given wall temperature $T_w = T_f$ corresponding to $Bi \to \infty$. Comparison is made of the temperatures at the two walls and at the middle of the slab, and of the rates of heat flow at the heated wall. In the finite difference calculations the slab was divided into 2, 4 and, in some cases, 8 sections; further the boundary conditions were satisfied with the help of auxiliary points outside the slab (see Section 8.2.6). The finite difference equation (8.2.2) was used with values for p as large as possible for solutions with a behaviour of the first type in Table 8.1; this yields $p = \frac{1}{2}$ for $Bi = 2$ and $p = \frac{1}{3}$ for a given wall temperature (see Eqs. (8.2.23) and (8.2.22)). The truncation errors in Table 8.3 are given as fractions of the maximum temperature difference occurring in the problem, that is $T_f - T_i$. The numerical errors of the finite difference solutions are negligible. Most of the values of the truncation error were obtained by linear interpolation, since the surfaces and the middle of the slab do not in general coincide with the midpoint of a section used in the difference calculation. For $Bi = 2$ interpolation in time was sometimes also necessary. In the case when the wall temperature is given, there is a discontinuity in the boundary conditions at $t = 0$, since $T_w = T_i$ for $t = 0$ and $T_w \neq T_i$ for $t = \varepsilon$ ($\varepsilon \to 0$ and $\varepsilon > 0$). This can be interpreted as a discontinuity in the initial temperature distribution (see also Section 8.2.5); then irregularities develop during the steps immediately following, if $p = \frac{1}{3}$ is used (see Section 8.2.3). One possible way to avoid this, although not applied here, is to use $p = \frac{1}{4}$ in the first steps and then change to $p = \frac{1}{3}$. Another possibility is to take for $T_{1,1}$ (the temperature in the point closest to the heated wall and at the end of the first time step) values from exact solutions and it is here sufficient to take values from the solutions for a semi-infinite body (see Section 7.4). This is called the variant B in distinction to variant A in which $p = \frac{1}{3}$ is used throughout.

If very few sections are used in the finite difference method, as in Table 8.3, useful results can only be expected for fully developed temperature profiles $(\tau \geqslant \frac{1}{16})$,† when the temperature already differs everywhere from the constant initial value. When this applies, the accuracy of the finite difference solutions obtained with only 4 sections would be sufficient

---

† Deviations from the initial temperature T_i occur at the insulated surface of the plate later than everywhere else. The temperature there deviates from T_i at times $\tau \geqslant \frac{1}{16}$ and for $Bi \geqslant 2$; this follows from Figs. 7.3 and 7.4.

for most practical purposes, because the truncation error for Bi → ∞ is equal to or less than 1·3 per cent for the variant A and 0·8 per cent for the variant B; for Bi = 2 it is equal to or less than 0·5 per cent. Even for two sections comparatively good results are obtained with truncation errors of 5·6 per cent, 3·0 per cent and 1·6 per cent in the above 3 cases. The truncation errors decrease with decreasing Bi, other quantities being the same, since then the temperature differences within the slab also decrease. Therefore errors for cases with $2 \leqslant$ Bi $< \infty$ would lie between those for Bi = 2 and Bi → ∞; for Bi $\leqslant 2$ they would be equal to or less than those for Bi = 2. Because of this argument the error estimate covers practically the whole Bi number range.

These results for the truncation error can even be applied when the temperature profiles are not fully developed, if the number of sections within the "penetration depth" is the same as was previously used for the whole slab (Fig. 8.7). The penetration depth is the distance between

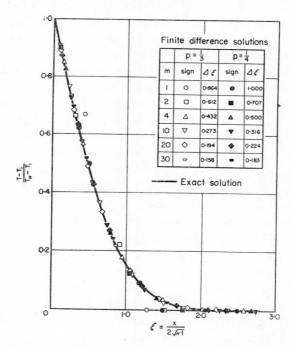

FIG. 8.7. Comparison between exact solutions of the differential and the finite difference solutions for a semi-infinite body with a given wall temperature T_w and constant initial temperature T_i. Auxiliary points for satisfying boundary conditions. Parameter $p = \dfrac{\varkappa \Delta t}{(\Delta x)^2} = 1/3$ and $1/4$. Fixed values of Δx; $\Delta \xi = \dfrac{\Delta x}{2\sqrt{(\varkappa t)}}$ and $t = m \Delta t$.

the heated surface and a point where the deviation from the initial temperature is small, say 1 per cent of the maximum temperature difference $T_f - T_i$. In most cases it is convenient before starting the finite difference calculations to decide on the minimum value of the penetration depth which is of interest and choose the size of the sections accordingly. Temperatures need be calculated only for a limited number of points close to the surface, since further interior temperatures do not change initially. When the temperatures further inside the slab do change, a progressively coarser division can be used.

So far the initial temperature distribution has been assumed constant. With an initial temperature distribution of uneven shape, particularly if it is discontinuous in places, more sections are necessary than for a uniform distribution, at least initially. Later on, as temperatures equalize, the division can be coarser than that for profiles which are not fully developed. In most engineering applications the initial temperature distributions are smooth and of linear, or parabolic form or of a similar simple shape; in these cases roughly the same connection between the accuracy and the section size can be assumed as for a constant initial temperature. More accurate estimates could be made with the help of the principle of superposition, using the source solutions of Section 8.2.3 and Fig. 8.2 where the truncation error of the source solution is given.

For variable heat transfer coefficients and variable medium temperatures, suitable mean values during a time interval Δt must be assumed for both. Therefore the time step must not be too large so that proper account can be taken of variations in h and T_f. For rocket propelled vehicles acceleration times are often very short so that far smaller time intervals of Δt must be used than would be necessary with respect to the behaviour of the solutions. In many cases Δt is chosen as a suitable fraction of the flight time which is of interest.

Variations in h are less important for the truncation error because it is only moderately influenced by even large variations of Bi according to Table 8.3. As regards the influence of variations in T_f, the truncation error is assumed the same as for constant T_f, but referred to the mean value of $T_f - T_i$ during the period of heating. Another possibility is to estimate errors for each time step separately and to add them suitably, taking into account the fact that errors spread in the same way as the temperatures themselves.

The results of this chapter can now be summarized. The truncation error was obtained by comparison with exact solutions for a slab with Bi $\to \infty$ and Bi $= 2$; and for constant values of the initial temperature, the heat transfer coefficient and the temperature of the external medium. By general considerations, partly based on physical reasoning, error estimates were extended to cover (a) the whole range of the Biot modulus, (b) spatial variations of the initial temperature, and (c) variations in time of the external heat transfer conditions. These estimates are, of course, no rigorous proof, but are a sufficiently reliable guide for practical purposes. The truncation errors given above refer to solutions obtained with the largest possible value of Δt with respect to a certain type of behaviour. Solutions for a slab and for $\text{Bi} = 2$ obtained with $p = \frac{1}{2}$, $\frac{1}{3}$ and $p \to 0$ were compared with each other in Ref. 6.3 and showed no significant influence of p on the truncation error for the slab divided into 2 and 4 sections. Therefore no worthwhile gain in accuracy is in general obtained, if the values of p, and hence also of Δt, used are smaller than those required either for convergence or to allow for rapid changes in the external heat transfer conditions.

8.2.8 *Non-linear boundary conditions*

The finite difference method is of particular advantage in solving problems with non-linear boundary conditions such as occur in heat transfer by free convection or heat radiation at the surface. In such cases the ordinary analytical methods fail (for semi-analytical methods see Section 7.7).

Free convection can be dealt with easily, because according to Section 3.5 the heat transfer coefficient h changes only in a moderate degree with the temperature difference $T_f - T_w$ between the external medium and the wall. Therefore it suffices in most cases to put in the finite difference equations

$$h_m = B_{m-1}(T_{f,m-1} - T_{w,m-1})^a \tag{8.2.26}$$

where the coefficient B and the temperature difference $T_f - T_w$ are taken at the beginning of the previous time step, when they are known. a is in most cases between $\frac{1}{4}$ and $\frac{1}{3}$. The numerical calculations proceed as if the conditions for the heat transfer were a known function of the time.

If thermal radiation and forced convection in a gas occur simultaneously at a surface, the heat flow there is (see also Section 2.9):

$$q_w = h(T_{aw} - T_w) + C_R[T_\infty^4 - T_w^4] \tag{8.2.27}$$

h is the heat transfer coefficient, T_{aw} is the adiabatic wall temperature for forced convection heat transfer, C_R is the radiation constant of the body (see Section 3.6) and T_∞ is the ambient temperature of the surroundings.

Equation (8.2.27) written in finite difference form, and with all quantities taken at the time $t = m\,\Delta t$, reads

$$T_{w,m} - T_{1,m} = s_h(T_{aw,m} - T_{w,m}) + s_{ra}[T_{\infty,m}^4 - T_{w,m}^4] \qquad (8.2.28)$$

where

$$s_h = \frac{h\Delta x}{2k} \quad \text{and} \quad s_{ra} = \frac{C_R \Delta x}{2k} \qquad (8.2.29)$$

Equation (8.2.28) can be brought into the same form as Eq. (2.9.4), if

$$T_{c,m} = \frac{1}{1+s_h}\,[T_{1,m} + s_h\,T_{aw,m} + s_{ra}(T_{\infty,m})^4] \qquad (8.2.30)$$

and

$$P = \frac{s_{ra}}{1+s_h}\,(T_{c,m})^3 \qquad (8.2.31)$$

All quantities for calculating $T_{c,m}$ and P are known. Hence we have finally

$$P\left(\frac{T_{w,m}}{T_{c,m}}\right)^4 + \frac{T_{w,m}}{T_{c,m}} - 1 = 0 \qquad (8.2.32)$$

Solutions for $T_{w,m}/T_{c,m}$ can be directly read from Fig. 2.21, replacing T_g/T_c by $T_{w,m}/T_{c,m}$; finally $T_{w,m}$ follows, because $T_{c,m}$ is known from Eq. (8.2.30). If some or all of the quantities h, T_f and T_1 change with time, mean values during the time interval Δt have to be used.

If an auxiliary point outside the body is used to satisfy the boundary conditions, $T_{0,m}$ follows from $T_{w,m}$ with the help of Eq. (8.2.15a). Additional conditions for the behaviour of solutions then arise as has been shown in Section 8.2.6. Because these conditions are not simple when thermal radiation is involved, it is best to use the same conditions as for a given wall temperature. For instance this would be $p \leqslant \frac{1}{3}$ according to Eq. (8.2.22), for the first type of behaviour (see Table 8.1).

8.2.9 Finite difference equations for cylindrical and spherical bodies and layers

Boundary conditions are again satisfied with the help of auxiliary points. Using an arrangement of the sections for finite difference calculations as in Fig. 8.8, the midpoint of section n is at a distance $r = (n-\frac{1}{2})\,\Delta r$ from the centre of a cylinder, a sphere or layers of these shapes. The finite difference forms of the expression in brackets on the right-hand side of Eq. (3.1.18) for a point midway between the points n and $n+1$ or between n and $n-1$ are respectively:

$$\left(r^j \frac{\partial T}{\partial r}\right)_{n\pm\frac{1}{2}} \approx \pm\left[n - \frac{1}{2} \pm \frac{1}{2}\right]^j (\Delta r)^{j-1}(T_{n\pm 1,m} - T_{n,m}) \qquad (8.2.33)$$

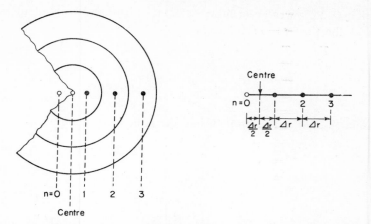

FIG. 8.8. Arrangement of sections in the finite difference method near the centre of a cylindrical or spherical body or layer.

with

$$j = \begin{cases} 1 \text{ for cylinder} \\ 2 \text{ for sphere} \end{cases} \qquad (8.2.34)$$

Further, for a point n

$$\left[\frac{1}{r^j}\frac{\partial}{\partial r}\left(r^j\frac{\partial T}{\partial r}\right)\right]_n \approx \frac{1}{\left(n-\frac{1}{2}\right)^j(\Delta r)^{j+1}}\left[\left(r^j\frac{\partial T}{\partial r}\right)_{n+\frac{1}{2}} - \left(r^j\frac{\partial T}{\partial r}\right)_{n-\frac{1}{2}}\right] \qquad (8.2.35)$$

If thermal properties are assumed constant, the equation for cylindrical and spherical heat conduction in finite difference form follows from Eqs. (8.2.33) and (8.2.35):

$$T_{n,m+1} = p_{r,n+1}T_{n+1,m} + p_{r,n-1}T_{n-1,m} + (1-p_{r,n+1}-p_{r,n-1})T_{n,m} \qquad (8.2.36)$$

where

$$p_{r,n+1} = \left(\frac{n}{n-\frac{1}{2}}\right)^j p, \quad p_{r,n-1} = \left(\frac{n-1}{n-\frac{1}{2}}\right)^j p, \quad p = \frac{\varkappa\Delta t}{(\Delta r)^2} \qquad (8.2.37)$$

Calculations proceed in the same way as for linear heat flow, but the temperature coefficients change with distance from the centre. For most problems of interest the temperature gradient at the centre vanishes initially. Hence it also does so later on; therefore with $T_{0,m}$ and $T_{1,m}$ as the temperatures in the points on both sides of the centre and at equal distances from it, one obtains $T_{0,m} = T_{1,m}$. Following the arguments of Sections 8.2.3 and 8.2.6 the solutions behave as the first and second types, if

$$p_{r,n+1} + p_{r,n-1} \leqslant 1 \qquad (8.2.38)$$

Therefore it follows from Eqs. (8.2.37) and (8.2.38) that for cylinders and cylindrical layers

$$p \leqslant \frac{1}{2} \tag{8.2.39}$$

which is the same as for linear flow. For spheres and spherical layers

$$p \leqslant \frac{4n^2 - 4n + 1}{8n^2 - 8n + 4} \tag{8.2.40}$$

The fraction on the right hand side of the inequality is $\frac{1}{4}$ at $n = 1$, $\frac{9}{20}$ at $n = 2$ and rapidly approaches $\frac{1}{2}$ for increasing n. If the expressions for $p_{r,n+1}$ and $p_{r,n-1}$ in Eq. (8.2.37) are expanded for large values of n, one obtains

$$p_{r,n+1} = 1 + \frac{j}{2n}, \quad p_{r,n-1} = 1 - \frac{j}{2n} \tag{8.2.41}$$

With these expressions for the p's the conditions for behaviour of the first type becomes $p = \frac{1}{2}$ for both cylinder and sphere. Conditions for the third and fourth types can be found in a similar way as in Section 8.2.3, but are not given here.

8.3 One-dimensional heat flow. An implicit difference equation

Divergence and instability of the finite difference equation (8.2.2) occur f p exceeds a certain value, because the finite difference expressions on the left-and right-hand sides of Eq. (8.2.1) refer to different times, as has been discussed in Section 8.2.1. This can be avoided by using an implicit finite difference equation first given by Crank and Nicolson in Ref. 8.5. The finite difference expression for the time derivative is the same as in Eq. (8.2.1), but the second derivative with respect to space is a mean value between the times $m\Delta t$ and $(m+1)\Delta t$:

$$\frac{1}{\Delta t}(T_{n,m+1} - T_{n,m}) = \frac{\varkappa}{2(\Delta x)^2}[T_{n-1,m+1} + T_{n-1,m} + T_{n+1,m+1} + T_{n+1,m} - 2T_{n,m} -$$
$$- 2T_{n,m+1}] \tag{8.3.1}$$

On introducing p, defined by Eq. (8.2.3) this equation becomes:

$$-\frac{p}{2}T_{n-1,m+1} + (1+p)T_{n,m+1} - \frac{p}{2}T_{n+1,m+1} = (1-p)T_{n,m} + \frac{p}{2}(T_{n-1,m} + T_{n+1,m})$$
$$\tag{8.3.2}$$

The temperatures on the right-hand side of the equation are known, but those on the left-hand side are unknown. Assume a finite region for one space variable divided into N sections. Further, assume boundary conditions at both ends of the region as for heat transfer by forced convection; use auxiliary points for satisfying the boundary conditions as previously and the same finite difference form for the boundary conditions as in Eq. (8.2.19):

$$T_{0,m} = \frac{1-s_{0,m}}{1+s_{0,m}}\,T_{1,m} + \frac{s_{0,m}}{1+s_{0,m}}\,(T^{(0)}_{f,m}+T^{(0)}_{f,m+1}) \qquad (8.3.3a)$$

$$T_{N+1,m} = \frac{1-s_{N,m}}{1+s_{N,m}}\,T_{N,m} + \frac{s_{N,m}}{1+s_{N,m}}\,(T^{(N)}_{f,m}+T^{(N)}_{f,m+1}) \qquad (8.3.3b)$$

The subscripts 0 and N at s as well as corresponding superscripts at T_f refer to heat transfer conditions at $x = \frac{1}{2}\Delta x$ and at $x = (N+\frac{1}{2})\Delta x$ respectively. Take Eq. (8.3.3a) and the N equations obtained from Eq. (8.3.2) by putting $n = 1, 2, \ldots N$; this system of equations is the same as that of Eqs. (6.3.2) with the following values for the coefficients:

$$\left.\begin{array}{c} D^{(1)}_{0,m} = \dfrac{1-s_{0,m}}{1+s_{0,m}}\,; \quad D^{(2)}_{0,m} = \dfrac{s_{0,m}}{1+s_{0,m}}\,(T^{(0)}_{f,m}+T^{(0)}_{f,m+1}) \\[2mm] A_{n,n-1} = A_{n,n+1} = \dfrac{p}{2}\,; \quad A_{n,n} = 1+p \\[2mm] B_{n,m} = (1-p)T_{n,m} + \dfrac{p}{2}\,(T_{n-1,m}+T_{n+1,m}) \end{array}\right\} \qquad (8.3.4)$$

if T_n and $T_{n\pm1}$ in Eq. (6.3.2b) are replaced by $T_{n,m+1}$ and $T_{n\pm1,m+1}$ respectively, and $B_n = B_{n,m}$. Then the same method of solution can be used as in Section 6.3. In the resulting system of equations $D^{(2)}_n$ always depends on time and $D^{(1)}_n$ does so in general. They are therefore written in the present notation as $D^{(1)}_{n,m}$ and $D^{(2)}_{n,m}$; $D^{(1)}_{n,m}$ depends on time only if s does. As an example the temperatures in a slab with zero temperature on one surface and zero rate of heat flow at the other surface have been calculated by the present method with $p = \frac{2}{3}$ and with the thickness divided into only two sections. The auxiliary quantities $D^{(1)}_{n,m}$ and $D^{(2)}_{n,m}$, and the finite difference solutions are given in Table 8.4 for five time steps. Agreement with the exact analytical solution of Section 7.5 is surprisingly good despite the small number of sections. Compared with the same example treated in Section 8.2.7 by the explicit finite difference equation (8.2.2) with $p = \frac{1}{3}$, the number of time steps is now halved, while the amount of computational effort is more than doubled, but the accuracy of the results is also higher.

Solutions of this implicit finite difference equation converge and are stable for all values of p, see Ref. 8.1.

TABLE 8.4. Finite difference solution for a slab with zero temperature on one surface and zero heat flow at the other surface. Initially the temperature is constant and equal to 1. Solutions obtained by the implicit finite difference equation (8.3.2) and the slab divided into two sections. Auxiliary points ($n=0$ and $n=3$) for satisfying boundary conditions. (a) Calculation scheme

time $\tau = \varkappa t/\delta^2$	m		$n=$ 0	1	2	3
—	—	$D_{n,m}^{(1)}$	-1	0·1667	0·2069	—
0	0	$T_{n,0}$	-1	1	1	1
		$D_{n,0}^{(2)}$	0	0·1667	0·6552	—
$\frac{1}{6}$	1	$T_{n,1}$	$-0·3043$	0·3043	0·8261	0·8261
		$D_{n,1}^{(2)}$	0	0·1377	0·4333	—
$\frac{1}{3}$	2	$T_{n,2}$	$-0·2288$	0·2288	0·5464	0·5464
		$D_{n,2}^{(2)}$	0	0·0911	0·2923	—
$\frac{1}{2}$	3	$T_{n,3}$	$-0·1525$	0·1525	0·3686	0·3686
		$D_{n,3}^{(2)}$	0	0·0614	0·1968	—
$\frac{2}{3}$	4	$T_{n,4}$	$-0·1028$	0·1028	0·2482	0·2482
		$D_{n,4}^{(2)}$	0	0·0414	0·1325	—
$\frac{5}{6}$	5	$T_{n,5}$	$-0·0693$	0·0693	0·1671	0·1671
		$D_{n,5}^{(2)}$	0	0·0279	0·0893	—

TABLE 8.4. (*cont.*) (b) Comparison with exact solution of the differential equation for 2 points: $n = 1·5$ (mid point) and $n = 2·5$ (adiabatic surface), for the mean temperature across the slab and for the surface rate of heat flow. Difference solutions for $n = 1·5$ and $2·5$ obtained from (a) by linear interpolation, for T_{mean} with the help of the trapezoidal formula for integration and for q_w with the help of

$$\Delta T/\Delta x = (T_{1,m} - T_{0,m})/\Delta x$$

τ	1/6		1/3		1/2		2/3		5/6	
	Exact	Approx.	Exact	Approx.	Exact	Approx.	Exact	Approx.	Exact	Approx.
$T_{1·5}$	0·6042	0·5652	0·3957	0·3876	0·2622	0·2606	0·1738	0·1755	0·1152	0·1182
$T_{2·5}$	0·8334	0·8261	0·5591	0·5464	0·3708	0·3686	0·2457	0·2482	0·1629	0·1671
T_{mean}	0·5395	0·5272	0·3562	0·3590	0·2360	0·2415	0·1564	0·1672	0·1037	0·1095
$\dfrac{\delta q_w}{k}$	1·3750	1·2170	0·8799	0·9152	0·5824	0·6100	0·3860	0·4112	0·2559	0·2772

If the heat transfer conditions are constant in time, the system of equations (8.3.2) and (8.3.3) can be solved directly (Ref. 8.6), so that

$$T_{n,m+1} = \sum_{j=1}^{N} K_{n,j} T_{j,m} \tag{8.3.5}$$

where $K_{n,j}$ are constants which are calculated once and for all.

8.4 One-dimensional heat flow in thin shells with external heat transfer. An explicit finite difference equation

Consider a shell with uniform temperature throughout its thickness δ and with external heat transfer by forced convection on one surface and zero heat flow at the other surface as indicated in Section 3.2. The differential equation of heat conduction parallel to the surface of the shell is given by Eq. (3.2.6) in which the bar above T is now dropped. In a similar way as in Section 8.2.1 two finite difference equations are derived from Eq. (3.2.6):

$$T_{n,m+1} = p(T_{n+1,m} + T_{n-1,m}) + (1-2p-2p_h)T_{n,m} + 2p_h T_{n,m}^{(f)} \tag{8.4.1}$$

and

$$T_{n,m+1} = \frac{1}{1+p_h} \{ p(T_{n+1,m} + T_{n-1,m}) + (1-2p-p_h) T_{n,m} + p_h(T_{n,m}^{(f)} + T_{n,m+1}^{(f)}) \} \tag{8.4.2}$$

where p is defined in Eq. (8.2.3) and

$$p_h = \frac{h\Delta t}{2\rho c\delta} \tag{8.4.3}$$

h is the heat transfer coefficient, ρ the density and c the specific heat of the shell. The superscript f at T refers to the external medium. In Eq. (8.4.1) the finite difference expression for the external heat flow is taken at the beginning of the time interval extending from $m \Delta t$ to $(m+1)\Delta t$ while in Eq. (8.4.2) it is the mean between the corresponding expressions at the times $m \Delta t$ and $(m+1)\Delta t$. The difference between the two equations (8.4.1) and (8.4.2) is similar to that between the two finite difference forms of the boundary conditions as discussed in Section 8.2.6.

The conditions for convergence and for the behaviour of the solutions can now be investigated in a way similar to that used in Section 8.2.4 for Eq. (8.2.2). Again, only the first time step needs to be considered, therefore $T_{n,m}^{(f)}$ can be put to zero without impairing the generality of the results. The terms $-2p_h T_{n,m}$ and $-p_h T_{n,m}$ on the right-hand side of Eqs.

(8.4.1) and (8.4.2) respectively correspond to internal heat sources and because of this the conditions for the first and second types of behaviour were found to be non-identical.† The first type of behaviour would not suffice for acceptable solutions, because these could have negative temperatures resulting from positive initial temperatures, which would be physically impossible. Otherwise, conditions for the behaviour of the solutions are similar to those for heat flow in the interior of a solid body and are summarized in Table 8.5. In order to obtain estimates for the truncation error (Ref. 6.3), we consider separately the errors in the following cases: (a) transient heat flow without external heat transfer, (b) transient temperature increases with a uniform distribution of the temperature along the surface of the shell and (c) steady state heat flow. It is assumed that the truncation error of the complete finite difference equation does not exceed the sum of the errors occurring in the three partial problems (a) to (c) above. Error estimates for (a) and (c) have already been made in Sections 8.2.7 and 6.7 and the remaining case (b) is treated below.

Neglecting heat conduction in Eq. (3.2.6) and assuming $T_f = 0$, an exact solution follows readily (again, the bar above T in Eq. (3.2.6) is now dropped):

$$T = T_i \, e^{-t*} \qquad (8.4.4)$$

T_i is the initial temperature. h may depend on time and hence

$$t* = \frac{1}{\rho c \delta} \int_0^t h \, dt . \qquad (8.4.5)$$

Corresponding solutions are now sought by the finite difference method. Neglecting the terms due to heat conduction in Eq. (8.4.1) or — which is the same—putting $p = 0$, and assuming $T_f = 0$, one obtains:

$$T_{m+1} = (1 - 2p_h) T_m \qquad (8.4.6)$$

In the same way one obtains from Eq. (8.4.2):

$$T_{m+1} = \frac{1 - p_h}{1 + p_h} T_m \qquad (8.4.7)$$

Exact solutions of Eqs. (8.4.6) and (8.4.7) are

$$T_{m+1} = (1 - 2p_h)^m T_i \qquad (8.4.8)$$

---

† When investigating conditions for the first and second type of behaviour as in Section 8.2.4 the initial temperatures to be considered are all possible combinations of the values $0, +1, -1$ for the first type and $0, +1$ for the second type (see also Table 8.1).

TABLE 8.5. Limitations on the magnitude of p and p_h in Eqs. (8.4.1) and (8.4.2) given by an inequality or by a time constant

		Type of behaviour of solutions			
		I	II	III	IV
Eq. (8.4.1)	Inequality	$p + \frac{p_h}{2} \leqslant \frac{1}{2}$	$p + p_h \leqslant \frac{1}{2}$	$p + \frac{2}{3} p_h \leqslant \frac{1}{3}$	$p + \frac{1}{2} p_h \leqslant \frac{1}{4}$
	Time constant τ	$\frac{1}{2}\left(\frac{x}{(\Delta x)^2} + \frac{h}{4\rho c\delta}\right)^{-1}$	$\frac{1}{2}\left(\frac{x}{(\Delta x)^2} + \frac{h}{2\rho c\delta}\right)^{-1}$	$\frac{1}{3}\left(\frac{x}{(\Delta x)^2} + \frac{h}{3\rho c\delta}\right)^{-1}$	$\frac{1}{4}\left(\frac{x}{(\Delta x)^2} + \frac{h}{4\rho c\delta}\right)^{-1}$
Eq. (8.4.2)	Inequality	$p \leqslant \frac{1}{2}$	$p + \frac{p_h}{2} \leqslant \frac{1}{2}$	$p + \frac{1}{3} p_h \leqslant \frac{1}{3}$	$p + \frac{1}{4} p_h \leqslant \frac{1}{4}$
	Time constant τ	$\frac{1}{2}\left(\frac{x}{(\Delta x)^2}\right)^{-1}$	$\frac{1}{2}\left(\frac{x}{(\Delta x)^2} + \frac{h}{4\rho c\delta}\right)^{-1}$	$\frac{1}{3}\left(\frac{x}{(\Delta x)^2} + \frac{h}{6\rho c\delta}\right)^{-1}$	$\frac{1}{4}\left(\frac{x}{(\Delta x)^2} + \frac{h}{8\rho c\delta}\right)^{-1}$

and

$$T_{m+1} = \left(\frac{1-p_h}{1+p_h}\right)^m T_i \tag{8.4.9}$$

respectively. If the truncation error ε is defined as $\varepsilon = (T-T_m)/(T_f-T_i)$ ($T =$ exact solution, $T_m =$ finite difference solution), its largest value during transient heating is (Ref. 6.3)

$$\varepsilon_{\max} = \left| G^{\frac{1}{1-G}} - G^{\frac{G}{1-G}} \right| \tag{8.4.10}$$

In the case of Eq. (8.4.6) G in this expression is

$$G = -\frac{2p_h}{\ln(1-2p_h)} \tag{8.4.11}$$

and in the case of Eq. (8.4.7)

$$G = -\frac{2p_h}{\ln(1-p_h)-\ln(1+p_h)}, \tag{8.4.12}$$

ln is the natural logarithm. The maximum value of the truncation error is shown in Fig. 8.9 and is much larger for the finite difference equation (8.4.6) than for (8.4.7). The great advantage of using an equation of type (8.4.7) instead of (8.4.6) can be illustrated as follows. If the truncation error is to be at most 2 per cent of T_f-T_i, it follows from Fig. 8.9 that $p_h \leqslant 0\cdot05$ for Eq. (8.4.6), but $p_h \leqslant 0\cdot38$ for Eq. (8.4.7). If calculations

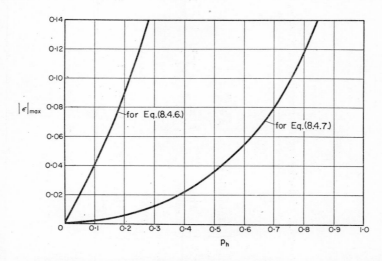

Fig. 8.9. Truncation error in finite difference calculations for transient heating of a shell with uniformly distributed wall temperatures.

are to cover 90 per cent of the total temperature increase, it would take about 22 steps in the first case, but only 3 steps in the second case. If T_f is variable, the above truncation error is assumed to be at least an approximate estimate.

The two equations (8.4.6) and (8.4.7) in the present simple example are the particular forms of Eqs. (8.4.1) and (8.4.2) respectively. Hence the maximum truncation error given by Eq. (8.4.10) or Fig. 8.9 is also an estimate for the maximum contribution to the truncation errors of Eqs. (8.4.1) and (8.4.2) owing to the external heat transfer as discussed at the beginning of this section.

The limitation on the magnitude of p_h and thus also on Δt can be expressed by a time constant so that $\Delta t \leqslant \tau_h$, where

$$\tau_h = \frac{2\rho c \delta}{h} (p_h)_{\max} \qquad (8.4.13)$$

The conditions for the different types of behaviour can also be expressed by time constants and these are given in Table 8.5. There are now two time constants for each type of behaviour; therefore the largest possible time step is equal to the smaller of the two time constants.

8.5 One-dimensional heat flow in composite structures. Method of lumped heat capacities and resistances

8.5.1 *General*

So far only sections of equal width have been considered in the finite difference method. Poor conductors are also important structural materials in aeronautics; windows, radomes, nose-cones and other such parts may be exposed to aerodynamic heating. In such materials heat very often penetrates only into the outer layers and then it is convenient for finite difference calculations to use sections of unequal width. Composite structures often consist of parts of different materials, and sections in shell structures may be of different thicknesses. In such complex structures it is more convenient to replace the structure by a model consisting of a series of heat reservoirs connected by heat resistances, rather than to divide the structure into a number of homogeneous bodies in contact with each other and with assumed boundary conditions at the interfaces. Models with lumped elements can be represented in a similar way as electrical circuits and they are derived by dividing the structure into homogeneous units of suitable size. Each unit is replaced by a reservoir with a heat capacity equal to that of the unit. Between two adjacent reservoirs a heat resistance is assumed of the same size as for steady heat

flow between the midpoints of the units (Fig. 8.10). If the initial phase
of heat transfer is of interest or if heat transfer conditions at the surface

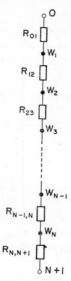

Heat reservoir
Auxiliary point with given temperature
Thermal resistance

FIG. 8.10. A series of simply connected heat reservoirs connected by intermediate
heat resistances.

change rapidly and the temperature changes inside the body are of interest,
then one uses reservoirs having small heat capacities in those parts of the
model which are in the vicinity of the heated surface. During a later phase of
heat transfer it is sufficient to use a simpler model with a coarser division.

The heat capacities of gas layers are in general negligible, but their
thermal resistances may be large. Heat transfer through gas layers can also
occur by free convection and by thermal radiation; in both cases the relation between the rate of heat flow and temperature difference is non-linear,
but linear approximations can often be used as in Section 3.1.3. The thermal
contact between mating surfaces of solids may not be perfect, as for instance in riveted and bolted joints (see Section 3.7).

8.5.2 *A system of differential equations valid for linear laws of heat transfer*

A simply connected linear circuit as in Fig. 8.10 is the most important
case and is treated first. Assuming heat transfer with a linear relation

between the rate of heat flow and the temperature difference, the balance of heat flow for each reservoir leads to a differential equation of the first order; using conductivities K rather than resistances R, one obtains $(K = 1/R)$

$$W_n \frac{dT_n}{dt} = K_{n-1,n}(T_{n-1}-T_n)+K_{n,n+1}(T_{n+1}-T_n) \qquad (8.5.1)$$

W_n and T_n are the heat capacity and the temperature respectively of the reservoir n, $K_{n-1,n}$ and $K_{n,n+1}$ are the heat conductivities between reservoir n and the two neighbouring reservoirs $n-1$ and $n+1$ respectively. For N reservoirs a system of differential equations is obtained

$$\frac{dT_n}{dt} = \frac{K_{n-1,n}}{W_n}(T_{n-1}-T_n)+\frac{K_{n,n+1}}{W_n}(T_{n+1}-T_n), \quad n = 1,2...N \qquad (8.5.2)$$

The temperatures T_0 and T_{N+1} are known; they are in many cases the temperatures of an external medium into which heat transfer occurs. In that case one obtains by adding corresponding resistances:

$$\frac{1}{K_{01}} = \frac{1}{K_{w1}} + \frac{1}{F_1 h_1} \qquad (8.5.3)$$

where K_{01} is the conductance between the temperature point 1 inside the body and point 0 outside it, K_{w1} is the conductance between the surface and point 1, h_1 the heat transfer coefficient and F_1 the area of the cross section at the heated surface.

8.5.3 *Exact solutions in special cases*

If T_0, T_{N+1} and all the coefficients $\dfrac{K}{W}$ in Eq. (8.5.2) are constants, exact solutions are of the form

$$T_n = \sum_{p=1}^{N} B_n^{(p)} e^{-\lambda_p t}+B_n^{(0)}, \qquad n = 1,2,3...N \qquad (8.5.4)$$

and can be obtained by introducing these expressions into Eq. (8.5.2). In each equation constant terms and terms containing $e^{-\lambda_p t}$ with a particular value of λ_p must satisfy each equation of the system 8.5.2 separately and this yields N^2 homogeneous equations for the coefficients $B_n^{(p)}$ $(p \neq 0)$ and N inhomogeneous equations for the $B_n^{(0)}$'s. In addition one obtains N equations by introducing the given initial temperatures into the system of Eqs. (8.5.4). The homogeneous equations can be arranged into N subgroups; their determinants are of the same form and must be equal to zero. Hence there follow the N eigenvalues λ_p and then the coefficients $B_n^{(p)}$, provided that all the eigenvalues are different from each other. If $k_1,k_2,...$ of the eigenvalues have the same values, $r_1,r_2...$, the sum in Eq. (8.5.4) has to comprehend only the simple eigenvalues, while for each multiple eigenvalue a term of the form $P_{k_l-1}(\exp\{-r_l t\})$ has to be added with P_{k_l-1} as a polynomial of the (k_l-1) degree and $l = 1,2....$ If T_0 and T_{N+1} are not constants, exact solutions can be found[†], but the procedure becomes more laborious. However, if external heat transfer conditions vary the heat transfer coefficient h usually varies too and hence at least one coefficient K/W in Eq. (8.5.2) varies; this method can not then be used.

The calculation of the eigenvalues is tedious unless the number of reservoirs is very small. Therefore, and because the method is restricted to cases with constant h, it is not important for finding the temperature distributions in structures.

8.5.4 *Numerical solutions*

The system of ordinary differential equations (8.5.2) with given initial emperatures can be solved by standard numerical methods, such as repeated integration and the methods of Runge and Kutta or of Adams (see for instance Ref. 7.3.1). Further, finite difference methods can be used and one of these methods is treated in detail in the following sections. Compared with the above standard methods the finite difference method used here is faster, and this is a great advantage, particularly when a desk calculator is used, but its accuracy is in general less though sufficient for most engineering purposes.

Among more recent methods are direct solutions by an analogue-type computer (Refs. 8.7 and 8.8) whose limited accuracy is in general sufficient for heat conduction problems. Because it is much more difficult to differentiate satisfactorily than to integrate on a computer of this type the system of differential equations is transformed by integrating both sides of each equation. This is now a standard procedure. For the presen purpose units for addition, subtraction, multiplication and integration would be required in the analogue calculator; in addition, function generators are necessary if T_0, T_{N+1}, h_1 and h_N change with time.

8.5.5 *Finite difference method*

Proceeding similarly as in Section 8.2.1, the derivatives of temperature with respect to time on the left-hand side of the system (8.5.2) are replaced by the finite difference expression $\dfrac{1}{\Delta t}(T_{n,m+1}-T_{n,m})$ and the temperatures

---

† E. KAMKE, Differentialgleichungen. Lösungsmethoden und Lösungen. Bd. 1, Gewöhnliche Differentialgleichungen. 7. Auflage. Akademische Verlagsgesellschaft, Leipzig (1961).

on the right-hand side of the equation are taken at the time $t = m\Delta t$; thus one obtains a system of explicit difference equations each of which is similar to Eq. (8.2.2):

$$T_{n,m+1} = p_{n-1,n} T_{n-1,m} + p_{n+1,n} T_{n+1,m} + (1 - p_{n-1,n} - p_{n+1,n}) T_{n,m} \quad (8.5.5)$$

with

$$p_{n-1,n} = \frac{K_{n-1,n}\Delta t}{W_n}, \quad p_{n+1,n} = \frac{K_{n,n+1}\Delta t}{W_n} \quad (8.5.6)$$

The subscripts at p are not interchangeable. Eq. (8.5.5) can be conceived as a general form of the difference Eq. (8.2.2) for sections of different size. The conditions for the behaviour of solutions for this system of difference equations can be investigated similarly as in Section 8.2.4 and the result is given in Table 8.6. The definition of the different types of behaviour is given in Table 8.1 of Section 8.2.4. As in Section 8.4 these conditions can be expressed by time constants which are also given in the table. Because terms corresponding to "internal heat sources" are absent in Eq. (8.5.5), conditions for the first and second type coincide. Besides, there is only one condition and therefore also only one time constant. For the third and fourth types there are two conditions and two corresponding time constants for each type and for each reservoir. In addition there are in general two conditions and two corresponding time constants for the first and the last reservoir in the series because of considerations of accuracy similar to those of Section 8.4 and this will be discussed later on. It is of great advantage to express all conditions for the behaviour of solutions by one or more time constants for each reservoir. The largest possible time step for the whole system of finite difference equations is then equal to the smallest of the individual time constants.

For the circuit of Fig. 8.10 the boundary conditions are simple. The first and the last point (0 and $N+1$) may for instance be known wall temperatures or the given temperatures of an external medium. In the case of an adiabatic wall the end point of the circuit is omitted in the calculations. If the heat flow at a surface is given, say on the surface next to reservoir 1, the first term in the Eq. (8.5.2) with the particular value $n = 1$, i.e. $\frac{K_{0,1}}{W_1} (T_0 - T_1)$, is replaced by $(q_w F_0)/W_1$ (q_w intensity of the heat flow to the surface, F_0 the area of the exposed surface) and the Eq. (8.5.5) becomes,

$$T_{1,m+1} = p_0 + p_{2,1} T_{2,m} + (1 - p_{2,1}) T_{1,m} \quad (8.5.7)$$

with

$$p_0 = \frac{q_w F_0 \Delta t}{W_1} \quad (8.5.8)$$

TABLE 8.6. Limitations on the magnitude of the parameters p in Eq. (8.5.5) given by an inequality which with the help of Eq. (8.5.6) yields $(\Delta t)_{max} = \tau$

	I and II	III	IV
		Type of behaviour of solutions	
Inequality	$p_{n-1,n}+p_{n+1,n} \leqslant 1$	$p_{n-1,n}+p_{n+1,n}+p_{n,n-1} \leqslant 1$ $p_{n-1,n}+p_{n+1,n}+p_{n,n+1} \leqslant 1$	$p_{n-1,n}+p_{n+1,n}+2p_{n,n-1} \leqslant 1$ $p_{n-1,n}+p_{n+1,n}+2p_{n,n+1} \leqslant 1$
Time constant τ	$\dfrac{W_n}{K_{n-1,n}+K_{n+1,n}}$	$\left(\dfrac{K_{n-1,n}+K_{n+1,n}}{W_n} + \dfrac{K_{n,n-1}}{W_{n-1}} \right)^{-1}$ $\left(\dfrac{K_{n-1,n}+K_{n+1,n}}{W_n} + \dfrac{K_{r,n+1}}{W_{n+1}} \right)^{-1}$	$\left(\dfrac{K_{n-1,n}+K_{n+1,n}}{W_n} + 2\dfrac{K_{n,n-1}}{W_{n-1}} \right)^{-1}$ $\left(\dfrac{K_{n-1,n}+K_{n+1,n}}{W_n} + 2\dfrac{K_{n,n+1}}{W'_{n+1}} \right)^{-1}$

In any case no additional conditions of convergence arise from the boundary conditions.

However, there may be limitations on the magnitude of Δt with regard to accuracy; these arise from the heat transfer condition between an end point with given temperature and its neighbouring magazine. In order to investigate this limitation on Δt, the circuit of Fig. 8.10 is reduced to one reservoir and one point with given temperature, either $n = 0$ and $n = 1$ or $N+1$ and N in the figure. The circuit then corresponds to a shell with external heat transfer which has been treated already in Section 8.4. As in that section, one finds here, also, that the time step Δt, is limited with respect to accuracy. In the present case one obtains

$$\Delta t \leqslant \tau_{k\mp 1} = \frac{2W_k}{K_{k\mp 1,k}} (p_h)_{max} \qquad (8.5.9)$$

The upper sign in the subscripts is used when $k = 1$ and the lower when $k = N$. $(p_h)_{max}$ is the largest possible value of p_h for a given truncation error and it can be read from Fig. 8.9 in which the curve "for Eq. (8.4.6)" refers to a finite difference equation for the reservoirs 1 and N of the same form as Eq. (8.5.5), while the curve "for Eq. (8.4.7)" refers to a different form viz. (k being either 1 or N),

$$T_{k,m+1} = \frac{1}{1+p_{k\mp 1,k}} [p_{k\mp 1,k}(T_{k\mp 1,m+1}+T_{k\mp 1,m}) + p_{k\pm 1,k}T_{k\pm 1,m}$$
$$+ (1-p_{k\mp 1,k}-p_{k\pm 1,k}) T_{k,m}] \qquad (8.5.10)$$

which yields more accurate solutions than Eq. (8.5.5), particularly, if T_0 and T_{N+1} change quickly with time. The two new time constants defined by Eq. (8.5.9) have to be added to those arising from the conditions of convergence.

Heat transfer by simultaneous forced convection and thermal radiation at a surface can be taken into account in a similar way as for a continuous body in Section 8.2.8. Suppose this kind of heat transfer to occur between point 0 and 1 in Fig. 8.10. Then the first term on the right-hand side of Eq. (8.5.2) is replaced by $\dfrac{K_{w,1}}{W_1}(T_w - T_1)$ where $K_{w,1}$ is the conductivity between reservoir 1 and the surface (subscript w) whose temperature T_w is determined by Eqs. (5.5.2)–(5.5.5); in these equations all temperatures are to be taken at the same instant. In Fig. 8.10 T_w takes the place of T_0 as the temperature in the end point of the circuit. Corresponding time constants can be calculated with the help of a "linearized form" for the rate of radiative heat flow with h_{eff} taken at its maximum value (see Section 3.1.3).

The possibilities of selecting time constants for solid bodies are often limited. For instance, a thin, but not negligible, layer of insulating material between two thick layers of a good conductor yields a small time constant which may severely limit the time step for the computations with finite difference equations of the explicit type. Difficulties of this type can sometimes be removed by a rearrangement of the division into sections, but the physical units may be so small that this method is not successful. A rather crude method is to redistribute some heat capacities and heat resistances in the equivalent circuit in order to eliminate one or more of the isolated reservoirs having the smallest time constants. Such a procedure is proposed in Ref. 6.3.

Other possibilities of avoiding these difficulties appear to be in the use of implicit finite difference equations of types similar to those which are always stable and convergent, as in the case of sections of equal size in a homogeneous body, i.e. when there is only one value of p in the difference equations (see for instance Section 8.3 and Refs. 8.1 and 8.11). At least a relaxation, if not a removal, of the stability limitations on Δt can be expected even in the present case of heat reservoirs and resistances of unequal magnitude. This is, however, not pursued further here.

8.6 Two-dimensional and multi-directional heat flow in composite structures. Method of lumped heat capacities and resistances

The methods developed in the previous sections for one-dimensional heat flow can be extended to cases with two- and three-dimensional heat flow or to cases where any number of reservoirs exchange heat with each other. An important case of application to aeronautical structures is for solid wings in which the temperatures cannot be assumed constant in the cross-sections. An example of heat flow in many directions is the heat exchange between structural elements and the load inside the structure such as electronic equipment, fuel and pay-load. As in the preceding section, models consisting of heat reservoirs and thermal resistances are derived from solids or structures and they are represented in a form similar to electrical circuits. It is assumed that each reservoir exchanges heat with a number of other reservoirs in a way determined by the connections in the circuit. Then the balance of heat flow for a reservoir is

$$W_n \frac{dT_n}{dt} = \sum K_{j,n} (T_j - T_n) \qquad (8.6.1)$$

where the summation is to be extended over all reservoirs which are in contact with the reservoir n. $K_{j,n}$ is the conductance between the reservoirs j and n. For N reservoirs there results a system of ordinary differential equations of the first order which is obtained from Eq. (8.6.1) by putting $n = 1, 2,... N$. These equations differ from Eq. (8.5.1) by there being now in general more than two terms on the right-hand side of each equation. Each of the methods of solution mentioned previously in the one-dimensional case can now be used. If an analogue computer is used and if the heat flows between reservoirs are linearly related to the temperature differences, the number of integrating units is the same as if the reservoirs were connected in series, but the number of connections between the integrating units is increased. If the finite difference method is used, explicit expressions similar to (8.5.5) can be obtained, but the number of terms on the right hand side of the equation is increased. The further treatment is a generalization of that for the straight circuit in Section 8.5. Convergence of the solution is again obtained by limiting the size of the time step Δt to be not larger than the smallest of all the time constants which for the first and second types of behaviour of the solutions is

$$\tau = W_n \left[\sum K_{j,n} \right]^{-1} \tag{8.6.2}$$

The summation sign has the same meaning as in Eq. (8.6.1).

For the third and fourth types of behaviour similar time constants are obtained as in Section 8.5, but for each reservoir the number of time constants is equal to the number of connections with other reservoirs. In addition there is a limit on Δt with respect to the accuracy of the solutions for reservoirs adjacent to points with a given temperature. This is similar to Section 8.5 and can also be treated in a similar way. The same applies also, if heat is transferred between reservoirs by thermal radiation and free convection.

8.7 Other approximate methods of solution

8.7.1 *A summary of further finite difference equations*

In Richtmyer's book (Ref. 8.1) 13 finite difference equations meriting attention are listed for the simple heat conduction equation (3.1.16). Included among this number are the two equations treated in Sections 8.2.1 and 8.3 and certain special cases, for instance Eq. (8.2.2) with $p = \frac{1}{6}$. Further, in this list there is an explicit form which is always stable; it is, however, not treated here.

An important property is the truncation error which in Richtmyer's book refers to the difference equations rather than to their solutions, in contrast to the preceding part of this chapter. The truncation error for Eq. (8.2.2) for instance is given as $O(\Delta t) + O[(\Delta x)^2]$ where the notation indicates that the truncation error is composed of two parts proportional to Δt and $(\Delta x)^2$ respectively. The truncation error expressed in this way is mainly useful for comparisons. For Eq. (8.2.2) with $p = \frac{1}{6}$ the truncation error becomes $O[(\Delta t)^2] = O[(\Delta x)^4]$ and for the implicit equation (8.3.2) it is $O[(\Delta t)^2] + O[(\Delta x)^2]$. For further details see Richtmyer's book.

So far only step by step methods have been treated and in these the temperatures obtained at any time step are final. Allen and Severn (Ref. 8.9) first introduced relaxation methods for treating transient heat conduction. The one-dimensional equation of heat conduction is now treated in a "two-dimensional" grid with spatial distance and time as the coordinates. At the beginning a guess is made for the unknown temperatures in the whole range of the space and time variables. Then the residuals of the equation for transient heat conduction are made zero in a way similar to that in Chapter 6 for steady heat conduction. In connection with this method Liebmann (Ref. 8.10) used an implicit finite difference equation of the form:

$$T_{n,m} - T_{n,m-1} = p(T_{n-1,m} - 2T_{n,m} + T_{n+1,m}) \qquad (8.7.1)$$

which was previously given by Laasonen (Ref. 8.11) and which is also listed in Ref. 8.1. This finite difference equation is stable for all values of the parameter p. The residual of the equation is

$$q_{n,m} = p(T_{n-1,m} + T_{n+1,m}) - (1+2p)T_{n,m} + T_{n,m-1} \qquad (8.7.2)$$

Liebmann also gave an extension to two-dimensional problems and developed electrical analogues for this method of solution (see Ref. 8.12 and Chapter 10).

8.7.2 *Integral form of the heat conduction equation. Variational methods*

The following method is well known in other spheres of mechanics, for instance in boundary layer theory; it is applied here to heat conduction problems (Ref. 8.13). An integral form of the one-dimensional equation of heat conduction is derived by integrating Eq. (3.1.16) with respect to x from $x = 0$ to $x = \delta$.

$$\frac{d}{dt} \int_0^\delta \rho c T dx = -k \left(\frac{\partial T}{\partial x}\right)_0 + k \left(\frac{\partial T}{\partial x}\right)_{x=\delta} \qquad (8.7.3)$$

The surfaces of the body are at $x = 0$ and $x = \delta$, where the boundary conditions are given. The temperature profile is of the form

$$\frac{T - T_i}{T_c - T_i} = F\left(\frac{x}{b} ; \quad \gamma_0, \gamma_1 \cdots \gamma_n\right) \qquad (8.7.4)$$

where T_i is the initial temperature, T_c a suitable reference temperature, b a characteristic length either constant or varying with time and γ_0, $\gamma_1,...,$ γ_n are parameters. For a semi-infinite body b is the penetration depth and for a slab it is the thickness. Introducing Eq. (8.7.4) into (8.7.3) yields an ordinary differential equation for b. Polynomials are very often used to represent the temperature profiles.

As an example, take the case of a semi-infinite body with a constant wall temperature T_w, which is given at $x = 0$, and a uniform initial temperature T_i (Ref. 8.13); the temperature distribution in the body is assumed as follows

$$\Theta = \frac{T-T_i}{T_w-T_i} = \begin{cases} \gamma_0+\gamma_1\dfrac{x}{b}+\gamma_2\left(\dfrac{x}{b}\right)^2, & \text{for } x \leqslant b \\ 0, & \text{for } x \geqslant b \end{cases} \qquad (8.7.5)$$

The coefficients γ_0, γ_1 and γ_2 are partly determined from one boundary condition

$$x = 0;\; \Theta = 1 \qquad (8.7.6a)$$

The other boundary condition

$$x \to \infty;\; \Theta = 0 \qquad (8.7.6b)$$

is already satisfied by Eq. (8.7.5). Two additional conditions are required in order to determine all coefficients. It is plausible to assume at the penetration depth that

$$x = b;\; \Theta = 0 \text{ and } \frac{d\Theta}{dx} = 0 \qquad (8.7.7)$$

Equations (8.7.6a) and (8.7.7) yield $\gamma_0 = 1$, $\gamma_1 = -2$ and $\gamma_2 = 1$. With these quantities introduced into the temperature distribution, Eq. (8.7.3) yields:

$$b\frac{db}{dt} = 6\varkappa \qquad (8.7.8)$$

With the initial condition $t = 0$, $\Theta = 0$ the solution is

$$b = t\sqrt{(12\varkappa t)} \qquad (8.7.9)$$

Comparison with the exact solution can be made in Fig. 8.11 where the solutions with temperature profiles approximated by polynomials of third and fourth degree are also shown. With increasing degree of the polynomial, the number of the coefficients γ also increases and one condition must be added for every unit increase in the order of the polynomial. In the present case $\left(\dfrac{\partial^2\Theta}{\partial x^2}\right)_{x=b} = 0$ has been added for the third order polynomial and $\left(\dfrac{\partial^3 \Theta}{\partial x^3}\right)_{x=b} = 0$ for the fourth order polynomial.

The well-known variational methods are also based on integral forms of the fundamental equations. Biot (Refs. 8.14 and 8.15) has introduced such methods for solving heat conduction problems. As compared with

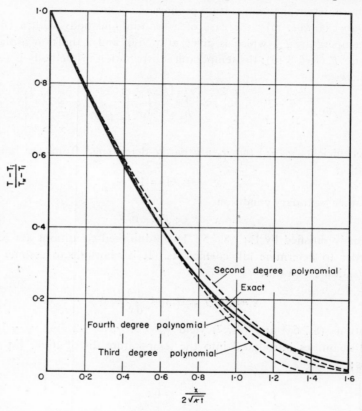

FIG. 8.11. Approximate solutions for the temperatures in a semi-infinite body as in Fig. 8.7; using an integral method with the temperature distribution approximated by second, third and fourth degree polynomials.

the previous integral method, the assumed analytical expression for the temperature distribution now contains more than one parameter to be determined by the variational principle and thus the solutions are in general improved. However, in most examples given by Biot, only one parameter was used in the analytical expression for the temperature profiles; hence similar results could be also obtained by the simple integral method discussed at the beginning of this section.

8.8 Examples

8.8.1 *A skin reinforced by an integral stiffener*

An example of a temperature distribution in the steel structural element of Section 7.7 was calculated in Ref. 8.17 by the finite difference method. This case is the same as that treated in Ref. 9.4 and in Section 9.3, where details of the structure are given. The structure was replaced by the model of Fig. 9.1 (c) with temperature variations in the skin considered. Half the length and half the pitch of the stiffener were each divided into 4 sections (see Fig. 8.12). The temperatures in the stiffener were obtained with the help of Eq. (8.2.2) and $p = 0.411$, and those in the skin with

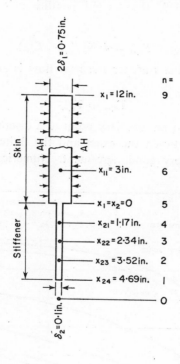

AH = Aerodynamic heating

FIG. 8.12. Model of a skin and an integral stiffener with the same dimensions as in Section 9.3.

the help of Eq. (8.4.2) with the same p and $p_h = 0.351$. The time step was the maximum possible, 30·3 sec, satisfying the conditions for the first and second types of behaviour of solutions for the stiffener ($p \leqslant 1/2$, see Section 8.2.4) and for the first type of behaviour for the skin ($p \leqslant 1/2$, see Table 8.5). Because of the term for external heat transfer in Eq. (8.4.2) there is a contribution to the truncation error of the solutions of not more than 1·5 per cent with the above value of p_h as follows from Fig. 8.9. In this particular case the boundaries for the skin and the stiffener were assumed to coincide with the temperature points; an arrangement which however, is not recommended in general for large values of Δx and Δt (see also Section 8.2.6). At the junction the temperatures and the rates of heat flow are to be continuous; the first condition is automatically satisfied in the present case. With the same material in skin and stiffener and with $2\dfrac{\delta_1}{\delta_2}\dfrac{\Delta x_2}{\Delta x_1} = 4\cdot39$, the second condition is in finite difference form:

$$T_{5,m} - T_{4,m} = 4\cdot39(T_{6,m} - T_{5,m}).\qquad(8.8.1)$$

At the mid point of the stiffener the heat flow is zero and this yields there

$$T_{2,m} = T_{0,m}\qquad(8.8.2)$$

with $n = 0$ referring to an auxiliary point at a distance Δx from the mid point. Comparison between the exact and the finite difference solutions in Fig. 8.13 shows very good agreement. Numerical computation with

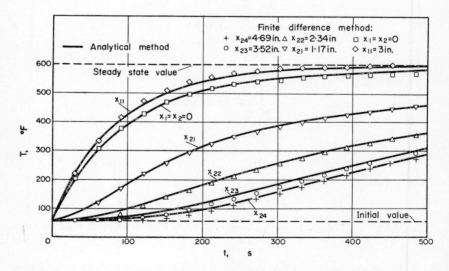

FIG. 8.13. Comparison between the temperature distributions obtained by the finite difference method and the analytical method of Ref. 9.4. x_{1n} and x_{2n} refer to the points given in Fig. 8.12.

a desk calculator required only two hours. When a high speed computer is used, the sectional division could be finer. An advantage of the numerical method is that cases with variable h and T_{aw} and even with temperature dependent material properties can be taken into account with only a modest increase in computational work.

8.8.2 *A sandwich wall*

The sandwich wall of Fig. 8.14 (Ref. 6.3) consists of metal sheets of which the upper skin is exposed to aerodynamic heating on its upper surface; at other surfaces the rate of heat flow is zero. Uniform tempera-

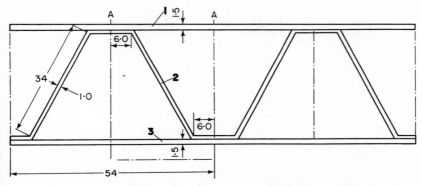

FIG. 8.14. A sandwich wall. Aerodynamic heating on the outer surface of part **1**.
Dimensions in mm.

tures are assumed across the thicknesses of the sheets. Where sheets overlap, the heat flow is not only parallel, but also normal to the surfaces of the sheets. Because of symmetry and because the heat transfer conditions are constant along the plate, it suffices to consider only the part which is within the lines AA in Fig. 8.14, and to assume zero heat flow at the faces of the cut. The method of Section 8.5 where lumped heat capacities and heat resistances are used, appears more convenient than a division into homogeneous parts with boundary conditions at the interfaces. When using a high speed computer, it would be possible to divide the structural element into sufficiently small units so that even the two-dimensional heat flow in the overlapping sheets could be found in detail. It will be shown that even a rather coarse division, as used here, yields good results. Therefore the part within AA in Fig. 8.14 is further simplified as shown in Fig. 8.15. Here the rate of heat flow between each end face of the vertical sheet and the skin is the same as that between the corresponding overlap of the skin and the stiffener in Fig. 8.14. Further, heat transfer in Fig. 8.15 is assumed to occur, under idealized conditions, between the end face of the vertical sheet and an equal area of the skin with a coefficient 6 times as large as the interface conductance between the skin and the stiffener, because their area of overlap is 6 times as large as the area of the end face. The material is aluminium ($\rho = 2850$ kg/m³, $c = 0.21$ kcal/(kg °C) and $k = 0.0375$ kcal/(m s °C)), the coefficient of external heat transfer at the upper skin is 0.0328 kcal/(m² s °C) and the temperature of the external medium (in flight, the adiabatic wall temperature) is 100°C. The conductance across the interface of the overlap

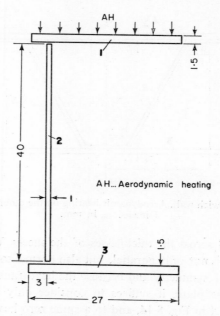

FIG. 8.15. Part AA of the sandwich wall of Fig. 8.14 as simplified for finite difference calculations. 1, 2 and 3 refer to corresponding parts in the previous figure. Dimensions in mm.

is 0.38 kcal/(m² s °C). Heat transfer starts suddenly with constant parameters and initially the temperature is uniform and zero. The division into four and ten sections, and the path of the heat flow is shown in Fig. 8.16. The solutions in Fig. 8.17 were obtained partly by an analogue-type computer using a system of differential equations each of the form of Eq. (8.10) and partly by finite difference equations such as in Eq. (8.5.5). In the latter case the division into sections was as in Fig. 8.16(a) for an early period of the heat flow, but later only three sections (not shown) were

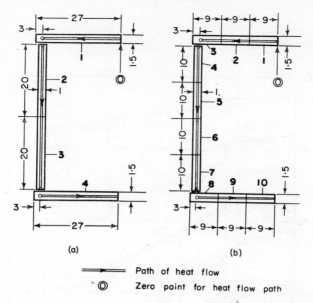

FIG. 8.16. The model of Fig. 8.15 divided into 4 and 10 sections for finite difference calculations. Dimensions in mm.

used. Comparison of results shows good agreement between the fine and the coarse divisions.

8.8.3 *A solid fin*

The next example is a titanium fin ($\rho = 4430$ kg/m³, $c = 0.13$ kcal/(kg °C) and $k = 0.0036$ kcal/(m s °C)) with a cross-section and a distribution of the heat transfer coefficient and the adiabatic wall temperature as in Fig. 8.18. The external boundary layer flow was assumed laminar for the first two sections, while for the rest of the sections it was turbulent. Accordingly, the initial temperature of the sections with laminar flow $T_{i,l}$ was assumed to differ from that of the sections with turbulent flow. Applying the criterion of Section 3.2 the temperature can be considered uniform throughout the thickness and hence the fin can be treated as a shell of variable thickness. Because the length of the sections and the heat transfer coefficients vary with distance from the leading edge, a division with graded sections is used. The temperature distributions of Fig. 8.19 were obtained by the method of Section 8.5 and the temperatures at the leading edge were found by extrapolation from those at the midpoints of the sections. Computations were made with the help of a high speed digital computer and required computing times of a few minutes only.

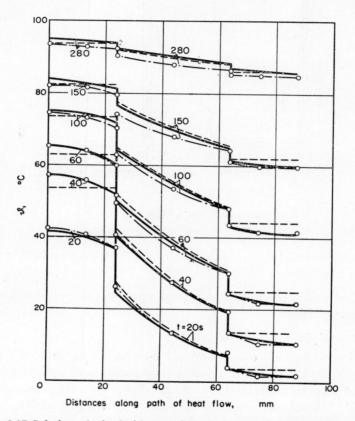

FIG. 8.17. Solutions obtained with an analogue computer using equations of the same form as Eq. (8.5.1) and with finite difference equations of Section 8.5. Division into 3, 4 and 10 sections.

----- Analogue computer. Division in 4 sections according to Fig. 8.16 (a).

——— Analogue computer. Division in 10 sections according to Fig. 8.16 (b)

o—·—o Finite difference method. Division in 4 sections according to Fig. 8.16 (a) and in 3 sections during the later phase of heat flow. ·

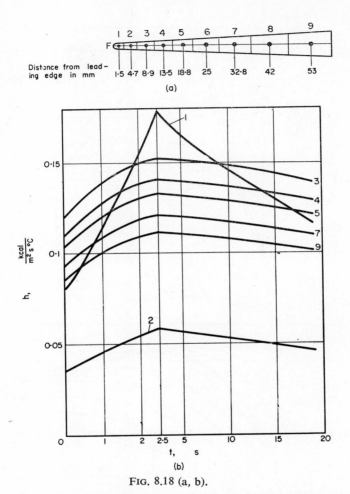

FIG. 8.18 (a, b).

Fig. 8.18(a). Cross-section of a solid titanium fin with sectional division for finite difference calculations, (b) distribution of the heat transfer coefficient along the surface of the fin and (c) distribution of the adiabatic wall temperature vs. time. Section numbering as in (a). Fig. 8.18(c) on next page.

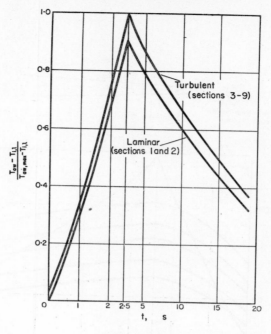

FIG. 8.18 (c).

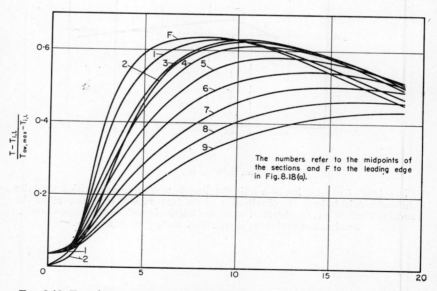

FIG. 8.19. Transient temperature distribution in the fin of Fig. 8.18. For initial temperature distribution see text.

8.8.4 *A solid wing*

In an early paper Kaye (Ref. 8.16) calculated an example of aerodynamic heating of a solid steel wing. Although this wing is of no great current interest, it is important for comparisons. The material is steel ($\rho = 486$ lbs/ft³, $c = 0.118$ Btu/(lb °F) and $k = 22$ Btu/(h ft °F)), the dimensions of the wing, the distributions of the heat transfer coefficient and the adiabatic wall temperature vs. time are shown in the Figs. 8.20 and 8.21. Constant conditions are assumed in the spanwise direction, thermal radiation is neglected and the thermal properties of the wing are assumed constant.

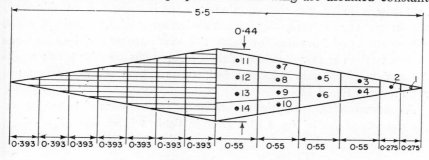

Dimensions in ft

Fig. 8.20. A solid steel wing treated by Kaye (Ref. 8.16). Arrangement of sections on the left-hand side as used by Kaye, on the right-hand side as used here.

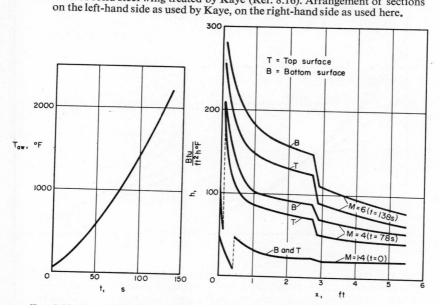

Fig. 8.21. The adiabatic wall temperature vs. time and distribution of the heat transfer coefficient along the surface of the wing.

Initially the flight speed corresponds to $M = 1·4$ at an altitude of 50,000 ft and the temperatures correspond to steady state conditions. Then the wing is accelerated from $M = 1·4$ to 6 with unit increase of M every 30 sec. Kaye divided the wing into 113 sections as shown on the left-hand side of Fig. 8.20 and it was necessary to use 32 steps. The result of Kaye's calculations for the mid section of the wing is shown in Fig. 8.24. In view of the relation between section size and accuracy of finite difference calculations (see Section 8.2.7) the same wing has been recalculated with a coarser sectional division. Because the wing is slender, the transverse heat flow is larger than that chordwise; hence it suffices to consider only the former when investigating the truncation error of the solutions, which can be estimated from that for slabs. For that purpose divisions into one or two sections and small values of the Biot modulus are of interest: results for a slab of constant thickness and constant heat transfer parameters are shown in Fig. 8.22.

An estimate of the truncation errors for the arrangement of the sections on the right-hand side of Fig. 8.20 is given in Table 8.7. Because $(T_{aw} - T_i)_{max}$

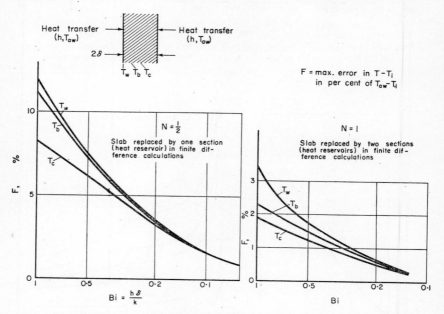

FIG. 8.22. Truncation errors F of the temperature solutions obtained by the finite difference method for a slab of constant thickness and constant heat transfer parameters. Small Biot moduli. Note, that heat transfer occurs here at both surfaces of the slab. (Subscripts w, b and c refer respectively to the wall, the section at a distance of $\delta/4$ from the wall and the midsection.)

TABLE 8.7. Estimate of maximum truncation error of the solutions $(T-T_i)/(T_{aw}-T_i)$ for the arrangement of sections on the right-hand side of Fig. 8.20

Section	$\mathrm{Bi} = \dfrac{h\,\delta}{k}$	Error
1	0·121	0·02
2	0·308	0·05
3 and 4	0·514	0·02
5 and 6	0·777	0·03
7 to 10	1·020	0·01
11 to 14	1·240	0·01

is in the present example about 2080°F, the largest error is about 100°F at station 2, but only 21°F at the midsection. Errors of this magnitude appear acceptable in many cases. The behaviour of solutions is to be of the first and second type. Calculating the corresponding time constants of the sections on the right hand side of Fig. 8.20, it was found that the smallest value was 9·85 sec for section 1 and the one next in magnitude was 26·8 sec for sections 8 and 9. In order to reduce the amount of computational work, section 1 with the smallest time constant was treated separately with the help of an auxiliary circuit shown in Fig. 8.23 for

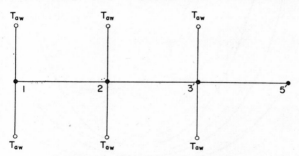

FIG. 8.23. Auxiliary circuit for reservoir 1 of the right-hand side of Fig. 8.20 (see also text).

which the sections 3 and 4 of the main circuit (on the right-hand side of Fig. 8.20) were combined to one section 3' and likewise 5 and 6 to 5'. The time step for the auxiliary circuit was 1/3 of that for the main circuit, hence 3 steps in the auxiliary circuit had to be made for 1 step in the main circuit. At the beginning of a period the temperatures in all sections and hence also those in the sections 1,2,3' and 5' of the auxiliary circuit are known. Here the temperatures in the sections 1,2 and 3' are obtained after the first step, those in the sections 1 and 2 after the second step and only the temperature in section 1 remains after the third step. Meanwhile no computations have been made in the main circuit where now one step is made. Then the temperatures in all sections are known and a new period can begin. Only 6 steps in the main circuit and 18 in the auxiliary circuit were necessary to cover the whole range of times. On comparing the results in Fig. 8.24 for the fine and the coarse sectional divisions, the

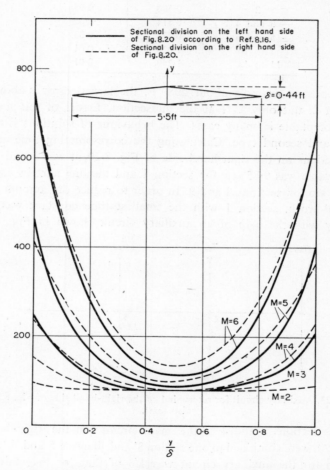

Fig. 8.24. Transient temperature distributions in the midsection of the solid wing of Fig. 8.20. Comparison of solutions obtained with the two different sectional divisions shown on the left-and right-hand sides of Fig. 8.20.

agreement lies within the expected error limits which is satisfactory considering that computations for the coarse division took only about 1/20th of the time for the fine division on the left-hand side of Fig. 8.20.

References

8.1   RICHTMYER, R. D., *Difference Methods for Initial-Value Problems*, Interscience Publ. New York (1957).

8.2   FORSYTHE, G. E. and WASOW, W. R., *Finite Difference Methods for Partial Differential Equations*, New York (1960).

8.3   SCHMIDT, E., Über die Anwendung der Differenzenrechnung auf technische Anheiz- und Abkühlungsprobleme. *Beiträge zur technischen Mechanik und technischen Physik. (August Föppl Festschrift.)* Berlin, 1924, pp. 179–189.

8.4   O'BRIEN, G. G., HYMAN, M. A. and KAPLAN, S., A study of the numerical solutions of partial differential equations, *J. Math. Physics*, **29**, 223–251 (1951).

8.5   CRANK, J. and NICOLSON, P., A practical method for numerical evaluation of solutions of partial differential equations of heat-conduction type, *Proc. Cambr. Phil. Soc*, **43**, 50–67 (1947).

8.6   LEPPERT, G., A stable numerical solution for transient heat flow, *J. Amer Soc. Naval Engng.* **65**, 4, 741–744 (1953).

8.7   HARTREE, D. R. and WOMERSLEY, J. R., A method for the numerical or mechanical solution of certain types of partial differential equations, *Proc. Roy. Soc, London*, A **161**, 353–366 (1937).

8.8   HOWE, R. M. and HANEMAN, V. S., The solution of partial differential equations by difference methods using the electronic differential analyzer, *Proc. West. Computer Conf., Los Angeles* (Feb. 1953), *New York* (1953), pp. 208–231.

8.9   ALLEN, D. N. de G. and SEVERN, R. T., The application of relaxation methods to the solution of non-elliptic partial differential equations. Part I: The heat conduction equation, *Quart. J. Mech. Appl. Math.* **4**, pt. 2, 209–222 (1951).

8.10 LIEBMANN, G., The solution of transient heat flow and heat transfer problems by relaxation, *Brit. J. Appl. Phys.* **6**, 129–135 (1955).

8.11 LAASONEN, P., Über eine Methode zur Lösung der Wärmeleitungsgleichung, *Acta. Math.* **81**, 309–317 (1949).

8.12 LIEBMANN, G., A new electrical analog method for the solution of transient heat-conduction problems, *Trans. A.S.M.E.* **78**, 3, 655–665 (1956).

8.13 REYNOLDS, W. C. and DOLTON, T. A., Use of integral methods in transient heat-transfer analysis, A.S.M.E. Paper 58-A-248 (1959).

8.14 BIOT, M. A., New methods in heat flow analysis with application to flight structures, *J. Aero. Sci.* **24**, 12, 857–873 (1957).

8.15 BIOT, M. A., Thermodynamics and heat flow analysis by Lagrangian methods, I.A.S. Paper No. 59-137 (1959).

8.16 KAYE, J., The transient temperature distribution in a wing flying at supersonic speeds, *J. Aero. Sci.* **17**, 12, 787–807, 816 (1950).

8.17 SCHUH, H., On the calculation of temperature distribution and thermal stresses in parts of aircraft structures at supersonic speeds, *J. Aero. Soc.* **21**, 8, 575–576 (1954).

8.18 FREED, N. H. and RALLIS, C. J., Truncation error estimates for numerical and analog solutions of the heat-conduction equation, *Trans. A.S.M.E. (Journal of Heat Transfer)* **83**, Series C, 3, 382–383 (1961).

CHAPTER 9

HEAT FLOW IN PARTICULAR STRUCTURAL ELEMENTS

IN THIS chapter a skin reinforced by a stiffener is treated in detail because this structural element is typical for aircraft and, except for simple shells, slabs and similar simple bodies, it is the only one which has hitherto been treated at length. Apart from the interest which this structural element merits for its own sake, it illustrates two points: first, the difficulties and advantages of solving a problem generally, i.e. for the whole range of parameters and, possibly, presenting results in the form of general charts. It should be noticed that for this purpose analytical as well as numerical methods could be used. Solutions of this type do exist, of course, for simple external heat transfer conditions, but can be extended by the methods of Section 7.7 to cover general boundary conditions even including heat transfer by radiation and free convection and arbitrary flight conditions. Secondly, it illustrates the advantages and limitations of the analytical method, which is used throughout the present chapter with a few exceptions. From what follows, it appears quite clear that numerical methods are preferable for more complex structures.

The structural elements and heat transfer conditions considered in this section are idealized by suitable assumptions in order to simplify the analytical treatment. The simplifications refer to the form of the structure, to the neglect of contact resistances, to the heat transfer conditions and the flight programme which determines the external heat transfer. Further the external heat transfer parameters are assumed not to vary along the surfaces. In the case of a skin reinforced by stiffeners the influence on the temperature distribution of some of these neglected quantities is investigated separately.

9.1 A skin reinforced by integral stiffeners

9.1.1 *Differential equation for heat flow. External heat transfer by forced convection*

This structural element was first treated by Hoff (Ref. 9.1); it is derived from the wing of Fig. 9.1(a) by considering an infinite row of sections with constant height (Fig. 9.1(b)). If the heat transfer conditions are symmetrical on the wing, it is sufficient to consider that part of the structure which lies within the broken lines A–A in Fig. 9.1(b) and which can

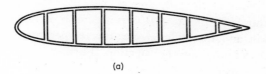

(a)

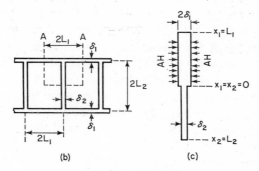

(b)   (c)

AH Aerodynamic heating

FIG. 9.1. (a) A wing consisting of a skin reinforced by integral stiffeners. (b) Row of wing sections with equally spaced stiffeners of uniform height. (c) Model for one-dimensional heat flow in part A–A of (b).

be further simplified to the shell of Fig. 9.1(c). The temperature is assumed to be uniform throughout the thicknesses of the skin and the stiffener and this is valid for the conditions which were given in Section 3.2. Further, constant thermal properties are assumed. With the usual notations and those used in Fig. 9.1(a–c) the equations determining the temperature distribution in the structural element are:

$$\frac{\partial T_1}{\partial x_1} = 0, \qquad x_1 = L_1 \qquad (9.1.1)$$

$$\frac{\partial T_1}{\partial t} = \varkappa_1 \frac{\partial^2 T_1}{\partial x_1^2} + \frac{h_f}{\rho_1 c_1 \delta_1}(T_f - T_1), \qquad 0 \leqslant x_1 \leqslant L_1 \qquad (9.1.2)$$

$$T_1 = T_2; \quad 2\delta_1 k_1 \frac{\partial T_1}{\partial x_1} = -\delta_2 k_2 \frac{\partial T_2}{\partial x_2}, \qquad x_1 = x_2 = 0 \qquad (9.1.3)$$

$$\frac{\partial T_2}{\partial t} = \varkappa_2 \frac{\partial^2 T_2}{\partial x_2^2}, \qquad 0 \leqslant x_2 \leqslant L_2 \qquad (9.1.4)$$

$$\frac{\partial T_2}{\partial x_2} = 0, \qquad\qquad x_2 = L_2 \qquad (9.1.5)$$

Subscripts 1 and 2 refer to the skin and the stiffener respectively. The boundary conditions at $x_1 = L_1$ and at $x_2 = L_2$ follow from conditions of symmetry, those at $x_1 = x_2 = 0$ correspond to perfect thermal contact between the skin and the stiffener, i.e. the temperature and the rate of heat flow are continuous at the junction. Further assumptions are: (a) constant initial temperature T_i at $t = 0$, (b) a sudden increase in flight speed followed by constant flight conditions, (c) external heat transfer by forced convection with the coefficient h_f and the reference temperature T_f constant and (d) heat transfer inside the structure occurring only by heat conduction in the solid part of the structure. Assumption (a) is valid if internal heat sources are absent and constant flight conditions prevail for a sufficiently long time prior to the acceleration of the wing, so that the temperature distribution in the structure becomes uniform. Condition (b) appears at first sight to be very crude but since the heat propagation inside the structure is relatively slow, the time for acceleration to the final speed is in many cases not very important, particularly for the thermal stresses. However, in order to clarify this point to some extent the influence of acceleration times on the temperature distribution in the structure is investigated separately in Section 9.1.7. If, as assumed, only forced convection contributes to the external heat transfer, T_f in Eq. (9.1.2) is equal to the adiabatic wall temperature T_{aw}. If radiative heat transfer is also important, its influence may approximately be taken into account by using the "linearized" expression h_{eff} and the equilibrium temperature T_g as given in Section 3.1.3; then in the above formulae h_f is to be replaced by $h_f + h_{eff}$ and T_f by T_g. As a consequence of the condition (c) above, the dependence of h_f on the ratio of wall temperature to adiabatic wall temperature (see Section 2.3.2) can be taken into account only by suitable mean values. By assumption (d) heat transfer by free convection and thermal radiation inside the structure is excluded. In many cases this appears realistic for light alloy structures, but not for those made of steel and its alloys. Neglect of these modes of heat transfer tends to give temperature differences, and hence also thermal stresses, that are too high. The influence of these modes of heat transfer is treated in Section 9.1.6.

9.1.2 *Solutions for a simplified problem*

Hoff (Ref. 9.1) assumed a uniform temperature distribution in the skin even in the vicinity of the junction, and hence the first term on the right-hand side of Eq. (9.1.2) is omitted. Further, skin temperatures are calculated without regard to the heat lost to the stiffener. The following non-dimensional quantities are introduced:

(a) for the temperatures

$$\Theta_1 = \frac{T_1 - T_i}{T_f - T_i} \text{ and } \Theta_2 = \frac{T_2 - T_i}{T_f - T_i} \tag{9.1.6}$$

(b) for the time

$$\tau = \frac{h_f t}{\rho_1 c_1 \delta_1} \tag{9.1.7}$$

and (c) for the space variable

$$\xi_2 = x_2 \sqrt{\left(\frac{\rho_2 c_2 h_f}{\rho_1 c_1 \delta_1 k_2}\right)} \tag{9.1.8}$$

The Eqs. (9.1.1)–(9.1.5) have now to be re-written in the new variables, but details are not given here. However, it is noted that owing to our simplifying assumptions, the second of the Eqs. (9.1.3) is now neglected and the boundary conditions at $x_2 = \xi_2 = 0$ in the new notation become simply:

$$\Theta_2(0, \tau) = \Theta_1(\tau) \tag{9.1.9a}$$

On account of a uniform temperature in the skin, $\partial^2/\partial x_1^2 = 0$ in Eq. (9.1.2) and this yields:

$$\Theta_1 = 1 - e^{-\tau} \tag{9.1.9b}$$

Thus the present problem has been reduced to that of finding the temperature in the stiffener with one end-face at a temperature given by Eq. (9.1.9b) and with no flow of heat at the other end-face. With no heat losses at the surfaces of the stiffener, the solution of the present problem is the same as that for a slab whose boundary conditions at the surfaces are the same as those at the end-faces of the stiffener. Such a solution is readily found in Ref. 3.1.1 (2nd ed., p. 104) and reads in our notation:

$$\Theta_2(\xi_2, \tau) = 1 - \frac{\cos(\Lambda_2 - \xi_2)}{\cos \Lambda_2} \exp\{-\tau\} -$$

$$-2\Lambda_2^2 \sum_{j=0}^{\infty} (-1)^j \frac{\cos \beta_j [1 - (\xi_2/\Lambda_2)]}{\beta_j (\Lambda_2^2 - \beta_j^2)} \exp\left\{-\beta_j^2 \frac{\tau}{\Lambda_2^2}\right\} \tag{9.1.10}$$

where

$$\beta_j = \frac{2j+1}{2}\pi \tag{9.1.11}$$

and

$$\Lambda_2 = L_2 \sqrt{\left(\frac{\rho_2 c_2 h_f}{\rho_1 c_1 \delta_1 k_2}\right)} \tag{9.1.12}$$

For small times the rate of convergence of the series in Eq. (9.1.10) becomes slow. If the temperature changes of the skin have not yet spread

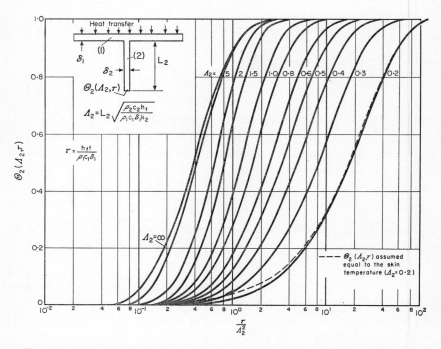

FIG. 9.2. Transient temperatures at the midpoint of the stiffener in the model of Fig. 9.1. Temperature variations along the surface of the skin neglected. For other assumptions see Section 9.1.1.

far into the stiffener the temperature distribution in the latter is best found from a solution for a semi-infinite region of ξ_2:

$$\Theta_{2,\text{si}}\left(\frac{\xi_2}{2\sqrt{\tau}}, \tau\right) = \text{erfc}\left(\frac{\xi_2}{2\sqrt{\tau}}\right) - u\left(\sqrt{\tau}, \frac{\xi_2}{2\sqrt{\tau}}\right)\exp\left\{-\frac{\xi_2^2}{4\tau}\right\} \tag{9.1.13}$$

where $\text{erfc}(x)$ is defined by Eq. (7.4.3). $u(x,y)$, with x and y as arbitrary variables, is related to the error function of complex argument as defined and tabulated in Ref. 3.1.1 (2nd ed., p. 486). In much the same way as for a slab in Section 7.5.1, general charts can be made for the temperature distribution in the stiffener. Thus the temperature at the midpoint of the stiffener is given in Fig. 9.2, and the temperature distribution for a semi-infinite region of the stiffener is given in Fig. 9.3, as calculated from Eqs. (9.1.10) and (9.1.13) respectively. For a finite stiffener the solution for a semi-infinite region is directly applicable, if times are so small that

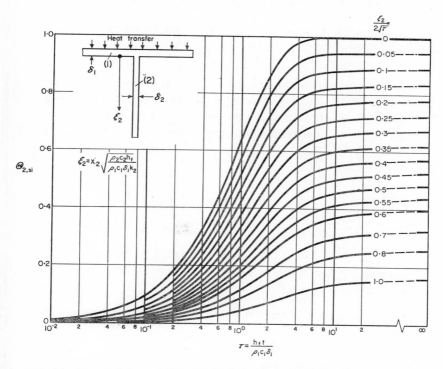

FIG. 9.3. Transient temperature distributions in the stiffener of Fig. 9.1 during the early phase of heat transfer. Temperature variations along the surface of the skin neglected.

a "temperature wave" emanating from $x_2 = 0$ has not yet penetrated beyond $x_2 = L_2$. With the help of the method of images, solutions for larger times can be found (see also Section 7.5.5). The sum of the temperature contributions of each pair of oncoming and reflected waves must be zero at $x_2 = 0$, because the temperature is given there. Therefore the temperature waves are reflected here with the same amplitudes, but with opposite signs. The rate of heat flow disappears at $x_2 = L_2$ and hence here the temperature waves are reflected unchanged. Thus the solution becomes:

$$\Theta_2(\xi_2, \tau) = \sum_{j=0}^{\infty} (-1)^j \left[\Theta_{2,\text{si}}\left(\frac{2j\Lambda_2 + \xi_2}{2\sqrt{\tau}}, \tau \right) + \Theta_{2,\text{si}}\left(\frac{2(j+1)\Lambda_2 - \xi_2}{2\sqrt{\tau}}, \tau \right) \right]$$

(9.1.14)

For small times which are of particular interest in aeronautics a few terms are sufficient in Eq. (9.1.14). The values for $\Theta_{2,\text{si}}$ can be read from Fig. 9.3.

9.1.3 *Solutions of the complete problem for small and large times*

The analytical treatment of the complete problem is sometimes made easier by first obtaining solutions for infinite regions of x_1 and x_2. Solutions of this type are of importance because the deviations of the uniform temperature in the skin are limited to a region of moderate extent near the junction between skin and stiffener and because small times are of particular interest in aeronautical applications. Besides Θ_1, Θ_2, τ and ξ_2 defined by Eqs. (9.1.6), (9.1.7) and (9.1.8), the following additional non-dimensional quantities are used:

$$\xi_1 = x_1 \sqrt{\left(\frac{h_f}{k_1 \delta_1} \right)}$$

(9.1.15)

$$\sigma^* = \frac{\delta_1}{\delta_2} \sqrt{\left(\frac{k_1 \rho_1 c_1}{k_2 \rho_2 c_2} \right)}$$

(9.1.16)

Equations (9.1.1)–(9.1.5) now read:

$$\frac{\partial \Theta_1}{\partial \xi_1} = 0, \qquad\qquad \xi_1 \to \infty \qquad (9.1.17)$$

$$\frac{\partial \Theta_1}{\partial \tau} = \frac{\partial^2 \Theta_1}{\partial \xi_1^2} - \Theta_1 + 1, \qquad 0 \leqslant \xi_1 < \infty \qquad (9.1.18)$$

$$\Theta_1 = \Theta_2; \quad 2\sigma^* \frac{\partial \Theta_1}{\partial \xi_1} = - \frac{\partial \Theta_2}{\partial \xi_2}, \quad \xi_1 = \xi_2 = 0 \qquad (9.1.19)$$

$$\frac{\partial \Theta_2}{\partial \tau} = \frac{\partial^2 \Theta_2}{\partial \xi_2^2}, \qquad\qquad 0 \leqslant \xi_2 < \infty \qquad (9.1.20)$$

$$\frac{\partial \Theta_2}{\partial \xi_2} = 0, \qquad\qquad \xi_2 \to \infty \qquad (9.1.21)$$

The solutions depend only on the parameter σ^*, besides the independent variables τ and ξ_1 or ξ_2. Applying the Laplace transformation (see Section 7.2 and Table 7.1) Eqs. (9.1.18)–(9.1.20) become:

$$\frac{d^2\overline{\Theta}_1}{d\xi_1^2} - (p+1)\overline{\Theta}_1 + \frac{1}{p} = 0, \qquad 0 \leqslant \xi_1 < \infty \qquad (9.1.22)$$

$$\overline{\Theta}_1 = \overline{\Theta}_2; \quad 2\sigma^* \frac{d\overline{\Theta}_1}{d\xi_1} = -\frac{d\overline{\Theta}_2}{d\xi_2}, \quad \xi_1 = \xi_2 = 0 \qquad (9.1.23)$$

$$\frac{d^2\overline{\Theta}_2}{d\xi_2^2} - p\overline{\Theta}_2 = 0, \qquad 0 \leqslant \xi_2 < \infty \qquad (9.1.24)$$

Bars above a quantity indicate a Laplace transform of the original quantity. Solutions for the temperatures $\overline{\Theta}_1$ and $\overline{\Theta}_2$ satisfying the boundary conditions, Eqs. (9.1.17) and (9.1.21) are:

$$\overline{\Theta}_1 = \frac{1}{p(1+p)}\left[1 - \frac{\exp\{-\xi_1\sqrt{(p+1)}\}}{1+2\sigma^*\sqrt{[(p+1)/p]}}\right] \qquad (9.1.25)$$

$$\overline{\Theta}_2 = \frac{2\sigma^*}{p(1+p)\left(\sqrt{\left(\dfrac{p}{1+p}\right)} + 2\sigma^*\right)}\exp\{-\xi_2\sqrt{p}\} \qquad (9.1.26)$$

Developing these expressions for large values of $s = p+1$ in Eq. (9.1.25) and p in Eq. (9.1.26) one obtains:

$$\overline{\Theta}_1 = \frac{1}{s(s-1)} -$$

$$- \frac{1}{(1+2\sigma^*)s^2}\left[1 + \frac{1}{s}\frac{1+\sigma^*}{1+2\sigma^*} + \frac{1}{s^2}\frac{6\sigma^{*2}+9\sigma^*+4}{4(1+2\sigma^*)^2} + \ldots\right]\exp\{-\xi_2\sqrt{s}\} \qquad (9.1.27)$$

$$\overline{\Theta}_2 = \frac{2\sigma^*}{(1+2\sigma^*)p^2}\left(1 - \frac{1+4\sigma^*}{2(1+2\sigma^*)p} + \frac{32\sigma^{*2}+18\sigma^*+3}{8(1+2\sigma^*)^2p^2} + \ldots\right)\exp\{-\xi_2\sqrt{p}\}$$
$$(9.1.28)$$

Re-transforming to the original variables with the help of Table 7.1 one obtains solutions which are valid for small times:

$$\Theta_1(\xi_1, \tau) = 1 - e^{-\tau}\left[1 + \frac{4\tau}{1+2\sigma^*}\,i^2\mathrm{erfc}\left(\frac{\xi_1}{2\sqrt{\tau}}\right) + \right.$$

$$\left. + \frac{1+\sigma^*}{(1+2\sigma^*)^2}(4\tau)^2 i^4\mathrm{erfc}\left(\frac{\xi_1}{2\sqrt{\tau}}\right) + \frac{6\sigma^{*2}+9\sigma^*+4}{4(1+2\sigma^*)^3}(4\tau)^3 i^6\mathrm{erfc}\left(\frac{\xi_1}{2\sqrt{\tau}}\right) + \ldots\right]$$
$$(9.1.29)$$

$$\Theta_2(\xi_2,\tau) = \frac{2\sigma^*}{1+2\sigma^*}\left[4\tau\,i^2\mathrm{erfc}\left(\frac{\xi_2}{2\sqrt{\tau}}\right) - \frac{1+4\sigma^*}{2(1+2\sigma^*)}(4\tau)^2 i^4\mathrm{erfc}\left(\frac{\xi_2}{2\sqrt{\tau}}\right) + \right.$$

$$\left. + \frac{32\sigma^{*2}+18\sigma^*+3}{8(1+2\sigma^*)^2}(4\tau)^3 i^6\mathrm{erfc}\left(\frac{\xi_2}{2\sqrt{\tau}}\right) + \dots\right] \qquad (9.1.30)$$

General solutions valid for larger times lead to integral expressions which are laborious to evaluate numerically. Hence the following results in Fig. 9.4

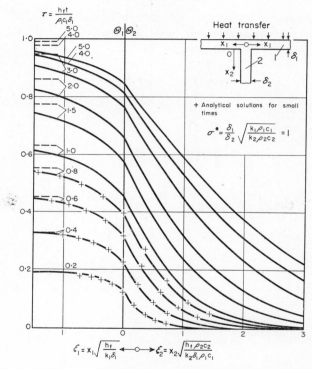

Fig. 9.4. Transient temperature distributions in the skin and stiffener of Fig. 9.1 during the early phase of heating; $\sigma^* = 1$. Temperature variation in the skin allowed for.

have been obtained by the finite difference method and, for small times, also by the analytical solutions given in Eqs. (9.1.29) and (9.1.30). The agreement between the results of the two methods is very good as Fig. 9.4 shows. There a typical example ($\sigma^* = 1$) is given for the temperature distribution. The temperature at the junction of the skin and the stiffener, and the "penetration depths" for both skin and stiffener are given in Figs. 9.5

and 9.6 for a number of values for σ^*. We use as a suitable definition of the non-dimensional penetration depths $\xi_{\beta,1}$ and $\xi_{\beta,2}$ for the skin and stiffener respectively:

$$\Theta_1(\xi_{\beta,1},\tau) = 0.05\,[\Theta_1(0,\tau)-\Theta_1(\infty,\tau)]+\Theta_1(\infty,\tau) \qquad (9.1.31a)$$

$$\Theta_2(\xi_{\beta,2},\,\tau) = 0.05\,\Theta_1(\infty,\tau) \qquad (9.1.31b)$$

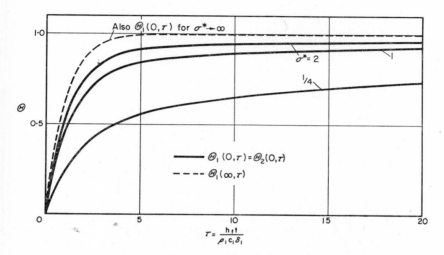

FIG. 9.5. Transient temperature $\Theta_1(0,t) = \Theta_2(0,t)$ at the junction of the skin and stiffener of Fig. 9.1 during the early phase of heating. For comparison skin temperature $\Theta_1(\infty,t)$ far away from the junction.

The solutions of Eqs. (9.1.29) and (9.1.30) are valid for times which are sufficiently small so that the penetration depths $\xi_{\beta,1}$ and $\xi_{\beta,2}$ are not much larger than Λ_1 (see Eq. (9.1.34)) and Λ_2 (see Eq. (9.1.12)) respectively.

For larger times solutions can be obtained by the method of images. Consider one reflection of each of the "waves" Θ_1 and Θ_2 of Eqs. (9.1.29) and (9.1.30) at $x_1 = L_1$ and $x_2 = L_2$ respectively. For the temperature of the skin the particular solution $1-\exp\{-\tau\}$ must be subtracted from the reflected wave in order to fulfil Eq. (9.1.2). The final solutions are, for the skin

$$T_1 = T_i+(T_f-T_i)\,[\Theta_1(\xi_1,\tau;\sigma^*)+\Theta_1(2\Lambda_1-\xi_1,\tau;\sigma^*)-1+\exp\{-\tau\}+\ldots]$$
$$(9.1.32)$$

and for the stiffener

$$T_2 = T_i+(T_f-T_i)\,[\Theta_2(\xi_2,\tau;\sigma^*)+\Theta_2(2\Lambda_2-\xi_2,\tau;\sigma^*)+\ldots] \qquad (9.1.33)$$

Λ_2 is defined by Eq. (9.1.12) and Λ_1 follows from Eq. (9.1.15):

$$\Lambda_1 = L_1 \sqrt{\left(\frac{h_f}{k_1 \delta_1}\right)} \tag{9.1.34}$$

Both solutions are valid as long as $\Theta_1(2\Lambda_1, \tau; \sigma^*)$ and $\Theta_2(2\Lambda_2, \tau; \sigma^*)$ remain small. Waves partly transmitted and partly reflected at the junction are more complicated to deal with and are not treated here.

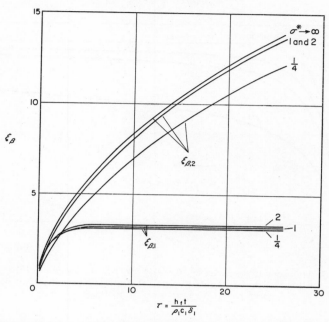

FIG. 9.6. Approximate values of the non-dimensional penetration depths vs. non-dimensional time in the skin and stiffener of Fig. 9.1 during the early phase of heating. Penetration depths defined by Eq. (9.1.31).

Solutions of Eqs. (9.1.1) – (9.1.5) for finite lengths of the skin and the stiffener have been given independently by Parkes (Ref. 9.2) and Pohle and Oliver (Ref. 9.3) in the form of series converging rapidly for large times. If the material in the skin and the stiffener is the same, the temperature distributions are, according to (Ref. 9.3):

$$T_1 - T_f = \sum_{j=1}^{l} B_j \cosh \beta_j (L_1 - x_1) e^{-\varkappa \alpha_j^2 t} + \sum_{j=l+1}^{\infty} B_j \cos \beta_j (L_1 - x_1) e^{-\varkappa \alpha_j^2 t} \tag{9.1.35}$$

and

$$T_2 - T_f = \sum_{j=1}^{\infty} A_j \cos \alpha_j (L_2 - x_2) e^{-\varkappa \alpha_j^2 t} \tag{9.1.36}$$

where the coefficients B_j and A_j become for $j = 1, 2..., l$:

$$B_j = -2\,(T_i - T_f)\left[\cosh\beta_j L_1 + \frac{\beta_j^2 k\,\delta_1}{h_f \sin\alpha_j L_2}\left\{L_2\,\frac{\cosh\beta_j L_1}{\cos\alpha_j L_2}\, + \right.\right.$$

$$\left.\left. + L_1 \frac{\delta_1}{\delta_2}\,\frac{\cos\alpha_j L_2}{\cos\beta_j L_1}\right\}\right]^{-1} \qquad (9.1.37)$$

$$A_j = B_j\,\frac{\cosh\beta_j L_1}{\cos\alpha_j L_2}, \qquad (9.1.38)$$

and for $j = l+1,\ l+2,..., \infty$

$$B_j = -2\,(T_i - T_f)\left[\cos\beta_j L_1 - \frac{\beta_j^2 k\,\delta_1}{h_f \sin\alpha_j L_2}\left\{L_2\,\frac{\cos\beta_j L_1}{\cos\alpha_j L_2} + L_1 \frac{\delta_1}{\delta_2}\,\frac{\cos\alpha_j L_2}{\cos\beta_j L_1}\right\}\right]^{-1}$$

$$(9.1.39)$$

$$A_j = B_j\,\frac{\cos\beta_j L_1}{\cos\alpha_j L_2} \qquad (9.1.40)$$

The eigenvalues become for $j = 1, 2,... l$,

$$\left.\begin{aligned}\alpha\tan\alpha L_2 &= \frac{\delta_1}{\delta_2}\,\beta\tanh\beta L_1 \\[2mm] \alpha^2 + \beta^2 &= \frac{h_f}{k\,\delta_1}\end{aligned}\right\} \qquad (9.1.41)$$

and for $j = l+1,\ l+2,..., \infty$

$$\left.\begin{aligned}\alpha\tan\alpha L_2 &= -\frac{\delta_1}{\delta_2}\,\beta\tan\beta L_1 \\[2mm] \alpha^2 - \beta^2 &= \frac{h_f}{k\,\delta_1}\end{aligned}\right\} \qquad (9.1.42)$$

Results for the numerical example of Ref. 9.3 are presented and discussed in Section 9.3. Solutions for different materials in skin and stiffener have been given by Parkes (Ref. 9.2) who also gave results for 8 examples with differing dimensions and with steel and light alloy as materials. General charts for the temperature distributions in skin and stiffener which may be of different materials are given in Ref. 9.4, for the particular case $\sigma^* = 1$ and subject to a restriction on the size of L_2 given by

$$L_2 \geqslant \frac{1}{2}\,L_1\sqrt{\left(\frac{\varkappa_1}{\varkappa_2}\right)} \qquad (9.1.43)$$

These charts have been obtained by numerical methods.

9.1.4 *Rate of heat flow given at the surface of the skin*

For many cases of severe aerodynamic heating the rate of convective heat flow to the skin becomes approximately independent of the surface temperature. Further, if thermal radiation from the surface of the skin to the surroundings can be neglected, the balance of the heat flow at the surface of the skin is a known function of the time. Solutions are in general easier to obtain for boundary conditions of this type than for forced convection. The same applies also to the method of images for satisfying boundary conditions at the junction between skin and stiffener. Further, solutions with this type of external heat transfer are important for semi-analytical methods such as were discussed in Section 7.7.

The rate of heat flow at the surface of the skin is assumed to be uniformly distributed and equal to

$$\left.\begin{array}{ll} q_w = 0, & t < 0 \\ q_w = \rho_1 c_1 \delta_1 D t^{\frac{n}{2}}, & t \geqslant 0 \end{array}\right\} \tag{9.1.44}$$

n is an integer and D a constant. For constant rate of heat flow $n = 0$. Equation (9.1.2) is replaced by

$$\rho_1 c_1 \delta_1 \frac{\partial T_1}{\partial t} = k_1 \delta_1 \frac{\partial^2 T_1}{\partial x_1^2} + \rho_1 c_1 \delta_1 D t^{\frac{n}{2}} \tag{9.1.45}$$

while Eqs. (9.1.1) and (9.1.3)–(9.1.5) are the same. The following distances and lengths respectively:

$$x_k^* = \frac{x_k}{\sqrt{\varkappa_k}} \quad \text{and} \quad L_k^* = \frac{L_k}{\sqrt{\varkappa_k}}, \quad k = 1 \text{ or } 2 \tag{9.1.46}$$

and temperature differences:

$$\vartheta_k = T_k - T_i, \qquad k = 1 \text{ or } 2 \tag{9.1.47}$$

are introduced. Thus Eqs. (9.1.1), (9.1.45), (9.1.3)–(9.1.5) become

$$\frac{\partial \vartheta_1}{\partial x_1^*} = 0, \qquad x_1^* = L_1^* \tag{9.1.48}$$

$$\frac{\partial \vartheta_1}{\partial t} = \frac{\partial^2 \vartheta_1}{\partial x_1^{*2}} + D t^{\frac{n}{2}}, \qquad 0 \leqslant x_1^* \leqslant L_1^* \tag{9.1.49}$$

$$\vartheta_1 = \vartheta_2; \quad 2\sigma^* \frac{\partial \vartheta_1}{\partial x_1^*} = -\frac{\partial \vartheta_2}{\partial x_2^*}, \quad x_1^* = x_2^* = 0 \tag{9.1.50}$$

$$\frac{\partial \vartheta_2}{\partial t} = \frac{\partial^2 \vartheta_2}{\partial x_2^{*2}}, \qquad 0 \leqslant x_2^* \leqslant L_2^* \tag{9.1.51}$$

$$\frac{\partial \vartheta_2}{\partial x_2^*} = 0, \qquad x_2^* = L_2^* \tag{9.1.52}$$

As previously, solutions for small times are sought first; then the ranges of the variables x_1^* and x_2^* can be assumed infinite ($L_1^* \to \infty$, $L_2^* \to \infty$). Applying the Laplace transformation one obtains for the transformed temperature differences:

$$\bar{\vartheta}_{1,\text{si}} = D\left[\Gamma\left(1+\frac{n}{2}\right)\right]\left[\frac{1}{p^{2+\frac{n}{2}}} - \frac{\exp\{-x_1^*\sqrt{p}\}}{p^{2+\frac{n}{2}}(1+2\sigma^*)}\right] \tag{9.1.53}$$

$$\bar{\vartheta}_{2,\text{si}} = D\frac{2\sigma^*\Gamma\left(1+\frac{n}{2}\right)}{(1+2\sigma^*)p^{2+\frac{n}{2}}}\exp\{-x_2^*\sqrt{p}\} \tag{9.1.54}$$

The subscript "si" indicates solutions for a semi-infinite range of the variables x_1^* and x_2^*. $\Gamma(x)$ is the gamma function of argument x. The final solutions† become, by re-transforming with the help of Table 7.1:

$$\left.\begin{aligned}
\vartheta_{1,\text{si}}\left(\frac{x_1^*}{2\sqrt{t}},t\right) &= D\left(1+\frac{n}{2}\right)^{-1}t^{1+\frac{n}{2}} - \vartheta_{1,\text{si}}^* \\[2mm]
\vartheta_{1,\text{si}}^*\left(\frac{x_1^*}{2\sqrt{t}},t\right) &= D\frac{\Gamma\left(1+\frac{n}{2}\right)}{1+2\sigma^*}(4t)^{1+\frac{n}{2}}\,\text{i}^{2+n}\text{erfc}\left(\frac{x_1^*}{2\sqrt{t}}\right)
\end{aligned}\right\} \tag{9.1.55}$$

$$\vartheta_{2,\text{si}}\left(\frac{x_2^*}{2\sqrt{t}},t\right) = D\frac{2\sigma^*\Gamma\left(1+\frac{n}{2}\right)}{1+2\sigma^*}(4t)^{1+\frac{n}{2}}\text{i}^{2+n}\text{erfc}\left(\frac{x_2^*}{2\sqrt{t}}\right) \tag{9.1.56}$$

When times become large enough for the size of the stiffener pitches and heights to have a noticeable effect, the method of images (see Section 7.5.5) can be used to satisfy the boundary conditions at $x_1^* = L_1^*$ and $x_2^* = L_2^*$. Obviously the first term on the right hand side of Eq. (9.1.55) is a partial solution satisfying the inhomogeneous differential equation (9.1.45) and hence further terms need only satisfy the homogeneous part of the equations. The terms $\vartheta_{1,\text{si}}^*$ and $\vartheta_{2,\text{si}}^*$ in the Eqs. (9.1.55) and (9.1.56) correspond to the waves propagating from the junction $x_1^* = x_2^* = 0$; they are reflected on arriving at the respective boundaries at $x_1^* = L_1^*$ and $x_2^* = L_2^*$. After the reflection, the contributions to ϑ_1 and ϑ_2 are, respectively

$$-\vartheta_{1,\text{si}}^*\left(\frac{2L_1^*-x_1^*}{2\sqrt{t}},t\right) \quad \text{and} \quad \vartheta_{2,\text{si}}\left(\frac{2L_2^*-x_2^*}{2\sqrt{t}},t\right).$$

As time increases, more terms have to be added. The reflection factor is 1 at the end faces ($x_1^* = L_1^*$ and $x_2^* = L_2^*$) because there $\partial\vartheta/\partial x = 0$.

---

† The solution for a constant rate of heat flow has previously been obtained by Hoff (Ref. 9.5).

It is $K_{12}^{(R)} = \dfrac{2\sigma^* - 1}{2\sigma^* + 1}$ (see Section 7.5.5) at the junction for a wave coming

from region 1 and $K_{21}^{(R)} = \dfrac{1 - 2\sigma^*}{1 + 2\sigma^*}$ for a wave coming from region 2. Cor-

responding values for the transmission factor are $K_{12}^{(S)} = \dfrac{2}{1 + 2\sigma^*}$ and $K_{21}^{(S)} =$

$= \dfrac{4\sigma^*}{1 + 2\sigma^*}$. Taking into account all possible heat paths up to one reflection

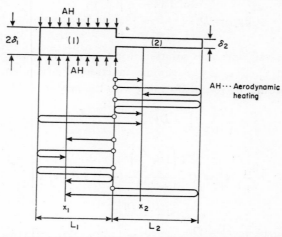

FIG. 9.7. Heat paths for the skin and the stiffener of Fig. 9.1 as used in the method of heat waves and images. Heat paths of increasing length up to at most one reflection at an end-face and one reflection or transmission at the junction.

or transmission at the interface (see Fig. 9.7), yields

$$\vartheta_1 = D \frac{t^{1 + \frac{n}{2}}}{1 + \frac{n}{2}} - \vartheta_{12}^* \tag{9.1.57}$$

$$\vartheta_2 = \vartheta_{21}^* \tag{9.1.58}$$

The two quantities ϑ_{12}^* and ϑ_{21}^* are:

$$\vartheta_{kl}^* = D(2\sigma^*)^{k-1} \frac{\Gamma\left(1 + \dfrac{n}{2}\right)}{1 + 2\sigma^*} (4t)^{1 + \frac{n}{2}} \{I(x_k^*) + I(2L_k^* - x_k^*) + \tag{9.1.59}$$

$$+ K_{kl}^{(R)} I(2L_k^* + x_k^*) - (2\sigma^*)^{l-k} K_{lk}^{(S)} I(2L_l^* + x_k^*)\}$$

where $k = 1$, $l = 2$ or $k = 2$, $l = 1$ and

$$I(x) = i^{n+2} \operatorname{erfc}\left(\frac{x}{2\sqrt{t}}\right) \tag{9.1.60}$$

If the rate of heat flow at the surface of the skin ($n = 0$ in Eq. (7.7.44)) is constant and the skin and the stiffener are made of the same material, a solution can be given in the form of a series converging rapidly for large times (Ref. 9.6):†

$$\vartheta_1 = \frac{q_w \delta_1}{k} \left\{ \frac{4\sigma^*\tau - \lambda(\lambda_1 - \zeta_1)^2}{2(\lambda + 2\sigma^*)} + \frac{\lambda\lambda_1^2[2\sigma^*(1 + 2\lambda^2) + 3\lambda]}{6(\lambda + 2\sigma^*)^2} + \right.$$

$$\left. + \frac{2}{\lambda_1} \sum_{j=1}^{\infty} \frac{\exp\{-\alpha_j^2\tau\}}{\alpha_j^3[(\lambda + 2\sigma^*)\cot(\alpha_j\lambda\lambda_1) - (1 + 2\lambda\sigma^*)\tan(\alpha_j\lambda_1)]} \frac{\cos[\alpha_j(\lambda_1 - \zeta_1)]}{\cos(\alpha_j\lambda_1)} \right\}$$

(9.1.61)

and

$$\vartheta_2 = \frac{q_w \delta_1 \sigma^*}{k} \left[\frac{2\tau + (\lambda\lambda_1 - \zeta_2)^2}{\lambda + 2\sigma^*} - \frac{\lambda\lambda_1^2(2 + \lambda^2 + 6\sigma^*\lambda)}{3(\lambda + 2\sigma^*)^2} - \right.$$

$$\left. - \frac{4}{\lambda_1} \sum_{j=1}^{\infty} \frac{\exp\{-\alpha_j^2\tau\}}{\alpha_j^3[(\lambda + 2\sigma^*)\cot(\alpha_j\lambda_1) - (1 + 2\lambda\sigma^*)\tan(\alpha_j\lambda\lambda_1)]} \frac{\cos[\alpha_j(\lambda\lambda_1 - \zeta_2)]}{\cos(\alpha_j\lambda\lambda_1)} \right]$$

(9.1.62)

where

$$\sigma^* = \frac{\delta_1}{\delta_2}, \quad \lambda = \frac{L_2}{L_1} \quad \text{and} \quad \lambda_1 = \frac{L_1}{\delta_1} \qquad (9.1.63)$$

and

$$\tau = \frac{\varkappa t}{\delta_1^2}, \quad \zeta_1 = \frac{x_1}{\delta_1} \quad \text{and} \quad \zeta_2 = \frac{x_2}{\delta_1} \qquad (9.1.64)$$

The eigenvalues α_j follow from

$$\tan(\alpha\lambda\lambda_1) + 2\sigma^*\tan(\alpha\lambda_1) = 0 \qquad (9.1.65)$$

Analytical solutions for the simplified model of Section 9.1.2 are less complicated. First an infinite region in the stiffener is considered and then one obtains from Eqs. (9.1.55) and (9.1.56) in the limit as $\sigma^* \to \infty$:

$$\vartheta_1(t) = D \frac{t^{1+\frac{n}{2}}}{1 + \frac{n}{2}} \qquad (9.1.66)$$

---

† A solution of this problem was earlier obtained by FREDRICK V. POHLE and IRVIN BERMAN, Thermal stresses in airplane wings under constant heat input. WADC TR 56–145(1956).

and

$$\vartheta_{2,\text{si}}(x_2^*, t) = D\left[\Gamma\left(1+\frac{n}{2}\right)\right](4t)^{1+\frac{n}{2}}i^{2+n}\operatorname{erfc}\left(\frac{x_2^*}{2\sqrt{t}}\right) \tag{9.1.67}$$

The temperature distribution in a stiffener of finite length follows from these equations with the help of the method of images as for Eq. (9.1.14):

$$\vartheta_2(x_2^*, t) = \sum_{j=0}^{\infty}(-1)^j\{\vartheta_{2,\text{si}}(2jL_2^*+x_2, t)+\vartheta_{2,\text{si}}[2(j+1)L_2^*-x_2^*, t]\} \tag{9.1.68}$$

From Ref. 3.1.1 (2nd ed.,p. 104) there follows a corresponding solution in the form of series which converge rapidly for large times, but which is restricted to constant rate of heat flow q_w at the surface of the skin (i.e. $n = 0$ in Eq. (9.1.66)):

$$\vartheta_2 = \frac{q_w}{\rho_1 c_1 \delta_1}\left[t + \frac{x_2^*}{2}(x_2^*-2L_2^*) + \right.$$

$$\left. +2L_2^{*2}\sum_{j=0}^{\infty}\frac{\sin(2j+1)\dfrac{\pi}{2}\dfrac{x_2^*}{L_2^*}}{\left[(2j+1)\dfrac{\pi}{2}\right]^3}\exp\left\{-\left[\frac{(2j+1)\pi}{2L_2^*}\right]^2 t\right\}\right] \tag{9.1.69}$$

9.1.5 *The influence of unsymmetrical heat transfer conditions at the upper and lower surfaces of a wing*

In hypersonic flight the rates of heat transfer on the surfaces of structures depend very strongly on the angle of attack. Therefore a different rate of heating on the upper and lower surfaces of a wing may occur, if the wing is flown at an angle of attack other than zero. The structure of Fig. 9.1(b) is again assumed, but the skin of the upper and lower surfaces may now be of different thicknesses. In view of that and because of the unsymmetrical heat transfer conditions the structural element within the broken lines in Fig. 9.1(b) is completed by the corresponding lower counterpart. Thus the model of Fig. 9.8(a) is obtained and can be simplified as previously to the shell of Fig. 9.8(b).

The set of equations determining the temperature distributions in this model is given by Eq. (9.1.1) and the following Eqs.:

$$\frac{\partial T_1}{\partial t} = \varkappa_1 \frac{\partial^2 T_1}{\partial x_1^2} + \frac{h_{f,u}}{\rho_1 c_1 \delta_1}(T_{f,u}-T_1), \qquad 0 \leqslant x_1 \leqslant L_1 \tag{9.1.70}$$

$$T_1 = T_2; \quad 2\delta_2 k_2 \frac{\partial T_2}{\partial x_2} = -\delta_1 k_1 \frac{\partial T_1}{\partial x_1}, \qquad x_1 = x_2 = 0 \tag{9.1.71}$$

$$\frac{\partial T_2}{\partial t} = \varkappa_2 \frac{\partial^2 T_2}{\partial x_2^2}, \qquad\qquad 0 \leqslant x_2 \leqslant 2L_2 \qquad (9.1.72)$$

$$T_2 = T_3; \quad 2\delta_3 k_3 \frac{\partial T_3}{\partial x_3} = \delta_2 k_2 \frac{\partial T_2}{\partial x_2}, \qquad x_2 = 2L_2; \; x_3 = 0 \quad (9.1.73)$$

$$\frac{\partial T_3}{\partial t} = \varkappa_3 \frac{\partial^2 T_3}{\partial x_3^2} + \frac{h_{f,l}}{\rho_3 c_3 \delta_3}(T_{f,l} - T_3), \qquad 0 \leqslant x_3 \leqslant L_3 \qquad (9.1.74)$$

$$\frac{\partial T_3}{\partial x_3} = 0, \qquad\qquad x_3 = L_3 \quad (9.1.74a)$$

where the subscripts u and l refer to heat transfer conditions on the upper and lower surfaces respectively. The subscripts 1, 2 and 3 refer to upper skin, stiffener and lower skin respectively. Otherwise the same assumptions as in Section 9.1.1 are made.

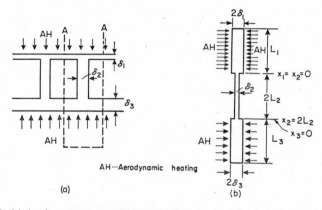

Fig. 9.8. (a) A wing structure as in Fig. 9.1, but upper and lower skins of different thickness and material as well as being exposed to different heat transfer conditions. (b) Model for one-dimensional heat flow in part A–A of Fig. 9.8(a).

First, consider the simplified model with uniform temperature distribution in the upper and the lower skins. Then the first term on the right-hand side of each of the Eqs. (9.1.70) and (9.1.74) disappears and the two skin temperatures T_1 and T_3 can be calculated separately. When T_1 and T_3 are known, the temperature in the stiffener can be obtained in the same way as for a "slab" of thickness $2L_2$, with different temperatures T_1 and T_3 given on the two surfaces of the slab. The solution is the sum of two component temperatures $\Theta_2^{(I)}$ and $\Theta_2^{(II)}$ which both satisfy Eq. (9.1.72) and the following boundary and initial conditions

$$x_2 = 0; \quad \Theta_2^{(I)} = \Theta_1; \quad \Theta_2^{(II)} = 0 \qquad\qquad (9.1.75)$$

$$x_2 = 2L_2; \quad \Theta_2^{(I)} = 0; \quad \Theta_2^{(II)} = \Theta_3 \qquad (9.1.76)$$

$$t = 0; \quad \Theta_2^{(I)} = \Theta_2^{(II)} = 0 \qquad (9.1.77)$$

where $\Theta = (T-T_i)/(T_f-T_i)$. The solutions for $\Theta_2^{(I)}$ and $\Theta_2^{(II)}$ are similar in type to the solutions in Section 9.1.2 except that at one of the boundaries the temperature instead of the rate of heat flow is equal to zero. Hence in the solutions for small times the reflection coefficients for the reflected "waves" are now -1 at both boundaries. Solutions for large times found by the method given in Ref. 3.1.1 are for instance for $\Theta_2^{(I)}$:

$$\Theta_2^{(I)} = 1 - \frac{\xi_2}{2\Lambda_2} - \frac{\sin(2\Lambda_2 - \xi_2)}{\sin 2\Lambda_2} \exp\{-\tau\} -$$

$$-8\Lambda_2^2 \sum_{j=1}^{\infty} (-1)^j \frac{\sin\left(j\pi\left[1 - \dfrac{\xi_2}{2\Lambda_2}\right]\right)}{j\pi(j^2\pi^2 - 4\Lambda_2^2)} \exp\left\{-\left(\frac{j\pi}{2\Lambda_2}\right)^2 \tau\right\} \qquad (9.1.78)$$

where τ, ξ_2 and Λ_2 are defined by Eqs. (9.1.7), (9.1.8) and (9.1.12) and h_f in these equations is to be replaced by $h_{f,u}$; Θ_1 in Eq. (9.1.75) is given by Eq. (9.1.9b). The expression for $\Theta_2^{(II)}$ is similar.

Next, a non-uniform temperature distribution is allowed in the upper and lower skins and the external heat transfer is by forced convection. For small times the temperatures due to the waves emanating from both skins can be superposed as long as waves from one end of the stiffener do not reach the other end. An analytical solution converging rapidly for large times has been given by Chen in Ref. 9.7, but the expressions in it are lengthy. Solutions become simpler if the rates of heat flow are given at the surfaces of the skins. Then for small times solutions can be obtained by superposing component temperatures due to the heat "waves" and the boundary conditions can be satisfied by the method of images. The procedure is similar to that in Section 9.1.4 with the difference that there are now three regions as shown in Fig. 9.8(b) with heat sources $q_{w,1}$ and $q_{w,3}$ in the regions 1 and 3 respectively. Also heat waves emanate from the interfaces between the regions 1 and 2 and between 2 and 3. Because reflections and transmissions can now be calculated easily, this procedure is useful for times which are of interest in aeronautical applications.

Further simplifications are possible if the structure is symmetrical so that the upper and lower skins are of the same thickness and the same material. However, heat transfer conditions are assumed unsymmetrical. Two heat flow rates $q_w^{(s)}$ and $q_w^{(a)}$ are introduced and they are related to the heat flow rates at the upper and lower skins as follows:

$$q_{w,1} = q_w^{(s)} + q_w^{(a)} \qquad (9.1.79)$$

$$q_{w,3} = q_w^{(s)} - q_w^{(a)} \qquad (9.1.80)$$

The temperature distributions due to $q_w^{(s)}$ are symmetrical and those due to $q_{w_{,1}}^{(a)}$ are anti-symmetrical with respect to the mid plane of the structure. Solutions for $q_w^{(s)}$ are the same as in Section 9.1.4 while those for $q_w^{(a)}$ differ in the boundary condition at $x_2 = L_2$, where $\vartheta_2 = T_2 - T_i$ is zero instead of the corresponding temperature gradient. Anti-symmetrical solutions are easily found, but are not treated here.

9.1.6 *Heat transfer by free convection and by thermal radiation between the skin and the stiffener*

We now assume that heat transfer occurs not only by conduction, but also by thermal radiation and by free convection through the internal cavities in the structure. For calculating the intensity of heat transfer due to these modes, "linearized" laws (see Section 3.1.3) are used. The temperature distribution in the skin is assumed uniform. Further, the radiative heat transfer is neglected between stiffeners. This would be approximately valid for large ratios of L_1/L_2. It is further assumed that the local radiative heat transfer can be approximated by $h_{\text{eff}}(T_1 - T_2)$ with h_{eff} as defined in Section 3.1.3. Because of these assumptions the following equations describe real conditions only approximately. Eq. (9.1.4) is now replaced by†

$$\rho_2 c_2 \delta_2 \frac{\partial T_2}{\partial t} = k_2 \delta_2 \frac{\partial^2 T_2}{\partial x^2} + 2 h_{\text{it}} (T_1 - T_2) \qquad (9.1.81)$$

where h_{it} is the coefficient for the internal heat transfer in the linearized law for both free convection and heat radiation. A constant mean value is assumed for h_{it}. A new non-dimensional constant

$$B = \frac{2 h_{\text{it}} \rho_1 c_1 \delta_1}{h_f \rho_2 c_2 \delta_2} \qquad (9.1.82)$$

is introduced, but otherwise the same non-dimensional quantities as in Section 9.1.2 are used. Thus Eq. (9.1.81) becomes with the help of Eq. (9.1.9b):

$$\frac{\partial \Theta_{2,\text{it}}}{\partial \tau} = \frac{\partial^2 \Theta_{2,\text{it}}}{\partial \xi_2^2} + B(1 - e^{-\tau} - \Theta_{2,\text{it}}) \qquad (9.1.83)$$

where the subscript "it" refers to the solution with all modes of internal heat transfer.

The initial condition is $\Theta_{2,\text{it}} = 0$ at $t = 0$ and the boundary conditions are: at $\xi_2 = 0$ as in Eq. (9.1.9) with $\Theta_{2,\text{it}}$ instead of Θ_2, and at $\xi_2 = \Lambda_2$ that $\partial \Theta_{2,\text{it}}/\partial \xi_2 = 0$.

---

† The heat capacity of the air in the enclosure between the skin and the stiffeners is neglected.

For $B < 1$ the following new non-dimensional distances and times are used

$$\left. \begin{array}{l} \xi_2^+ = \xi_2 \sqrt{(1-B)} \\ \tau^+ = (1-B)\tau \end{array} \right\} \qquad (9.1.84)$$

By substituting

$$\Theta_{2,\text{lt}}(\xi_2, \tau) = 1 - \frac{1}{1-B} e^{-\tau B} [1 - \Theta_2^{(1)}(\xi_2^+, \tau^+)] + \frac{B}{1-B} e^{-\tau} \qquad (9.1.85)$$

into Eq. (9.1.83) one obtains the following differential equation for the new quantity $\Theta_2^{(1)}(\xi_2^+, \tau^+)$:

$$\frac{\partial^2 \Theta_2^{(1)}}{\partial \tau^+} = \frac{\partial^2 \Theta_2^{(1)}}{\partial (\xi_2^+)^2} \qquad (9.1.86)$$

From the boundary conditions for $\Theta_{2,\text{lt}}$ those for $\Theta_2^{(1)}$ follow as:

$$\Theta_2^{(1)} = 1 - e^{-\tau^+}, \qquad \xi_2^+ = 0 \qquad (9.1.87)$$

and

$$\frac{\partial \Theta_2^{(1)}}{\partial \xi_2^+} = 0, \qquad \xi_2^+ = \Lambda_2 \sqrt{(1-B)} \qquad (9.1.88)$$

The initial condition for $\Theta_{2,\text{lt}}$ is satisfied, if

$$\Theta_2^{(1)}(\xi_2^+, 0) = 0 \qquad (9.1.89)$$

Thus $\Theta_2^{(1)}$ satisfies the same differential equation, and the same initial and boundary conditions as Θ_2 in Section 9.1.2, if ξ_2 and τ are replaced by the corresponding starred values. Thus $\Theta_2^{(1)}(\xi_2^+, \tau^+)$ is known and hence the final solution is given by Eq. (9.1.85). A numerical example for this method is given in Section 9.3.

For $B > 1$ Eqs. (9.1.84) are replaced by

$$\xi_2^{++} = \xi_2 \sqrt{(B-1)} \quad \text{and} \quad \tau^{++} = (B-1)\tau \qquad (9.1.90)$$

and Eq. (9.1.85) by

$$\Theta_{2,\text{lt}}(\xi_2, \tau) = 1 + \frac{e^{-\tau B}}{B-1} [1 - \Theta_2^{(2)}(\xi_2^{++}, \tau^{++})] - \frac{B}{B-1} e^{-\tau} \qquad (9.1.91)$$

One again obtains Eqs. (9.1.86), (9.1.88) and (9.1.89) with a superscript (2) on Θ and two-starred values of τ and ξ_2; but Eq. (9.1.87) is replaced by

$$\Theta_2^{(2)} = 1 - e^{\tau^{++}}, \qquad \xi_2^{++} = 0 \qquad (9.1.92)$$

A solution for $\Theta_2^{(2)}$ with the boundary condition Eq. (9.1.92) is given in Ref. 3.1.1 (2nd ed., p.105).

For the case $B = 1$,

$$\Theta_{2,\text{lt}} = 1 - [1 - \Theta_2^{(3)}(\xi_2, \tau) + \tau] e^{-\tau} \qquad (9.1.93)$$

which retains the original independent variables. Substituting this expression into Eq. (9.1.83) yields Eqs. (9.1.86), if $\Theta_2^{(1)}, \tau^+$ and ξ_2^+ are there replaced by $\Theta_2^{(3)}, \tau$ and ξ_2 respectively. With this change of notation, one obtains also Eqs. (9.1.88) and (9.1.89), but instead of Eq. (9.1.87) there is now:

$$\Theta_2^{(3)} = \tau, \quad \xi_2 = 0. \tag{9.1.94}$$

A solution for $\Theta_2^{(3)} (\xi_2, \tau)$ can also be found from Ref. 3.1.1.

Hoff (Ref. 9.8) treated the heating of a stiffener due to only radiative heat transfer occurring between the aerodynamically heated skin and the stiffener. The exact law for thermal radiation was used. Similar problems have also been treated by Gatewood (Ref. 9.9).

9.1.7 *The influence of flight plan on temperature distribution*

Previously, an instantaneous change of speed was assumed in order to simplify the analytical treatment. In the case of a supersonic aircraft with approximately uniform acceleration to constant flight conditions, certain calculated examples reported in Refs. 9.2 and 8.17 seem to indicate that in many cases the temperature distributions do not differ too much from those for an instantaneous change of speed, but occur at later times. It is interesting to investigate generally the magnitude of the acceleration times which would alleviate the temperature differences and, thereby, also the thermal stresses. The simplified model of Section 9.1.2 with internal heat transfer by conduction only is assumed.

Assuming a turbulent boundary layer for the external air flow, the heat transfer coefficient is roughly proportional to the speed of the vehicle u (see Section 2.3.2). Assume further a uniform acceleration at constant altitude from $t = 0$ to $t = t_0$ when the maximum speed is attained. For simplicity the initial speed is taken as zero and the initial temperature distribution as uniform and equal to the ambient air temperature T_∞. A non-dimensional time is introduced:

$$\tau = \frac{t h_{f,\max}}{\rho_1 c_1 \delta_1} \tag{9.1.95}$$

with $h_{f,\max}$ as the maximum heat transfer coefficient corresponding to constant flight conditions and with the other symbols as defined previously. Uniform temperature distribution in the skin is assumed as in Section 9.1.2. For a turbulent boundary layer at moderate supersonic speeds in air, the reference temperature T_f of the external medium is T_{aw} which follows from Eq. (2.2.7) with a recovery factor $\eta = 0.9$ and a ratio of the specific heat at constant pressure and at constant volume $\gamma = 1.40$.

The skin temperature is determined from the truncated Eq. (9.1.2), with $\partial^2/\partial x^2 = 0$, and reads in the present notation

$$\frac{dT_1}{d\tau} = \frac{h_f}{h_{f,\,\text{max}}} \left[T_\infty \left(1 + 0.18 M^2\right) - T_1 \right] \tag{9.1.96}$$

Because a uniform acceleration is assumed, then approximately $h_f \sim u \sim t$ and $M \sim t$. Introducing a constant

$$B = 0.18 T_\infty\, M_\text{max}^2 \tag{9.1.97}$$

and a temperature difference

$$\vartheta_1 = T_1 - T_\infty \tag{9.1.98}$$

Equation (9.1.96) becomes

$$\frac{d\vartheta_1}{d\tau} = B \left(\frac{\tau}{\tau_0}\right)^3 - \frac{\tau}{\tau_0}\,\vartheta_1 \tag{9.1.99}$$

where τ_0 is the non-dimensional form of the acceleration time t_0 obtained from Eq. (9.1.95). The solution of the above equation with $\vartheta_1 = 0$ at $\tau = 0$ becomes

$$\vartheta_1 = B \left[\left(\frac{\tau}{\tau_0}\right)^2 - \frac{2}{\tau_0} \left(1 - \exp\left\{ -\frac{\tau^2}{2\tau_0} \right\} \right) \right] \tag{9.1.100}$$

By first developing $\exp\{\ldots\}$ for small times and then calculating the expression within brackets [ ], one obtains $\vartheta_1 \sim \tau^3$. If the acceleration time t_0 is large compared with the time constant $\dfrac{\rho_1 c_1 \delta_1}{h_{f,\,\text{max}}}$ of the skin, then $\tau_0 \gg 1$ and $\vartheta_1 \sim \left(\dfrac{\tau}{\tau_0}\right)^2 = \left(\dfrac{t}{t_0}\right)^2$ for the major part of the acceleration time. Because a large reduction of the temperature differences in the structure is to be expected only for acceleration times of this magnitude, the skin temperature is assumed as follows:

$$\vartheta_1 = \left(\frac{t}{t_0}\right)^2 \vartheta_{1,\,\text{max}}, \qquad 0 \leqslant t \leqslant t_0 \tag{9.1.101a}$$

$$\vartheta_1 = \vartheta_{1,\,\text{max}}, \qquad t_0 \leqslant t < \infty \tag{9.1.101b}$$

A modified space variable and length are used in the stiffener as given by Eq. (9.1.46) with $k = 2$. The relative temperature $\vartheta(x_2^*, t) = T_2 - T_\infty$ is used; initially $\vartheta_2 = 0$ at $t = 0$, the boundary conditions are

$$\vartheta_2(0, t) = \vartheta_1(t), \qquad x_2^* = 0 \tag{9.1.102a}$$

and

$$\frac{\partial \vartheta_2}{\partial x_2^*} = 0, \qquad x_2^* = L_2^* \tag{9.1.102b}$$

Because of Eqs. (9.1.101) and (9.1.102a) the analytical solutions differ for $t < t_0$ and for $t > t_0$. Solutions for a semi-infinite solid are obtained from Ref. 3.1.1, (2nd ed., p. 63), for the boundary condition in Eqs. (9.1. 102a), and for $\vartheta_1(t)$ as given by Eq. (9.1.101a):

$$\vartheta_{2,\text{si}} = 32\,\vartheta_{1,\max}\left(\frac{t}{t_0}\right)^2 \text{i}^4\text{erfc}\left(\frac{x_2^*}{2\sqrt{t}}\right) \tag{9.1.103a}$$

The subscript "si" refers to a semi-infinite solid and $\text{i}^4\text{erfc}(x)$ is defined by Eq. (7.4.12). By the method of images, as explained in Section 7.5.5 one obtains, for a finite length of the stiffener,

$$\vartheta_2(x_2^*, t) = \vartheta_2^*(x_2^*, t) \equiv 32\,\vartheta_{1,\max}\left(\frac{t}{t_0}\right)^2 \sum_{j=0}^{\infty}(-1)^j\left\{\text{i}^4\text{erfc}\left(\frac{2jL_2^*+x_2^*}{2\sqrt{t}}\right)+\right.$$

$$\left.+\text{i}^4\text{erfc}\left[\frac{2(j+1)L_2^*-x_2^*}{2\sqrt{t}}\right]\right\} \tag{9.1.103b}$$

Because the analytical expression for ϑ_1 changes at $t = t_0$ another solution is required for $t > t_0$ with an initial temperature distribution which follows from Eq. (9.1.103b) if one puts $t = t_0$ there. The inconvenience of finding a solution with an initially non-uniform temperature is avoided by re-writing the boundary condition (9.1.102a), with ϑ_1 according to Eq. (9.1.101b), as follows:

$$\vartheta_2(0, t) = \vartheta_{1,\max}\left[\left(\frac{t}{t_0}\right)^2 - \left(\frac{t-t_0}{t_0}\right)^2 - 2\frac{t-t_0}{t_0}\right], \qquad t_0 \leqslant t < \infty \tag{9.1.104}$$

The value of the expression within the brackets [ ] is 1. To each term in these brackets there belongs a partial solution of Eq. (9.1.51) which satisfies both the initial and the boundary conditions of this problem. These partial solutions are in turn: $\vartheta_2^{(1)}$, $\vartheta_2^{(2)}$ and $\vartheta_2^{(3)}$; the first two follow directly from Eq. (9.1.103b) and the remaining one follows in a similar way as above with the help of Ref. 3.1.1. The complete solution for $t > t_0$ is thus:

$$\vartheta_2(x_2, t) = \vartheta_2^*(x_2^*, t) - \vartheta_2^*(x_2^*, t-t_0) -$$

$$-8\,\vartheta_{1,\max}\left(\frac{t-t_0}{t_0}\right)\sum_{j=0}^{\infty}(-1)^j\left[\text{i}^2\text{erfc}\left(\frac{2jL_2^*+x_2^*}{2\sqrt{(t-t_0)}}\right)+\text{i}^2\text{erfc}\left(\frac{2(j+1)L_2^*-x_2^*}{2\sqrt{(t-t_0)}}\right)\right]$$

$$\tag{9.1.105}$$

$\vartheta_2^*(x_2^*, t)$ is defined by Eq. (9.1.103b). By inspecting Eq. (9.1.105) one finds that the correct temperature distribution at $t = t_0$ is automatically satisfied and thus the use of Eq. (9.1.104) is justified.

For large times which are also of interest here, the series of Eqs. (9.1.103) and (9.1.105) converge too slowly. Solutions in the form of series which converge rapidly for large times follow from a corresponding general expression of Ref. 3.1.1 for a slab, for which the temperature is given at one surface and at whose other surface the heat flow is zero:

$$\vartheta_2(x_2^*, t) = \vartheta_2^*(x_2^*, t) \equiv \vartheta_{1,\max}\left[\left(\frac{t}{t_0}\right)^2 + \frac{L_2^{*2} t}{t_0^2}(z^2 - 1) + \right.$$
$$+ \frac{L_2^{*4}}{12 t_0^2}(z^4 - 6z^2 + 5) -$$
$$\left. -4\frac{L_2^{*4}}{t_0^2}\sum_{j=0}^{\infty}(-1)^j \frac{\exp\left\{-\left[(2j+1)\frac{\pi}{2}\right]^2 \frac{t}{L_2^{*2}}\right\}}{\left[(2j+1)\frac{\pi}{2}\right]^5}\cos(2j+1)\frac{\pi}{2}z\right]$$
$$0 \leqslant t \leqslant t_0$$

$$\left.\begin{array}{c}\\\\\\\\\\\\\\\\\\\\\end{array}\right\} \quad (9.1.106)$$

where z stands for $(L_2^* - x_2^*)/L_2^*$, and

$$\vartheta_2(x_2^*, t) = \vartheta_2^*(x_2^*, t) - \vartheta_2^*(x_2^*, t - t_0) - 2\vartheta_{1,\max}\left[\frac{t - t_0}{t_0} + \right.$$
$$+ \frac{L_2^{*2}}{2 t_0}(z^2 - 1) +$$
$$\left. +2\frac{L_2^{*2}}{t_0}\sum_{j=0}^{\infty}\frac{(-1)^j \cos(2j+1)\frac{\pi}{2}z}{\left[(2j+1)\frac{\pi}{2}\right]^3}\exp\left\{-\left[(2j+1)\frac{\pi}{2}\right]^2\frac{t - t_0}{L_2^{*2}}\right\}\right]$$
$$t_0 \leqslant t < \infty$$

$$\left.\begin{array}{c}\\\\\\\\\\\\\\\\\\\\\end{array}\right\} \quad (9.1.107)$$

If the material in the skin and the stiffener is the same, the thermal stresses for large values of L_1/L_2 are proportional to $\vartheta_1(t) - \vartheta_2(L_2^*, t)$ as follows from the corresponding formulas given in Refs. 9.1 or 9.3. This temperature difference is plotted as a fraction of its largest possible value $\vartheta_{1,\max}$ in Fig. 9.9 against the square root of the time ratio t/t_0 with $\sqrt{t_0}/L_2^*$ as parameter. From the figure it follows that noticeable reductions in the thermal stresses due to a gradual acceleration of a vehicle can be expected only if $\sqrt{t_0}/L_2^* > 1$.

For rocket propulsion the flight plan is different, and steady flight conditions occur at most for only short times. Hence the boundary conditions vary with time and the general methods of Sections 7.7 or Chapter

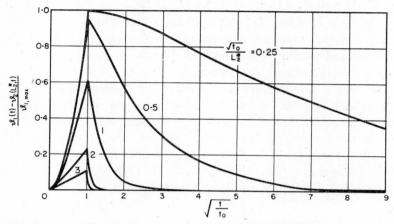

FIG. 9.9. The influence of acceleration times on the largest temperature differences in the model of the wing structure of Fig. 9.1. Temperature differences given as a fraction of their maximum possible value vs. square root of the ratio of time t to acceleration time t_0. For other assumptions see text.

8 have to be used. However, under conditions of severe aerodynamic heating the rate of heat flow q_w at the surface is approximately independent of the surface temperature and hence is a known function of the time. For the two time histories of q_w given in Fig. 9.10 the temperature distribution in the structure can be obtained as above by the following

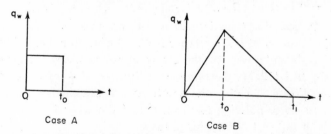

Case A

Case B

FIG. 9.10. Two idealized cases of the time history of the rate of surface heat flow q_w as may occur for rocket propelled vehicles.

procedure which is valid regardless of possible simplifications to the temperature distribution in the skin. In case A q_w can be expressed as

$$q_w = \rho_1 c_1 \delta_1 D_0, \quad 0 \leqslant t \leqslant t_0 \qquad (9.1.108)$$

$$q_w = 0, \quad t < 0 \quad \text{and} \quad t > t_0 \qquad (9.1.109)$$

The corresponding temperatures can be found from Section 9.1.4:

$$\vartheta_{k\square}(x_k^*, t) = \vartheta_k(x_k^*, t; D_0; 0), \qquad 0 \leqslant t \leqslant t_0 \qquad (9.1.110)$$

and

$$\vartheta_{k\square}(x_k^*, t) = \vartheta_k(x_k^*, t; D_0; 0) - \vartheta_k(x_k^*, t-t_0; D_0; 0), \qquad t_0 \leqslant t < \infty \quad (9.1.111)$$

where the sign $\square$ refers to solutions with a time history for q_w of rectangular form as given in Fig. 9.10 (case A). The subscripts $k = 1,2$ refer to the skin and stiffener respectively. $\vartheta_k(x_k^*, t; D; n)$ is a solution of Section 9.1.4, the significance of the parameters D and n following from Eq. (9.1.44). For a skin-stiffener with non-uniform temperature distribution in the skin, ϑ_k is given by Eqs. (9.1.57)–(9.1.60) for short times and any value of n, and by Eqs. (9.1.61)–(9.1.65) for large times but $n = 0$ only. For the same problem, but with a uniform temperature distribution assumed in the skin, ϑ_2 is given by Eq. (9.1.68) for small and by Eq. (9.1.69) for large times; ϑ_1 follows from Eq. (9.1.66).

In case B of Fig. 9.10 q_w can be expressed by

$$q_w = D_0 t, \qquad\qquad 0 \leqslant t \leqslant t_0 \qquad (9.1.112)$$

$$q_w = D_1(t-t_0) + D_0 t_0, \qquad t_0 \leqslant t \leqslant t_1 \qquad (9.1.113a)$$

There is a relation between D_0, D_1 and t_1 as follows from Eq. (9.1.113a) by putting in it $t = t_1$ and $q_w = 0$. For reasons similar to those for which a boundary condition previously was written in the form of Eq. (9.1.104), we now re-write Eq. (9.1.113a) as

$$q_w = D_0 t + (D_1 - D_0)(t-t_0), \qquad t_0 \leqslant t \leqslant t_1 \qquad (9.1.113b)$$

t_1 is the time for which q_w again becomes zero and remains so infinitely. Hence an expression analogous to Eq. (9.1.113b) is:

$$q_w = 0 = D_0 t + (D_1 - D_0)(t-t_0) - D_1(t-t_1), \qquad t_1 \leqslant t \leqslant \infty \quad (9.1.113c)$$

D_0 and D_1 are the time-derivatives of the rate of heat flow during $0 \leqslant t \leqslant t_0$ and $t_0 \leqslant t \leqslant t_1$ respectively. During the first time interval $0 \leqslant t \leqslant t_0$ the solutions for the temperatures corresponding to the heat flow of Eq. (9.1.112) are the same as in Section 9.1.4 for the same rate of heat flow. For $t_0 \leqslant t \leqslant t_1$ the solutions are obtained as the sum of two components corresponding to the first and the second term on the right hand side of Eq. (9.1.113b); this yields:

$$\vartheta_{k\triangle} = \vartheta_k(x_k^*, t; D_0; 2) + \vartheta_k(x_k^*, t-t_0; D_1-D_0; 2), \qquad t_0 \leqslant t \leqslant t_1 \quad (9.1.114)$$

The sign $\triangle$ refers to the form of the surface heat-input of case B in Fig. 9.10; otherwise the same notations are used as previously. For $t \geqslant t_1$ one obtains:

$$\vartheta_{k\triangle} = \vartheta_k(x_k^*, t; D_0; 2) + \vartheta_k(x_k^*, t-t_0; D_1-D_0; 2) - \vartheta_k(x_1^*, t-t_1; D_1; 2),$$
$$t \geqslant t_1 \qquad\qquad (9.1.114a)$$

In some cases a better approximation to real flight conditions may be

$$q_w = q_{w,\max} \sin\left(\frac{\pi}{t_0} t\right) \tag{9.1.115}$$

where $q_{w,\max}$ is the maximum intensity of heat flow and t_0 the time from the start of heating to the onset of cooling. Solutions for the structural element of Section 9.1.1 were given by Goldberg (Ref. 9.10) and commented upon by Shih-Yuan Chen (Ref. 9.11). These solutions are in the form of series converging rapidly for large values of the time.

9.2 A skin reinforced by a stiffener with a thermal contact resistance at the joint

It is now assumed that the stiffener has a flange (Fig. 9.11) which is bolted, riveted or bonded to the skin. If w is the length of the flange in contact with the skin and h_{ct} is the heat transfer coefficient across the

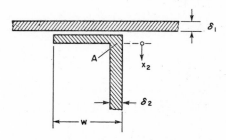

FIG. 9.11. A stiffener bolted, riveted or bonded to a skin.

nterface of the joint (for numerical values of h_{ct} see Section 3.7) the boundary condition at the junction of the flange and stiffener (A in Fig. 9.11) is

$$-k_2 \frac{\partial T_2}{\partial x_2} = \frac{w h_{ct}}{\delta_2} (T_1 - T_2) \tag{9.2.1}$$

where the temperature distributions in the entire skin and the flange are assumed uniform. Other conditions and notations are the same as in Section 9.1.2. It would be consistent with the assumptions made hitherto to assume the zero point for x_2 at the junction A between stiffener and flange. Then, however, the thermal resistance to heat flow in the direction parallel to the surface of the flange would be neglected, as would the heat capacity of the flange. These omissions can approximately be taken into account by a suitable increase in the geometrical length L_2 of the stiffener.

Assuming, as in Section 9.1.2, heat transfer by forced convection at the surface of the skin, the solution for the uniformly distributed temperature in the skin is given by Eq. (9.1.9b) from which follows for the skin temperature itself:

$$T_1 = T_i + (T_f - T_i)\exp\{-\tau\} \tag{9.2.1a}$$

with τ given by Eq. (9.1.7). Then the present problem is simplified to solving Eq. (9.1.4) with external heat transfer at $x_2 = 0$ with a coefficient

$$h_{ct}^* = \frac{w h_{ct}}{\delta_2} \tag{9.2.2}$$

into a "medium" with the temperature T_1 as given by Eq. (9.2.1a) and with the boundary condition Eq. (9.1.5) at $x_2 = L_2$. Assuming h_{ct} is independent of temperature the solution follows from the general formula in Ref. 3.1.1, (2nd ed., p. 127) and is:

$$\Theta_2 = 1 - \frac{\text{Bi}\cos\left[\Lambda_2\left(1 - \dfrac{\xi_2}{\Lambda_2}\right)\right]}{(\text{Bi}\cot\Lambda_2 - \Lambda_2)\sin\Lambda_2}\exp\{-\tau\} +$$

$$+ 2\,\text{Bi}\Lambda_2^2 \sum_{j=1}^{\infty} \frac{\cos\left[\beta_j\left(1 - \dfrac{\xi_2}{\Lambda_2}\right)\right]\exp\left\{-\dfrac{\beta_j^2 \tau}{\Lambda_2^2}\right\}}{(\text{Bi} + \beta_j^2 + \text{Bi}^2)(\beta_j^2 - \Lambda_2^2)\cos\beta_j} \tag{9.2.3}$$

with τ and Λ_2 defined by Eqs. (9.1.7) and (9.1.12) respectively; further,

$$\text{Bi} = \frac{h_{ct}^*}{k_2}L_2 = \frac{w L_2 h_{ct}}{k_2 \delta_2} \tag{9.2.4}$$

and β_j is defined by Eq. (7.5.4). A condition for the validity of the solution is $\Lambda_2 \neq \beta_j$.

A result more suitable for a qualitative assessment of the influence of a finite contact resistance is obtained from a solution for a given rate of heat flow at the surface. Hence Eq. (9.1.44) is used to determine the temperature of the skin. With the help of the Laplace transformations and correspondences in Table 7.1, in particular No. 6, the following result has been obtained for a semi-infinite range of x_2^*

$$\vartheta_2 = -D\,\frac{\Gamma\left(1 + \dfrac{n}{2}\right)}{(-\bar{h})^{2+n}}\left\{\exp\{\bar{h}x_2^* + \bar{h}^2 t\}\,\text{erfc}\left(\frac{x_2^*}{2\sqrt{t}} + \bar{h}\sqrt{t}\right) - \right.$$

$$\left. - \sum_{j=0}^{n+2}(-\bar{h}\sqrt{t})^j\,i^j\text{erfc}\left(\frac{x_2^*}{2\sqrt{t}}\right)\right\} \tag{9.2.5}$$

where

$$\bar{h} = \frac{w h_{ct}}{\delta_2 \sqrt{(k_2 \rho_2 c_2)}} \tag{9.2.6}$$

If the first term within the brackets { } on the right-hand side of Eq. (9.2.5) is expanded for large values of $\bar{h}\sqrt{t}$ one obtains with the help of Eq. (7.4.4)

$$\frac{\vartheta_2}{\vartheta_1} \approx 2^{n+2} \Gamma \left(2 + \frac{n}{2} \right) \left(i_j^{n+2} \operatorname{erfc} \left(\frac{x_2^*}{2\sqrt{t}} \right) - \frac{1}{2\bar{h}\sqrt{t}} i^{n+1} \operatorname{erfc} \left(\frac{x_2^*}{2\sqrt{t}} \right) + \dots \right) \tag{9.2.7}$$

According to Eq. (7.4.17)

$$\frac{i^{n+1} \operatorname{erfc}(x)}{i^{n+2} \operatorname{erfc}(x)} \approx 3 \tag{9.2.8}$$

for small values of x and for n between 0 and 4. From Eq. (9.2.7) it follows that the thermal contact resistance has small effect, if the second term in Eq. (9.2.7) is, say, only about 10 per cent of the first; for the time t_{ct} when this happens, it follows from Eq. (9.2.6) that:

$$t_{ct} \approx 200 \, k_2 \rho_2 c_2 \left(\frac{\delta_2}{w h_{ct}} \right)^2 \tag{9.2.9}$$

Whether the contact resistances are important or not for the maximum temperature differences in the structure (and hence also for the maximum thermal stresses) depends on the time t_{max} when these occur; contact resistances are important, if $t_{max} < t_{ct}$ and they are not, if $t_{max} > t_{ct}$.

For light alloys $k\rho c$ is about 10–20 (kcal/m² °C)²/sec (0·4–0·8 (Btu/ft² °F)²/sec) according to Table 7.2 and h_{ct} about 0·3–1·4 kcal/m²sec°C (200–1000 Btu/ft²h°F) according to Section 3.7; assuming $k\rho c = 15$, $h_{ct} = 0·6$ (both in metric units) and $w/\delta_2 = 10$, $t_{ct} \approx 80$ sec. Since aerodynamic heating of missiles is often severe, but of short duration with times of 10 sec to about a minute, the contact resistances in light alloy joints are important in many cases. This may not be so in the case of an aircraft when the heating is less intense but has a duration of some minutes or more. However, for ordinary steel or stainless steel structures, the contact resistances are in general important for both missiles and aircraft, because $k\rho c$ is between 3·8 (0·16) and 9·3 (0·39) and h_{ct} is about 0·07 (50);† hence the times when contact resistances become of small influence (see Eq. (9.2.9)) are much larger.

Thus far a uniform temperature distribution in the entire skin has been assumed. Next, the temperature drop in the skin near the junction of the

---

† Dimensions in metric (British) units as above.

skin and the stiffener is taken into account, but the flanges (Fig. 9.11) are assumed to be so short that the influence of their length on the temperature distribution in the skin can be neglected. The heat capacity of the flanges is also neglected or, as previously, approximately taken into account by a corresponding increase in the height of the stiffener. Then the model of Fig. 9.1(c) is again valid, but the first of the two boundary conditions in Eq. (9.1.3), $T_1 = T_2$, is replaced by Eq. (9.2.1). Other conditions are the same. Corresponding solutions have been given in Ref. 9.12 under the assumption that the spacing of the stiffeners is equal to their height ($L_1 = L_2$). A solution in the form of a series converging rapidly for large times is given there for a constant rate of heat flow q_w at the surface of the skin for $t > 0$. Further approximate solutions for small times are given in the same reference for a general form of q_w and, in more detail, for the particular form (B a constant):

$$q_w = B \frac{t}{t_0} \exp \left\{ -\frac{t}{t_0} \right\}, \quad t \geqslant 0 \qquad (9.2.10)$$

The numerical results of Ref. 9.12 confirm the above estimates regarding the influence of contact resistances on temperature distributions.

A solution for a non-uniform temperature distribution in the flange and the adjacent parts of the skin (Fig. 9.11) has been given by Frank (Ref. 9.13). The rate of heat flow q_w at the surface of the skin is assumed to be uniform, but a general function of time. Solutions are obtained in two steps. First, the heat capacity of the flange and its resistance to a heat flow parallel to the surface are neglected. This part of the problem is the same as in Ref. 9.12 except that the lengths of the skin and stiffener are now assumed infinite (solutions for small times). In the next step the heat capacity of the flange and its heat resistance are taken into account, thus allowing spatial variations of the temperature in the flange and in the adjacent parts of the skin. The temperature at the junction of flange and stiffener (A in Fig. 9.11) is now assumed as given from the solution of the first step. However, this assumption appears arbitrary and therefore the advantage gained by this refined but more complicated treatment appears doubtful. However, good agreement with an experiment is reported (Ref. 9.13).

Using the method of lumped heat capacities and lumped heat resistances (see Section 8.5) Griffith and Miltonberger (Ref. 9.14) calculated, with the help of an analogue-type calculating machine, the temperature distribution in a skin and stiffener. External heat transfer by forced convection only was assumed. Variations were made in the external heat transfer coefficient h_f ($h_f \delta_1/k = 0.02$, 0.2 and 2) in the joint heat transfer coefficient h_{ct} ($h_{ct}\delta_1/k = 0$, 0.03, 0.15, 0.36, ∞) and in the ratio of stiffener pitch to skin thickness ($L_1/\delta_1 = 10$, 20, 30). The thermal properties and h_{ct} were assumed to be independent of temperature. A number of cases were solved numerically in Ref. 9.14 and results are given in non-dimensional form.

9.3 Examples of aerodynamic heating of skins reinforced by stiffeners

First, the example of Hoff's early paper, Ref. 9.1, is given, because subsequently it has also been treated by other authors (for instance Refs. 9.2, 9.3). The structure considered is a skin reinforced by an integral stiffener as shown in Fig. 9.1 and it is mainly meant to be illustrative, but not necessarily representative of flight structures in general. The assumptions and notations used are the same as in Section 9.1.1. The dimensions in the example of Ref. 9.3 are $\delta_1 = 0.375$ in., $\delta_2 = 0.1$ in., $L_1 = 12$ in., $L_2 = 4.69$ in. Heat transfer by forced convection only is considered, with a heat transfer coefficient of $h_f = 90$ Btu/h(ft)^2°F and an adiabatic wall temperature of $T_{aw} = 600$°F. A constant initial temperature is assumed $T_i = 60$°F. The material is steel and its thermal properties are $\varkappa = 0.0186$ (in.)^2/sec, $\rho = 489.6$ (1bs)/(ft)^3 and $c = 0.1406$ Btu/1b°F. These values for h_f and T_{aw} quoted in Ref. 9.1 were taken from Ref. 8.16 and meant to correspond to a flight speed of $M = 3.1$ at an altitude of 50,000 ft (normal atmosphere) and to a turbulent boundary layer at 1 ft distance from the leading edge. Thermal radiation was neglected. However, at the time when the papers of Refs. 8.16 and 9.1 were prepared, insufficient was known about heat transfer in compressible turbulent boundary layers. Now, when more experimental results and better theories are available, other values would be chosen for the heat transfer data. For simplicity the above values for h_f and T_{aw} are retained, but it is noted that the correct values of the corresponding flight data are: altitude $H = 23,000$ ft and Mach number $M = 2.8$, if the distance from the leading edge is assumed to be 1.6 ft. The value for h_f follows from Eq. (2.3.1) if for c_f/c_{fi} the arithmetic mean is used between the two values corresponding to $T_w = T_i$ and $T_w = T_{aw}$ at $M = 2.8$ (see Fig. 2.5).

Solutions are considered first in which the temperatures are allowed to be non-uniform near the junction of skin and stiffener. It is assumed that heat transfer occurs externally by forced convection only and inside the structure by conduction only. The present example had been calculated numerically in Ref. 9.3 with the help of the Eqs. (9.1.35)–(9.1.42) and is presented in Fig. 9.12. Because $\sigma^* = 3.75$, an estimate from Fig. 9.5 shows that in this particular case the temperature variations along the skin are expected to be small. This is confirmed in Fig. 9.12 by comparison with the solutions for a uniformly distributed skin-temperature which were given earlier by Hoff (Ref. 9.1) and which were recalculated

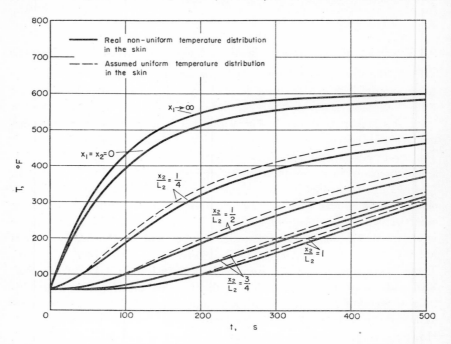

FIG. 9.12. A numerical example for transient temperatures in the wing of Fig. 9.1. Dimensions and heat transfer conditions are given in the text. Heat transfer inside the structure by heat conduction only.

here using Eqs. (9.1.10) or (9.1.14). When using the latter equation, only one or, at most, two terms had to be considered.

If external heat transfer by thermal radiation is also taken into account with a coefficient of emissivity of $\varepsilon = 0.9$ and the same flight conditions ($M = 2.8$, $H = 23,000$ ft) as above, the final equilibrium temperature would be $T_g = 581°F$ instead of being equal to the adiabatic wall temperature of 600°F when only forced convection is considered. The reason for the small difference between T_g and T_{aw} is that the altitude is low and there the convective heat transfer coefficient is large. For an altitude of 100,000 ft, but otherwise the same conditions, the equilibrium temperature is $T_g = 351°F$ against $T_{aw} = 468°F$.

Next, we consider internal heat transfer by free convection and thermal radiation between the skin and the stiffener.† The simplifications of Section 9.1.2 and the same dimensions as above are used. For the radiative and free-convection heat transfer the temperature characteristic for the skin is chosen as a mean value between $x_1 = x_2 = 0$ and $x_1 \to \infty$, and that for the stiffener is taken at $x_2 = L_2/2$ (see Fig. 9.1). Since these temperatures vary, we take the values at $t = 100$ sec when the temperature differences are not far from their maximum value (Fig. 9.12) and obtain $T_1 = 410°F$ and $T_2 = 100°F$. The heat transfer coefficient for free convection between skin and stiffener is assumed as half the value‡ for a vertical plate (see Eq. (3.5.8)) with $L = L_2 = 4.69$ in., $T_f = \dfrac{T_1 + T_2}{2} = 255°F$; hence $h_{con} = 0.5$ Btu/(h ft² °F). The "linearized" coefficient h_{ra} in radiative heat transfer is calculated from Eq. (3.1.10) with $C_R = \varepsilon C_\sigma$ ($\varepsilon = 0.9$)§ and yields $h_{ra} = 2.45$ Btu/(h ft² °F). From the combined coefficient for internal heat transfer $h_{it} = h_{con} + h_{ra}$ and Eq. (9.1.82) it follows that $B = 0.25$ and the temperature distributions in the stiffener, as calculated from Eq. (9.1.85), are shown in Fig. 9.13. The deviations from the corresponding case of heat flow by conduction only, are large in this example for all but very small times. This was to be expected since Hoff observed already in Ref. 9.1 that the convective mode of internal heat transfer is of the same order of magnitude as internal heat conduction. However, for missile structures of light alloy the influence of these additional modes of internal heat transfer is much less and may be neglected in many cases (Ref. 9.19). This is so for a number of reasons: flight times are shorter and speeds higher, hence heating is more rapid than for the steel structure treated above; also coefficients of emissivity are smaller and heat conductivities larger than for steel. Further, flight times are usually much shorter than was assumed above.

---

† In this case external radiative heat transfer was neglected in order to facilitate comparison with the previous case with internal heat transfer by conduction only.

‡ This assumption is only a rough estimate; a more accurate value could be obtained only by investigating the free-convection flow between the skin and the stiffener and this would be difficult. Besides, the heat capacity of the air in the cavity between the skin and the stiffener is neglected.

§ This value of C_R would be valid for large values of L_1/L_2 (ratio of pitch to height of the stiffener) and it is retained in the example because in our simplified treatment (uniform skin temperature) the size of the pitch has no influence on the temperature of the stiffener. For a ratio of $L_1/L_2 \approx 2.5$ as was used in Ref. 9.3 for the solution of the complete problem, C_R would be about 20 per cent less as follows from Ref. 9.8 provided $\varepsilon \approx 1$.

This can be confirmed by the following rough estimate. Consider the same type of structure as previously, except that it is made of aluminium with $\delta_1 = \delta_2 = 0.08$ in., and the same external heat transfer conditions as above. Assume a heat transfer coefficient for internal free convection

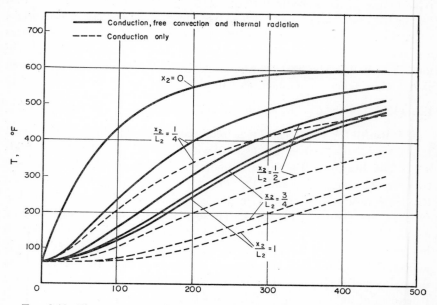

FIG. 9.13. The same case as in Fig. 9.12 but with three modes of heat transfer inside the structure: conduction, free convection and thermal radiation. Approximate solution of Section 9.1.6.

of 0.5 Btu/[(ft)^2 h °F] as previously, and a coefficient of emissivity of $\varepsilon = 0.2$ as for aged aluminium (Ref. 3.6.1); the previous value of h_{ra} for a steel structure is reduced by a factor $0.2/0.9$, which is equal to the ratio of the emissivities of light alloy and steel. Thus the combined "linearized" heat transfer coefficient for both modes of internal heat transfer is approximately $h_{it} = 1.05$ Btu/[(ft)^2 h °F]. Then one obtains from Eq. (9.1.82) that $B = 0.023$ and further $\Lambda_2 = 5.45$ according to Eq. (9.1.12), with $k = 70$ Btu/(ft h °F) for an aluminium alloy (see Table 7.2). Although it is not typical for a missile flight plan, instantaneous acceleration to constant flight conditions is assumed here for simplicity and this is believed to be permissible for a rough estimate. With internal heat transfer by conduction only the non-dimensional temperature $\Theta_2 = (T_2 - T_i)/(T_f - T_i)$ in the middle of the stiffener ($\xi_2 = \Lambda_2$) remains zero according to Fig. 9.2 for flight times of 10 and 20 sec. If the two additional modes of internal heat transfer are taken into account, the temperature at this point becomes $\Theta_{2,\text{it}}(\Lambda_2,\tau) = \dfrac{B}{2}\tau^2$ from Eq.(9.1.85) for small values of B and moderate values of τ. This yields temperatures $\Theta_{2,\text{it}}(\Lambda_2,\tau) = 0\cdot01$ and $0\cdot04$ for 10 and 20 sec respectively. Thus the temperature increases at the middle of the stiffener remain small, even if internal heat transfer by free convection and thermal radiation is taken into account.

Next we consider the influence of acceleration times on the two structures and under the same flight conditions. As mentioned in Section 9.1.7 the maximum thermal stresses are proportional to the maximum temperature difference between the middle of the stiffener and the skin, if L_1 is large. Hence these temperature differences are of particular interest and they are considered now when investigating the influence of flight plans. From Fig. 9.9 it follows that a favourable influence of the acceleration time t_0 on the temperature differences only becomes important for $V(t_0)/L_2^* > 0\cdot5$ (t_0 and L_2^* are defined in Sections 9.1.7 and 9.1.4 respectively), and in the steel and light alloy wings previously treated this yields: $t_0 > 300$ sec and $t_0 > 75$ sec respectively. From the same figure it follows that the maximum temperature differences within the structure fall to about half their highest possible value, if $\dfrac{Vt_0}{L_2^*} \approx 1\cdot2$ or, in the present cases, $t_0 \approx 1700$ sec and $t_0 \approx 450$ sec for steel and light alloy respectively. One of the assumptions in this estimate is that the time constants of the skin are small compared with the acceleration times and this is true in the present case, because the time constant is $(\rho_1 c_1 \delta_1)/h_{f,\max} = 86$ sec for the steel wing and 10 sec for the light alloy one.

Examples have been given in Refs. 9.15, and 9.16 for configurations of skins and stiffeners connected by angles and with finite contact resistance across the joints. In the first report direct analogue methods as described in Section 10 were used. In the second report the method of lumped heat capacities and heat resistances as in Section 8.6 was applied and numerical solutions were obtained with the help of an analogue-type calculating machine.

Thermal responses of a thin flat plate with one edge held at constant temperature have been given in Ref. 9.17 for a particular case of heat input at the surface similar to that occurring in the neighbourhood of nuclear explosions. Heat losses from the surfaces were due to convective heat transfer. The same problem for a typical aircraft structure has been treated in Ref. 9.18.

9.4 A shell with a discontinuity in thickness

In many structures shells are reinforced by local increases in thickness and under transient heating this causes temperature differences in the structure. As a first step in dealing with cases of this kind consider two semi-infinite shells (Fig. 9.14) of the same material, but with different

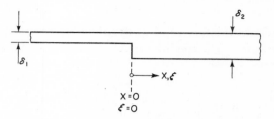

FIG. 9.14. A shell with a discontinuity in thickness.

thicknesses. The thermal contact between the two shells is assumed to be perfect. Other assumptions are the same as in Section 9.1.1. Using the same notation as previously, the equations for heat conduction in the two shells are:

$$\rho c \delta_1 \frac{\partial T_1}{\partial t} = \delta_1 k \frac{\partial^2 T_1}{\partial x^2} + h_f(T_f - T_1) \tag{9.4.1}$$

$$\rho c \delta_2 \frac{\partial T_2}{\partial t} = \delta_2 k \frac{\partial^2 T}{\partial x^2} + h_f(T_f - T_2) \tag{9.4.2}$$

where the subscripts 1 and 2 refer to the respective shells. The following non-dimensional quantities are introduced: Θ_1 and Θ_2 as defined in Eq. (9.1.6), a non-dimensional distance

$$\xi = x \sqrt{\left/\left(\frac{h_f}{\delta_1 k}\right)\right.} \tag{9.4.3}$$

and a non-dimensional time

$$\tau = \frac{h_f t}{\rho c \delta_1} \tag{9.4.4}$$

Equations (9.4.1) and (9.4.2) become

$$\frac{\partial \Theta_1}{\partial \tau} = \frac{\partial^2 \Theta_1}{\partial \xi^2} - \Theta_1 + 1 \tag{9.4.5}$$

$$\frac{\partial \Theta_2}{\partial \tau} = \frac{\partial^2 \Theta_2}{\partial \xi^2} - \frac{\delta_1}{\delta_2}(\Theta_2 - 1) \tag{9.4.6}$$

and the boundary conditions are

$$\frac{\partial \Theta_1}{\partial \xi} = 0, \qquad\qquad \xi \to -\infty \qquad (9.4.7)$$

$$\Theta_1 = \Theta_2; \qquad \frac{\partial \Theta_1}{\partial \xi} = \frac{\delta_2}{\delta_1}\frac{\partial \Theta_2}{\partial \xi}, \qquad \xi = 0 \qquad (9.4.8)$$

$$\frac{\partial \Theta_2}{\partial \xi} = 0, \qquad\qquad \xi \to \infty \qquad (9.4.9)$$

Constant initial T_i is assumed and hence

$$t = 0; \quad \Theta_1 = \Theta_2 = 0 \qquad\qquad (9.4.10)$$

Since analytical solutions valid for the whole range of time variables are in the form of integrals which are laborious to evaluate numerically, solutions have been obtained by the finite difference method of Chapter 8. The temperature distributions thus obtained are given in Fig. 9.15 for $\frac{\delta_2}{\delta_1} = 2$.

The temperature at the junction and the "penetration depths" are given in Figs. 9.16 and 9.17 for $\delta_2/\delta_1 = 1\cdot5$, $2\cdot0$ and $4\cdot0$. The penetration depth as defined for $\xi_{\beta,1}$ by Eq. (9.1.31a) indicates the distance from the junction within which non-uniform temperatures prevail; the definition of $\xi_{\beta,2}$ is analogous and given by Eq. (9.1.31b).

Here again there are many cases where it is of interest to assume that the rate of heat flow is given at the surface. The terms $h_f(T_f - T_1)$ and $h_f(T_f - T_2)$ in Eqs. (9.4.1) and (9.4.2) are then replaced by constants or functions of the time. In order to obtain simple analytical solutions, these functions are assumed to be $\rho c \delta_1 D_1 t^{n/2}$ and $\rho c \delta_2 D_2 t^{n/2}$ respectively. Introducing the quantity $x^* = x/\sqrt{\varkappa}$ and the temperature differences ϑ_1 and ϑ_2 as defined in Eq. (9.1.47) the differential equations for heat conduction become

$$\frac{\partial \vartheta_1}{\partial t} = \frac{\partial^2 \vartheta_1}{\partial x^{*2}} + D_1 t^{n/2}, \quad 0 \leqslant x^* < \infty \qquad (9.4.11)$$

$$\frac{\partial \vartheta_2}{\partial t} = \frac{\partial^2 \vartheta_2}{\partial x^{*2}} + D_2 t^{n/2}, \quad -\infty < x^* \leqslant 0 \qquad (9.4.12)$$

As previously, a constant initial temperature T_i is assumed, hence $\vartheta_1 = \vartheta_2 = 0$ at $t = 0$. The boundary conditions are the same as in Eqs. (9.4.7)–(9.4.9) except that ξ is replaced by x^*. The solution is again found with

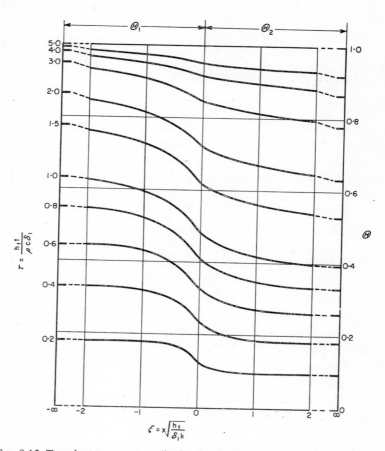

FIG. 9.15. Transient temperature distribution in the shell of Fig. 9.14. Thickness ratio $\delta_2/\delta_1 = 2$.

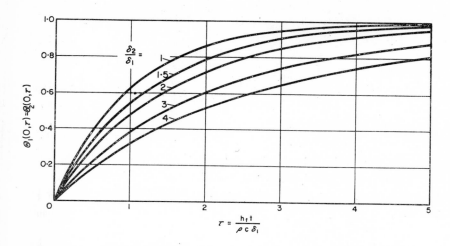

FIG. 9.16. The shell of Fig. 9.14. The temperature at the junction as a function of the non-dimensional time. Thickness ratios $\delta_2/\delta_1 = 1\cdot5$, 2, 3 and 4.

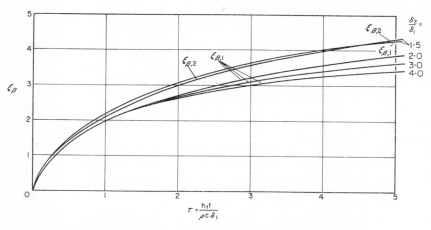

FIG. 9.17. The shell of Fig. 9.14. Approximate values of the penetration depth on both sides of the junction as a function of the non-dimensional time for a range of the thickness ratios $\delta_2/\delta_1 = 1\cdot5$ to 4.

the help of the Laplace transformation and follows the same lines as in Sections 7.4 and 9.1.4. With $\sigma^* = \delta_1/\delta_2$ the result is

$$\vartheta_1 = \frac{D_1}{1+\frac{1}{2}n}\, t^{1+\frac{n}{2}} + \frac{\Gamma\left(1+\frac{1}{2}n\right)}{1+\sigma^*}\,(D_2-D_1)(4t)^{1+\frac{n}{2}}\,i^{n+2}\mathrm{erfc}\left(\frac{x^*}{2\sqrt{t}}\right) \qquad (9.4.13)$$

$$\vartheta_2 = \frac{D_2}{1+\frac{1}{2}n}\, t^{1+\frac{n}{2}} + \frac{\Gamma\left(1+\frac{1}{2}n\right)}{1+\sigma^*}\,\sigma^*(D_1-D_2)(4t)^{1+\frac{n}{2}}\,i^{n+2}\mathrm{erfc}\left(\frac{-x^*}{2\sqrt{t}}\right)$$

$$(9.4.14)$$

The case of a thin skin (shell) supported by a frame with both skin and frame being aerodynamically heated from one side, has been treated by Schuh (Ref. 9.21); thereby the temperature in the frame was assumed uniform.

References

9.1   HOFF, N. J., Structural problems of future aircraft, Proceedings of the Third Anglo-American Aeronautical Conference p. 103–110, the Royal Aeronautical Society, London (1951).

9.2   PARKES, E. W., Transient thermal stresses in wings, *Aircraft Engineering* XXV, 298, 373–378 (1953).

9.3   POHLE, F. V. and OLIVER, H., Temperature distribution and thermal stresses in a model of a supersonic wing, *J. Aero. Sci.* **21**, 1, 8–16 (1954).

9.4.   SCHUH, H., Transient temperature distributions and thermal stresses in a skin-shear web configuration at high-speed flight for a wide range of parameters, *J. Aero. Sci.* **22**, 12, 829–836 (1955).

9.5   HOFF, N. J., Thermal buckling of supersonic wing panels, *J. Aero. Sci.* **23**, 11, 1019–1028 (1956).

9.6   BROOKS, W. A. JR., Temperature and thermal-stress distributions in some structural elements heated at a constant rate, NACA TN 4306 (1958).

9.7   CHEN, S.-Y., Transient temperature distribution and thermal stresses in a hypersonic unsymmetrical wing structure at angles of attack, A.S.M.E. Paper No. 58-SA-63 (1958).

9.8   HOFF, N. J., Comparison of radiant and conductive heat transfer in a supersonic wing, *J. Aero. Sci.* **23**, 7, 694–696 (1956).

9.9   GATEWOOD, B. E., *Thermal Stresses*, McGraw-Hill, New York (1957).

9.10   GOLDBERG, M. A., Investigation of the temperature distribution and thermal stresses in a hypersonic wing structure, *J. Aero. Sci.* **23** 11, 981–990 (1956).

9.11   CHEN, S.-Y., Comments on "Investigation of the temperature distribution and thermal stresses in a hypersonic wing structure", *J. Aero. Sci.* **24**, 7, 544–545 (1957).

9.12 BARBER, A. D., WEINER, J. H. and BOLEY, B. A., An analysis of the effect of thermal contact resistance in a sheet-stringer structure, *J. Aero. Sci.* **24**, 3, 232–234 (1957).

9.13 FRANK, I., Transient temperature distribution in aircraft structures, *J. Aero. Sci.* **25**, 4, 265–267 (1958).

9.14 GRIFFITH, G. E. and MILTONBERGER, G. H., Some effects of joint conductivity on the temperatures and thermal stresses in aerodynamically heated skin-stiffener combinations, NACA TN 3699 (1956).

9.15 QUINVILLE, J. A., Transient temperature distribution in typical aircraft structures due to aerodynamic heating. Thermal analyzer solution, Northrop Aircr. Inc. Rep. NAI 54–453 (1954).

9.16 QUINVILLE, J. A. and GORDON, C. K., Transient temperature distribution in typical aircraft structures due to aerodynamic heating. Lumped parameter solution, Northrop. Aircr. Inc. Rep. NAI 54–454 (1954).

9.17 AMBROSIO, A. and ISHIMOTO, T., Analytical studies of aircraft structures exposed to transient external heating, Pt. 1 and 2. WADC Tech. Rep. 54–579 : 1 and 54–579 : 2 (1954).

9.18 AMBROSIO, A., BUSSEL, B. and MACINNES, W. F., Temperature distributions in a typical aircraft structure due to transient external heating, Vol. I. T-33 Airplane. WADC Techn. Rep. 52–216/1 (1953).

9.19 GATEWOOD, B. E., Approximate procedures for transient thermal stresses in missile structures, I.A.S. Preprint No. 578 (1956).

9.20 POHLE, F. V., LARDNER, T. J. and FRENCH, F. W., Temperature distribution and thermal stresses in structures with contact resistances, Polytech. Inst. Brooklyn, Dep. Aero. Engng. and Appl. Mech. Rep. No. 557 (1960).

9.21 SCHUH, H., Temperature distributions, thermal stresses and thermal buckling of thin skins supported by frames, Third Int. Congr. Aero. Sci., Paper No. ICAS–42, The Institute of the Aerospace Sciences, New York (1962).

CHAPTER 10

ANALOGUES

10.1 General

One must distinguish between direct and indirect analogues or analogue computers. In a direct analogue the analogous variable has the same significance everywhere within the analogue system, while in an indirect analogue this need not be so and solutions are obtained with the help of a mathematical model. A direct analogue to one-dimensional heat flow can be an electrical network of capacitances and resistances in which there is a direct analogy between corresponding points in the thermal and in the electrical system. In an example of an indirect analogue the equation of heat conduction and the boundary conditions are transformed into finite difference equations which are the mathematical model to be solved by an analogue. Indirect analogues may range from simple devices for solving particular mathematical problems to general purpose computers. Only some examples of the former type of indirect analogues are dealt with here.

Analogues can further be divided into continuous and discrete types; in the first, continua such as metal sheets are used, and in the second type lumped elements such as resistances and capacitances are used.

Among the many possible systems, only mechanical and electrical systems have been used to any extent in heat flow problems. Analogue systems become much simpler if the relation between the rates of heat flow and the temperature differences is linear.

The scale of analogous quantities can be chosen at will and this is done from certain practical points of view. For direct analogues the similarity laws to be discussed later on in Chapter 11 are automatically satisfied and one need not consider them specifically, except in cases of transient heat flow, where the time as a physical quantity of the original problem is usually retained in the analogue. The time scales in the original problems and in their analogues are in many cases different, but this is of no real significance.

10.2 Steady heat flow

There is not much interest in analogues for one-dimensional heat flow, since calculations are easier in these cases. For two-dimensional heat flows, analytical and numerical solutions often become difficult because of the shape of the boundaries. Steady heat flow by conduction is governed by the Laplace equation which is important in many branches of physics and engineering. A well-known mechanical analogue of the continuous type consists of the viscous flow of a liquid between two plates; if the motion is sufficiently slow, the rate of mass flow corresponds to the rate of heat flow and the pressure to the temperature (Ref. 10.4). The streamlines of the flow can be made visible by introducing dyes; lines of constant pressure (corresponding to isothermals) are orthogonal to the streamlines. Boundaries of any shape can be placed in the flow field. Even heat flow with internal sources can be dealt with by this method, if there are sources of liquid emanating from the walls (Ref. 10.5).

In an electrical analogue of the continuous type one uses electrically conducting papers or an electrolytic tank. Electrically conducting papers of constant thickness are available for various values of the specific resistance. The boundaries are obtained by cutting the paper to the desired form and the external heat transfer conditions there can be represented by suitable resistances between the boundaries and the reference points for the temperatures of the external medium. The voltage at any point is analogous to the temperature, and the electrical current density to the density of the heat flow. Lines of constant voltage can be found with the help of a voltmeter and a contact sliding on the surface of the paper. The density of the heat flow is obtained from the voltage gradient in the same direction and from the resistivity R of the sheet, which is the resistance between two parallel edges of a square and is independent of the size of the square, i.e.

$$i_n = -\frac{1}{R}\frac{\partial V}{\partial n} \tag{10.1}$$

where n is a distance in a direction characterized by the subscript n. Composite bodies can be simulated by using sheets of different thicknesses. Heat sources can be represented by local supplies of electrical current.

In an electrolytic tank the metal sheet is replaced by a conducting liquid, otherwise the arrangement is similar except that alternating currents must be used to avoid polarization of the liquid.

An electrical analogue of the discrete type consists of networks of resistances where each point corresponds to a point in the heat flow field and the resistances between the mesh-points correspond to the specific resistance of the field.

10.3 Transient heat flow

A mechanical analogue for transient heat flow by conduction which uses liquid flow in tubes and capillaries is known by the name of Hydrocal (Ref. 10.6). This analogue is of the discrete type with vertical tubes representing heat reservoirs and capillaries representing thermal resistances. The rate of fluid flow between two vertical tubes is

$$Q_{n-1,n} = K_{n-1,n}(H_n - H_{n-1}) \qquad (10.2)$$

where H_{n-1} and H_n are the heights of the fluid levels in the tubes $n-1$ and n and $K_{n-1,n}$ is the reciprocal of the resistance for the fluid flow in the capillary. The equation of motion for a system of tubes as in Fig. 10.1 is

$$W_n \frac{dH_n}{dt} = K_{n,n-1}(H_{n-1} - H_n) + K_{n,n+1}(H_{n+1} - H_n) \qquad (10.3)$$

where the subscript n refers to the nth tube, $K_{n,n-1}$ is the reciprocal of the capillary resistance between the tube n and $n-1$ and W_n is the cross-section of area of the nth tube.

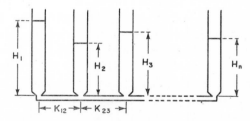

FIG. 10.1. A fluid flow analogue of the discrete type ("Hydrocal").

Obviously Eq. (10.3) is of the same form as Eq. (8.5.1), if W_n, $K_{n,n-1}$ and H_n are the quantities analogous to the heat capacities, conductances and temperatures. In the equipment for this mechanical analogue, each tube has a tap so that initially the level of the liquid in the tube can be adjusted to correspond to the initial temperature of the corresponding heat reservoir. An additional tap common to all tubes is often arranged so that the flow of the liquid can be stopped at any moment for reading the instantaneous liquid levels. Boundary conditions corresponding to heat transfer by forced convection at the surfaces can be satisfied by keeping the end tubes at a level corresponding to the temperature of the external medium and connecting these tubes to neighbouring ones by a capillary whose flow resistance is equal to the reciprocal of the external heat transfer coefficient. If the temperature of the external medium is constant, the liquid level in the corresponding tube is kept constant by using a tank with a large cross-section instead of a tube. The analogue can be used for complex bodies and for non-linear problems which arise in the case of thermal properties varying with temperature, of radiative heat transfer at the surfaces and so on. Extensions are also possible to two- and three-dimensional heat flow and even to ablation problems, but then the equipment becomes more complicated. An application of this mechanical analogue to a problem of heat flow in structures is given in Ref. 10.7.

For linear problems electrical analogues are easier to handle and more flexible than mechanical ones. A direct analogue of the discrete type can be constructed with the help of electrical resistances and capacitances and such an arrangement for one-dimensional heat flow is shown in Fig. 10.2.

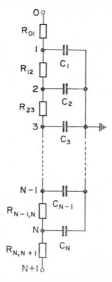

FIG. 10.2. An example of an electrical analogue of the direct and discrete type for one-dimensional heat flow with capacitors and resistors.

Heat reservoirs correspond to the capacities and thermal resistances to the electrical resistances as follows by comparison with Fig. 8.10. Further, the voltage at each point corresponds to a temperature and the electrical current between two capacitances to a heat flow, both quantities referring to analogous points in the two systems. If the initial temperature distributions are arbitrary, the points $0, 1, \ldots, N+1$ must initially be connected to electrical sources, so that an analogous initial distribution of the voltages at these points is obtained; at the start of heat transfer these connections are broken unless there are internal heat sources. As mentioned in Section 10.1

the time scale can be chosen at will and there are two practical possibilities. The time constants can be made large, so that all changes occur slowly and can be read directly on instruments or registered by electromechanical devices (plotters): or the time constants are small, so that the whole process can be repeated many times per second and may be displayed as a standing pattern on a cathode ray tube. The advantage of the last method lies in the possibility of using smaller capacitances and making all changes of the parameters visible immediately; the disadvantage is the greater complexity of the equipment. The solution of non-linear problems requires more elaborate equipment. For details see Ref. 10.1.

An example of an indirect analogue is a method due to Liebmann, Ref. 8.12. The starting point is the implicit finite difference equation Eq. (8.7.1) which re-written with voltages instead of temperatures becomes:

$$V_{n,m} - V_{n,m-1} = p(V_{n-1,m} - 2V_{n,m} + V_{n+1,m}), \tag{10.4}$$

In contrast to Chapter 8 this equation is used here in a step-by-step procedure where the voltages at the time $t = (m-1)\Delta t$ and at all places $x = n\Delta x$, $(n = 1,...N)$ are known and the corresponding voltages at $t = m\Delta t$ are sought. The analogue for solving Eq. (10.4) is the circuit of Fig. 10.3; the balance of the electrical currents at node n corresponds to Eq. (10.4) if all nodes are kept at the voltages indicated in Fig. 10.3 and if

$$R_p = pR_x \tag{10.5}$$

R_x can be chosen at will. The computer based on this circuit is shown in Fig. 10.4. The voltages $V_{n,m-1}$ already known are adjusted by sliding resistances R_0', R_1', ... R_n' and then the unknown voltages can be read by connecting a voltmeter to the points $1, 2, ..., n$, one at a time. The resistances $R_{0,1}$, ... and $R_{p,1}$ ... have to be large compared with the resistances R' so that the voltages $V_{0,m-1}$, $V_{1,m-1}$, ... depend only on the position of the resistances R'. In order to avoid adjustments by hand, servo-mechanisms and automatic recording units have been proposed. As equipment of this type becomes more elaborate, it would become a special-purpose analogue-computer.

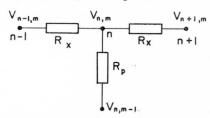

FIG. 10.3. The basic circuit for an electrical analogue of the indirect and discrete type due to Liebmann (Ref. 8.12).

It depends on the circumstances whether a direct analogue, an analogue computer or a digital computer is preferable for solving a given problem. For steady heat flow problems with linear relations between the rate of

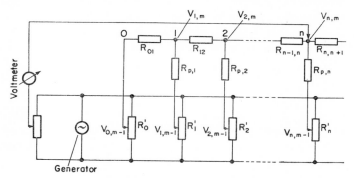

FIG. 10.4. A computer based on the basic circuit of Fig. 10.3.

heat flow and the temperature differences, direct analogues can be easily constructed, often largely with standard laboratory equipment. For moderate accuracies these analogues are useful and inexpensive, particularly for two-dimensional cases. Analogues are valuable for transient problems, when parameters in a design have to be optimized, and when a large number of temperature distributions of a similar type have to be found.

If available, the general purpose digital computer is best where moderate or small amounts of work of varying types are involved. It also has great advantages whenever "non-linear" boundary conditions or similar complications occur.

References

General:

10.1 KARPLUS, W. J., *Analog Simulation*, MacGraw-Hill, New York (1958).
10.2 KARPLUS, W. J. and SOROKA, W. W., *Analog Methods—Computation and Simulation*, MacGraw-Hill, New York (1959).
10.3 SOROKA, W. W., Simulation in science and technology. *Appl. Mech. Reviews* **13**, 9, 621–623 (1960).

Particular:

10.4 HELE-SHAW, H. S., The flow of water, *Nature* **58**, 34–36 (1898), The motion of a perfect liquid, *Proc. Roy. Inst.* **16**, 49–64 (1899).
10.5 MOORE, A. D., Fields from fluid flow mappers, *J. Appl. Phys.* **20**, 790–804 (1949).
10.6 MOORE, A. D., The hydrocal, *Ind. Engng. Chem.* **28**, 704–708 (1936).
10.7 KNUTH, E. L. and KUMM, E. L., Application of hydraulic analog method to one-dimensional transient heat flow, *Jet Prop.* **26**, 649–654, 659 (1956).

CHAPTER 11

SIMILARITY LAWS AND MODEL-TESTING FOR HEAT FLOW IN STRUCTURES†

SIMILARITY laws can be obtained from a non-dimensional form of the fundamental equations of a problem. Such equations have been used previously, especially in simple cases when general results were sought. The above method is used here, but the same results could also be obtained by dimensional analysis.

If similarity laws could be found, it would be possible to calculate in a simple way the influence of changes in the scale, in the flight plan, or in the thermal properties of the materials from the known temperature distribution of a certain case; or to give requirements for laboratory simulation of heating on the prototype or on models. In this chapter similarity laws are derived and some applications are discussed. The treatment is theoretical and refers to temperature problems only. For instance, no discussion is given here as to whether model testing is practical, either for finding temperature distributions only, or for mechanical strength tests under elevated transient temperatures. In fact, one can foresee many difficulties in model testing, and its practical importance is open to doubt at present. However, laboratory simulation of the heating of structures is already being widely used. In this connection, similarity laws are of some interest.

A number of books deal with similarity laws and model testing in general (see for instance Refs. 11.1 and 11.2), but only a few papers treat corresponding aspects in the heating of structures (Refs. 11.3 and 11.4).

---

† This chapter deals largely with the same problems as treated earlier by Sobey (Ref. 11.3.) This paper was known to the author and he used it to a large extent for this chapter. However, in comparison with Ref. 11.3 the approach is somewhat different here, being more in line with the rest of the monograph, but the conclusions are, by and large, the same. In some cases the similarity laws could be relaxed here, because regard was taken of the analytical expressions for heat transfer coefficients. The author is indebted to Mr. A. J. Sobey for reading and commenting upon an early version of this chapter.

11.1 Internal heat flow by conduction only. Integral structures

11.1.1 *External heat flow by forced convection*

We assume for the present either an integral structure or one in which the similarity conditions for finite conductances across interfaces are satisfied, as discussed later on in Section 11.4. For simplicity, the thermal properties are first assumed constant, but in Section 11.3 the influence of variable thermal properties is investigated separately. Heat transfer by free convection or by thermal radiation inside the structure is assumed to be either absent or negligible; further, on external surfaces the losses by thermal radiation are considered to be small. Evaporation or melting is excluded. The equation of heat conduction in a Cartesian coordinate system reads

$$\frac{\partial T}{\partial t} = \varkappa_M \left(\frac{\partial^2 T}{\partial x^2} + \frac{\partial^2 T}{\partial y^2} + \frac{\partial^2 T}{\partial z^2} \right) \tag{11.1.1}$$

$\varkappa_M$ is the thermal diffusivity of the material of the structure. Initially the distribution of the temperature in the structure is:

$$t = 0; \qquad T = T_i^*(x, y, z) \tag{11.1.2}$$

On external surfaces the boundary conditions are of the form (see Section 3.1.3)

$$-k_M \left(\frac{\partial T}{\partial n} \right)_{w1} = [h_f^*(x, y, z, t)]_{w1} [T_{aw}^*(x, y, z, t) - T]_{w1} \tag{11.1.3}$$

The subscript $w1$ characterizes outer surfaces and n is a distance normal to these surfaces and directed towards the inside of the structure. The parameters of the external heat flow, here denoted by h_f^* † and T_{aw}^*, may vary with time and along the surface of the structure ‡ ; to each of these parameters as well as to the initial temperature there corresponds a constant reference value: h_f, T_{aw} and T_i. Inside the structure the rate of heat flow may be zero on certain boundaries, but this yields no additional similarity conditions.

The following non-dimensional quantities are introduced with L as a characteristic length of the structure

$$\xi = \frac{x}{L}, \qquad \eta = \frac{y}{L}, \qquad \zeta = \frac{z}{L} \tag{11.1.4}$$

---

† h is here assumed to be independent of the wall temperatures; for turbulent boundary layers and high supersonic Mach numbers the deviations from this assumption may be large (see Chapter 2); this dependence on T_w could be taken into account by a method similar to those of Section 11.3 for temperature-dependent thermal properties.

‡ The variation of T_{aw} along the surface is small (see Chapter 2) and can usually be neglected.

$$\tau = \frac{\varkappa_M t}{L^2} \tag{11.1.5}$$

Considering bodies and structures which have similar geometry, Eq. (11.1.1) is transformed into a non-dimensional form with Θ_I as a suitable non-dimensional temperature:

$$\frac{\partial \Theta_I}{\partial \tau} = \frac{\partial^2 \Theta_I}{\partial \xi^2} + \frac{\partial^2 \Theta_I}{\partial \eta^2} + \frac{\partial^2 \Theta_I}{\partial \zeta^2}, \tag{11.1.6}$$

where

$$\Theta_I = \frac{T - T_i}{T_{aw} - T_i} \tag{11.1.7}$$

Equations (11.1.2) and (11.1.3) become:

$$\tau = 0; \quad \Theta_I = F_i \tag{11.1.8}$$

and

$$-\left(\frac{\partial \Theta_I}{\partial (n/L)}\right)_{w1} = \text{Bi}\,[F_h (F_{aw} - \Theta_I)]_{w1} \tag{11.1.9}$$

In these equations

$$\text{Bi} = \frac{h_f L}{k_M} \tag{11.1.10}$$

is a non-dimensional heat transfer coefficient, and

$$F_i = \frac{T_i^* - T_i}{T_{aw} - T_i}, \quad F_h = \frac{h_f^*}{h_f}, \quad F_{aw} = \frac{T_{aw}^* - T_i}{T_{aw} - T_i} \tag{11.1.11}$$

Similar solutions of Eq. (11.1.6) are of the form

$$\Theta_I = \Theta_I (\text{Bi}; \xi, \eta, \zeta, \tau) \tag{11.1.12}$$

They satisfy the initial and the boundary conditions, Eqs. (11.1.8) and (11.1.9) and depend only on one similarity parameter, Bi, and on the non-dimensional space and time variables given by Eqs. (11.1.4) and (11.1.5). If no additional parameters are to occur in Eq. (11.1.12), the initial temperature distribution must depend on ξ, η and ζ only:

$$F_i = F_i (\xi, \eta, \zeta) \tag{11.1.13}$$

and similarly there must be for F_h and F_{aw}:

$$F_j = F_j (\xi, \eta, \zeta, \tau), \quad j = h \text{ or aw} \tag{11.1.14}$$

If these requirements are satisfied, the distributions of h_f^* and T_{aw}^* are similar in space and time and that of T_i^* is similar in space.

In flight the local heat transfer parameters h_f^* and T_{aw}^* depend on the external flow field and this in turn depends on the altitude H^*, the flight Mach number M^* and the atmospheric conditions, for which a standard is assumed here. Consider similar flight plans with M^*/M and H^*/H being functions of τ only, where M and H are constant reference values. According to Chapter 2 h_f^* depends in a general way on M^* and Re_x (the local Reynolds number), and T_{aw}^* on the ambient temperature and M^*. Therefore similar flight plans are incompatible with Eq. (11.1.14) except in particular cases, since similarity requires the functions in Eq. (11.1.14) to depend only on the variables ξ, η, ζ, τ, but not on any parameter.

If aerodynamic heating is to be simulated in a laboratory, then h_f^* and T_{aw}^* are determined from the flight conditions to be simulated. Similarity for F_h and F_{aw} can then be easily preserved, even if a model is used, i.e. if either $\varkappa$ or L, or both, differ from corresponding values of the prototype.

These results can be summarized as:

Similarity law 1.1:

Assume bodies or structures of similar geometry with (a) internal heat flow by conduction only, (b) heat transfer on external surfaces following a linear relation between the rate of heat flow and the temperature difference, (c) constant thermal properties and (d) negligible thermal resistances across interfaces† of any joints present. Then the temperature distributions are similar under the following conditions: (1) The similarity parameter Bi is the same, (2) the distribution of the parameters for external heat transfer must be similar in space and in time, that of the initial temperature must be similar in space and (3) the thermal properties at similar points must be in a constant ratio, if the bodies or the structures are composed of different materials.

The rate of heat flow at the surface of the structure is important for model testing and it is:

$$q_w^* = -k_M \left(\frac{\partial T}{\partial n}\right)_{w1} = -\frac{k_M}{L}(T_{aw}-T_i)\left(\frac{\partial \Theta_I}{\partial (n/L)}\right)_{w1} \qquad (11.1.15)$$

A corresponding non-dimensional expression is:

$$\frac{q_w^* L}{k_M(T_{aw}-T_i)} = F_q(\mathrm{Bi}, \xi, \eta, \zeta, \tau) \qquad (11.1.16)$$

As a particular case when similar flight plans are possible consider sudden acceleration to a constant speed at a constant altitude. Then

---

† Unless the thermal resistances satisfy the similarity conditions of Section 11.3.

$M^* = M$. Assume heat transfer as on an ideal flat plate at zero incidence with either laminar or turbulent flow along the entire length of the plate. Then according to Section 2.3.2, to a good approximation (see footnote † on page 18):

$$h_f^* \sim \rho_\infty c_{p,\infty} u_\infty \left(\frac{u_\infty x}{\nu_\infty} \right)^{-l} f(M) \qquad (11.1.17)$$

$\rho_\infty, c_{p,\infty}, \nu_\infty$ are respectively the density, the specific heat at constant pressure and the kinematic viscosity, all at ambient conditions; u_∞ is the flight speed, x the distance from the leading edge, l the exponent in the friction law and $f(M)$ the ratio of the compressible to the incompressible friction coefficient (see Chapter 2). $c_{p,\infty}$ and μ_∞ do not change much for altitudes up to about 140 km or about 500,000 ft. Then from (11.1.17) it follows that $h_f \sim (\rho_\infty u_\infty)^{1-l} L^{-l} f(M)$; now $F_h = F_h(\xi)$ and hence similarity in h_f^* is satisfied. Further

$$\text{Bi} \sim \frac{(\rho_\infty u_\infty L)^{1-l}}{k_M} f(M) \qquad (11.1.18)$$

If the same structure (i.e. L and k_M being the same) is exposed to external heating due to different flight conditions, then it follows from (11.1.18) and condition (1) of similarity law 1.1 that only one of the two flight parameters M and H can be chosen as desired, because ρ_∞ depends on H, and u_∞ on H and M. The initial temperature distribution must also be similar and (3) of similarity law 1.1 satisfied.

For structures of different size and made of different materials, but of similar geometry 3 of the 4 quantities H, M, L and k_M can be chosen as desired.

Next, we consider the simulation of aerodynamic heating in the laboratory with the help of radiation lamps or other suitable heat sources. These must be so controlled that the desired rate of heat flow on the surface of the structure is simulated as closely as possible. For this purpose use is often made of a servo-controller and a computer to which the values of the external heat transfer parameters h_f^* and T_{aw}^* are supplied.

If the prototype, i.e. L and k_M being the same, is tested under conditions of simulated heating, the heat transfer coefficient h_f must be the same as in flight as follows from Eq. (11.1.10), but the adiabatic wall temperature and the initial temperature can be different. In this case the temperature levels of the structure are different in the test and in flight.

Tests on models are made in order to save expense, therefore models have to be of smaller size than the prototype (L a characteristic length)

$$L_m < L_p \qquad (11.1.19)$$

and at the surfaces the rates of heating are to be lower

$$(q_w^*)_m < (q_w^*)_p \qquad (11.1.20)$$

The subscript m refers to the model and p to the prototype. In a number of cases there is also a limit on the time scale of the model, because too rapid a heating rate may necessitate expensive instrumentation or may be disadvantageous in some other way. Therefore a possible third condition for model-testing is that events in the model should not occur faster than in the prototype:

$$t_m \geqslant t_p \qquad (11.1.21)$$

Again, the similarity law requires that the Biot modulus (see Eq. (11.1.10)) be the same. The inequality (11.1.20) yields, because of Eq. (11.1.16)

$$\left[\frac{k_M(T_{aw} - T_i)}{L} \right]_m < \left[\frac{k_M(T_{aw} - T_i)}{L} \right]_p \qquad (11.1.22)$$

If a limitation on the time scale is important, one obtains from Eqs. (11.1.5) and (11.1.21)

$$\left[\frac{L^2 (\rho c)_M}{k_M} \right]_m \geqslant \left[\frac{L^2 (\rho c)_M}{k_M} \right]_p \qquad (11.1.23)$$

Since $(\rho c)_M$ does not vary much among the materials in question, with a few exceptions at most in the ratio $1:2$ according to Table 7.2, it follows from (11.1.23) that the heat conductivity of the model should in most cases be smaller than that of the prototype because of the inequality (11.1.19). From (11.1.22) it follows that the rate of heating on the model can be reduced to any desired degree by choosing a sufficiently small temperature difference $T_{aw} - T_i$ in the test.

For illustration consider two examples. If, as assumed in this section, there are no requirements about the absolute level of the temperature, (11.1.22) could be satisfied in principle by choosing a low value of $T_{aw} - T_i$ for the model. Then the most stringent requirement comes from condition (11.1.21). Consider an aluminium-alloy prototype and a stainless steel model and $t_m/t_p = 2$; for τ to be the same for the prototype and the model, it follows that $L_m/L_p = 0.43$. Next, consider a stainless steel structure with $L_m/L_p = 1/6$ and $t_m/t_p = 2$. With $(\rho c)_M$ initially assumed to be of the same order of magnitude for the prototype and the model, one obtains: $(k_M)_m/(k_M)_p \approx 0.014$; hence from Table 7.2 models would have to be made of non-conducting materials such as plastics or glass.

11.1.2 *Rate of heat flow given at the outer surfaces*

The concept of "severe" aerodynamic heating was introduced in Section 1.2. It is used when the temperature increases at the heated surfaces are so small that they do not influence the rate of heat flow there, and this quantity can therefore be considered as given. The previous boundary condition, Eq. (11.1.3), is now replaced by

$$-k_M \left(\frac{\partial T}{\partial n} \right)_{w1} = q_w^*(x, y, z, t) \qquad (11.1.24)$$

and Eq. (11.1.7) is replaced by

$$\Theta_{II} = \frac{k_M (T - T_i)}{q_w L} \qquad (11.1.25)$$

q_w is the value of q_w^* at a characteristic point and at a fixed time. The non-dimensional quantities in Eqs. (11.1.4) and (11.1.5) are retained and Eq. (11.1.24) becomes

$$-\left[\frac{\partial \Theta_{II}}{\partial (n/L)} \right]_{w1} = \frac{q_w^*(x, y, z, t)}{q_w} \qquad (11.1.26)$$

A solution of Eq. (11.1.6) which satisfies the initial condition (11.1.8), with Θ_{II} instead of Θ_I, and the boundary condition (11.1.26) is

$$\Theta_{II} = \Theta_{II}(\xi, \eta, \zeta, \tau) \qquad (11.1.27)$$

No similarity parameter is required now, but only similarity in the geometry and in the distribution of the initial temperature Eq. (11.1.13), provided that the distribution of the rate of heat flow is:

$$\frac{q_w^*}{q_w} = F_q(\xi, \eta, \zeta, \tau) \qquad (11.1.28)$$

Again assuming steady-state values for the heat transfer parameters at any instant, then

$$F_q(\xi, \eta, \zeta, \tau) = F_q^{(1)}(\xi, \eta, \zeta) F_q^{(2)}(\tau) \qquad (11.1.29)$$

Similar flight plans compatible with Eq. (11.1.29) are, again, not possible except in special cases such as discussed before, because $q_w = h_f T_{aw}$.

Summarizing, one obtains:

Similarity law 1.2:

> Assume bodies or structures of similar geometry and (a), (c), and (d) of similarity law 1.1; assume further that the rates of heat flow at the surfaces are given. Then the temperature distributions are similar under the following conditions:
> (1) The distributions of the initial temperatures must be similar in space and that of the rates of heat flow at the surfaces must be similar in space and in time and (2) the third condition of similarity law 1.1 must be satisfied.

If the same structures, or structures of different size and of different materials but similar geometry, are exposed to different flight conditions, only similarity in F_i and F_q is required; if similar flight plans can be found there is no restriction on H and M. The temperature level is proportional to $(q_w L)/k_M$ as follows from Eq. (11.1.25).

For laboratory simulation of aerodynamic heating of a prototype, only the distributions F_i of the initial temperatures and, of course, that of the rates of heat flow need be similar. The same is also valid for models. The model requirements (11.1.19) and (11.1.20) are satisfied, because L and q_w can be chosen as desired, and for the third model requirement (11.1.21) the same applies as in Section 11.1.1.

11.2 Internal heat flow by conduction, free convection and thermal radiation. Integral structures

11.2.1 *External heat transfer by forced convection and thermal radiation*

It is now assumed that the structure experiences heat transfer on its outer surfaces not only by convection but also by thermal radiation; the corresponding boundary condition is

$$-k_M\left(\frac{\partial T}{\partial n}\right)_{w1} = h_f^*(T_{aw}^*-T)_{w1}-\varepsilon\, C_\sigma(T^4-T_\infty^4)_{w1} \qquad (11.2.1)$$

where ε is the coefficient of thermal emissivity, C_σ the radiation constant of a black body and T_∞ the ambient temperature (see also Section 3.6). Even if thermal radiation is important in the balance of heat flow in Eq. (11.2.1), the contribution due to the term T_∞^4 on the right-hand side of the equation is in most cases unimportant, and would complicate the following analysis. This term is therefore neglected and Eq. (11.2.1) is re-written as

$$-k_M\left(\frac{\partial T}{\partial n}\right)_{w1} = h_f^*(T_{aw}^*-T)_{w1}-\varepsilon\, C_\sigma[(T)_{w1}]^4 \qquad (11.2.2)$$

Inside the structure, heat transfer is assumed to occur not only by conduction but also by free convection of the air inside structural cavities and by thermal radiation between internal surfaces. The boundary conditions at inside surfaces are of the form

$$-k_M\left(\frac{\partial T}{\partial n}\right)_{w2} = [h_{it}^*(T_{it}-T)]_{w2}+\sum_j [C_{R,j}^*(T_j^4-T^4)]_{w2} \qquad (11.2.3)$$

h_{it}^* is the heat transfer coefficient for free convection inside the structure and T_{it} the respective reference temperature. The heat capacity of the fluid inside the structure is neglected; in many cases this is permissible when air is the fluid, but not for a liquid such as the fuel. Therefore T_{it} depends only on the temperature distribution in the structure and will not appear in Eq. (11.2.12) among the parameters determining a solution of Θ_{III}. The subscript $w2$ refers to inner surfaces. $C_{R,j}^{*}$ is the local radiation coefficient. The summation on the right-hand side of Eq. (11.2.3) is to be made for all surface elements in radiative heat transfer with the point considered; strictly, the sum should be replaced by an integral. The heat transfer coefficient h_{it}^{*} for free convection depends on the pressure p_{it} inside the structure (see also later in this section). It is assumed here that this pressure is related to the ambient air pressure and hence also to the altitude. This would not be true for pressurized cabins or the like.

The non-dimensional quantities introduced by Eqs. (11.1.4) and (11.1.5) are retained, but the non-dimensional temperature is now:

$$\Theta_{III} = \frac{T}{T_i} \tag{11.2.4}$$

Because of thermal radiation and free convection, the absolute level of the temperature is now important. Since the expression for the heat transfer coefficient h_{it}^{*} is complex, it would not be practical to retain it when proceeding with the analysis. From Eqs. (3.5.7) and (3.5.1) there follows:

$$h_{it}^{*} = C \frac{k_{it}}{L} \left[\frac{g L^3 \beta_{it} \mathrm{Pr}}{\nu_{it}^2} \right]^{a} |T - T_{it}|^{a} \tag{11.2.5}$$

where T_1 and T_2 in Eq. (3.5.1a) have been replaced by T and T_{it} respectively. a is between 1/3 and 1/4. The index "it" refers to the medium experiencing free convection. This medium is assumed to be an ideal gas with $\beta_{it} = 1/T_{it}$ and with $\rho_{it} = p_{it}/R T_{it}$; p_{it} is the pressure of the gas inside the structure and R the gas constant. According to Section 3.5 the material properties of the medium are to be taken at the temperature $T_m = \frac{1}{2}(T + T_{it})$; if they depend on temperature in a similar way as the quantities in Eq. (11.3.2), one may put

$$\mu_{it} = \mu(T_i) f_\mu\left(\Theta_{III}, \frac{T_{it}}{T_i}\right) \tag{11.2.6}$$

and similar expressions are valid for ρ_{it} and k_{it}; the function f_μ follows from the temperature dependence of μ. Further, in Eq. (11.2.3) $T - T_{it}$ is replaced by $T_i\left(\Theta_{III} - \dfrac{T_{it}}{T_i}\right)$. With these assumptions and modifications one obtains finally from Eq. (11.2.5)

$$h_{it}^{*} = \frac{k_{it}(T_i)}{L} \left[\frac{g L^3 p_{it}^2 \mathrm{Pr}}{[\mu_{it}(T_i)]^2 T_i^2 R^2} \right]^{a} f\left(\Theta_{III}, \frac{T_{it}}{T_i}\right) \tag{11.2.7}$$

where all functions of Θ_{III} and T_{it}/T_i, and the constant C have been collected in one function f.

If re-written in non-dimensional form, the equation of heat conduction becomes the same as Eq. (11.1.6) with Θ_{III} instead of Θ_I, and the boundary conditions are

$$-\left(\frac{\partial\Theta_{III}}{\partial(n/L)}\right)_{w1} = \frac{h_f L}{k_M}\left[F_h\left(\frac{T_{aw}}{T_i}F_{aw}^0 - \Theta_{III}\right)\right]_{w1} - \frac{\varepsilon C_\sigma L T_i^3}{k_M}[(\Theta_{III})_{w1}]^4$$

(11.2.8)

and

$$-\left(\frac{\partial\Theta_{III}}{\partial(n/L)}\right)_{w2} = \frac{k_{it}(T_i)}{k_M}[...]^a\left[F\left(\Theta_{III}, \frac{T_{it}}{T_i}\right)\right]_{w2} +$$

$$+ \sum_j\left[\frac{C_{R,j}^* L T_i^3}{k_M}(\Theta_{III,j}^4 - \Theta_{III}^4)\right]_{w2} \quad (11.2.9)$$

respectively. F_h is defined in Eq. (11.1.11) and

$$F_{aw}^0 = \frac{T_{aw}^*}{T_{aw}}$$

(11.2.10)

is a non-dimensional distribution of the adiabatic wall temperature and [...] in Eq. (11.2.9) means the expression within square brackets on the right-hand side of Eq. (11.2.7). From what has been said in Section 3.6.5 it can be concluded that the emissivity must be the same in similar cases, if values of C_R^* are to be in the same ratio at corresponding points. This ratio is one, because the shape factors of Section 3.6 are the same for bodies or structures of similar geometry.

The initial condition becomes in non-dimensional form

$$t = 0; \quad \Theta_{III} = F_i^0$$

(11.2.11a)

where

$$F_i^0 = \frac{T_i^*}{T_i}$$

(11.2.11b)

A solution of Eq. (11.1.6) satisfying the initial and the boundary conditions is of the general form

$$\Theta_{III} = \Theta_{III}\left(\frac{h_f L}{k_M}, \frac{T_{aw}}{T_i}, \frac{k_{it}(T_i)}{k_M}[...]^a, \frac{C_\sigma L T_i^3}{k_M}, \varepsilon, \xi, \eta, \zeta, \tau\right) (11.2.12)$$

Again, similarity requires that F_h and F_{aw}^0 are functions of ξ, η, ζ and τ only, and F_i^0 is only a function of ξ, η, ζ.

If the heat capacity of the fluid inside the structure is not negligible the ratio of the heat per unit volume ρc of the fluid to that of the material of the structure must be the same in similar cases. This follows from the balance of heat flow for the fluid inside the structure; the fluid can often be assumed to be at a uniform mean temperature.

These results may be summarized as:

Similarity law 2.1:

Assume bodies or structures of similar geometry and (c) and (d) of similarity law 1.1; further, (a) heat transfer to occur on external surfaces by forced convection and thermal radiation and (b) heat transfer inside the structure to occur by conduction, free convection of a gas (usually air) and by thermal radiation. Then the temperature distributions are similar under the following conditions: (1) the similarity parameters

$$\frac{h_f L}{k_M}, \quad \frac{T_{aw}}{T_i}, \quad \frac{k_{it}(T_i)}{k_M}\left[\frac{gL^3 p_{it}^2 \mathrm{Pr}}{[\mu_{it}(T_i)]^2 T_i^2 R^2}\right]^a, \frac{C_\sigma L T_i^3}{k_M}, \varepsilon \qquad (11.2.13)$$

are to be the same, (2) the distributions of the reference temperatures and the coefficients of external heat transfer by forced convection must be similar in space and in time, and the distribution of the initial temperatures must be similar in space, (3) the third condition of similarity law 1.1 to be satisfied; if the heat capacity of the medium for free convection inside the structure is important, the heat per unit volume of the fluid and of the structure must be in the same ratio.

The rate of heat flow at the surface of the structure q_w^* follows from the solution Θ_{III} and is in non-dimensional form

$$\frac{q_w^* L}{k_M T_i} = F_q(\ldots) \qquad (11.2.14)$$

where F_q depends on the same number of parameters and variables as Θ_{III}. If radiation is important in the external heat transfer only, equality in ε can be dropped, if, at the same time, the third similarity parameter becomes $\dfrac{\varepsilon C_\sigma L T_i^3}{k_M}$:

There are now three similarity parameters: $\dfrac{h_f L}{k_M} = \mathrm{Bi}$, $\dfrac{T_{aw}}{T_i}$ and $\dfrac{k_{it}(T_i)}{k_M}[\ldots]^a$ which are affected by flight conditions. Since flight plans are determined by two quantities: M and H, similar flight plans are not possible for the same structure. For structures of different size and made of different materials, but of similar geometry one of the 5 quantities H, M, L, k_M and T_i can be chosen as desired, the rest is then fixed, again if similar flight plans are possible.

If aerodynamic heating on a prototype is to be simulated in a laboratory, T_{aw} and T_i have to be the same in the test as in flight because of the equality in the second and the fourth similarity parameter. Because of the third and fourth similarity parameter, the air pressure p_{it} inside the structure must be the same for the test and the flight. If flight at high altitudes is to be simulated, the air pressure inside the structure must be small and less than that of the natural environment of the laboratory, if heat transfer by free convection inside the structure is at all important.

For simulated heating of models only the third and fourth similarity parameters of 11.2.13 need be considered, because the first two parameters can always be satisfied by a suitable choice of h_f and T_{aw}. The fourth similarity parameter is re-written by dropping the constant C_σ i.e.

$$\frac{L T_i^3}{k_M} = \text{same in prototype and model} \tag{11.2.15}$$

The third can be re-written with the help of the fourth similarity parameter and is

$$\frac{L^{3a-1} p_{it}^{2a}}{F(T_i)} \text{Pr} = \text{same in prototype and model} \tag{11.2.16}$$

Because of the fourth similarity parameter in (11.2.13), Eq. (11.2.14) can be re-written as

$$\frac{q_w^*}{(T_i)^4} = \text{same in prototype and model} \tag{11.2.17}$$

If the air pressure in the model can be chosen as desired, 2 of the 4 quantities k_M, L, p_{it} and T_i can be chosen as desired, the other quantities follow from the Eqs. (11.2.15) and (11.2.16), provided $a \neq 1/3$; for $a = 1/3$ only either p_{it} or T_i can be among the quantities to be chosen at will. If, however, the intensity of external heating is to be smaller than on the prototype the choice of the above two quantities is subject to the condition $(T_i)_m < (T_i)_p$ because of the inequality (11.1.20) and Eq. (11.2.17). If p_{it} is to be equal to the natural atmospheric pressure in the laboratory, only one of the quantities L and T_i can be chosen as desired, the other of the two and k_M are then determined; for $a = 1/3$, T_i is fixed and either L or k_M can be chosen at will. At any rate k_M would have to be smaller on the model than on the prototype, if the model requirements (11.1.19) and (11.1.21) are to be satisfied (see text following (11.1.23)).

11.2.2 *Rate of heat flow given at the outside surfaces*

For severe rates of heating the heat flow to the surfaces is not influenced appreciably by changes in the surface temperatures and therefore the contribution due to thermal radiation from external surfaces also becomes unimportant. Again, as in Section 11.1.2, the rate of heat flow to the external surfaces of bodies or structures is given. At inside surfaces the boundary conditions are the same as in Section 11.2.1. The non-dimensional quantities of Eqs. (11.1.4) and (11.1.5) are retained and the non-dimensional temperature is the same as in Eq. (11.2.4). The boundary condition, Eq. (11.1.24) now becomes with q_w as a reference value

$$-\left(\frac{\partial\Theta_{\mathrm{III}}}{\partial(n/L)}\right)_{w1} = \frac{q_w L}{k_M T_i}\,\frac{q_w^*}{q_w} \tag{11.2.18}$$

A solution of Eq. (11.1.6) satisfying the initial condition Eq. (11.1.8) and the boundary conditions Eq. (11.2.18) is of the general form

$$\Theta_{\mathrm{III}} = \Theta_{\mathrm{III}}\left(\frac{q_w L}{k_M T_i},\ \frac{k_{\mathrm{it}}(T_i)}{k_M}\ [\ldots]^a,\ \frac{C_\sigma L T_i^3}{k_M},\ \varepsilon,\ \xi,\eta,\zeta,\tau\right) \tag{11.2.19}$$

if F_i^0 and q_w^*/q_w are only functions of ξ, η, ζ, and ξ, η, ζ, τ respectively. Again, similar flight plans are not possible in general, but the possibilities are improved for special cases as compared with the previous section, because only the first two similarity parameters on the right-hand side of Eq. (11.2.19) refer to flight conditions.

The results can be summarized as:

Similarity law 2.2:

> Assume bodies or structures of similar geometry to satisfy the assumptions (c) and (d) of similarity law 1.1 and the assumption (b) of similarity law 2.1; further, assume that the rate of external heat flow is given. Then the temperature distributions are similar under the following conditions: (1) the similarity parameters

$$\frac{q_w L}{k_M T_i},\ \frac{k_{\mathrm{it}}(T_i)}{k_M}\left[\frac{g L^3 p_{\mathrm{it}}^2 \mathrm{Pr}}{[\mu_{\mathrm{it}}(T_i)]^2 T_i^2 R^2}\right]^a,\ \frac{C_\sigma L T_i^3}{k_M},\ \varepsilon \tag{11.2.20}$$

> are to be the same, (2) the distribution of the rate of heat flow must be similar in space and time, and that of the initial temperature must be similar in space and (3) the third condition of similarity law 1.1 to be satisfied.

For the same structure, only indentical flight plans are possible, as follows from condition (1). For structures of different size and of different materials, but similar geometry, similar flight plans are possible, in particular cases. Because q_w depends on H and M, and p_{it} on H, 2 of the 5 quantities: H, M, L, k_M and T_i can be chosen as desired if, again, $a \neq 1/3$. For $a = 1/3$ only either H or T_i can be among the quantities to be chosen as desired, because p_{it} depends on H. The other quantities are then fixed by the similarity requirement (1) of law 2.2, provided similar flight plans exist (see also Section 11.1.1).

If the prototype is tested under simulated heating, similarity requires T_i to be the same as in flight because of the third parameter in (11.2.20). Therefore pre-cooling or pre-heating of the structure may be necessary. If T_i is fixed, then equality in the second similarity parameter in (11.2.20) requires the pressure of the air inside the structure to be the same as in flight because of Eq. (11.2.16).

Next, consider testing of a model under simulated heating. If T_i is to be equal to the natural temperature in the laboratory, either L or one of the two quantities k_M or p_{it} can be chosen as desired, then all quantities are fixed; except when $a = 1/3$, then even p_{it} is fixed. Whether or not the rate of heat flow on the model is smaller than on the prototype, depends on the laboratory temperature being lower or higher than the T_i of the prototype because of Eq. (11.2.17). If, on the other hand, the initial temperature of the model can be chosen as desired, then the rate of heat flow on the model can be made smaller than on the prototype if $(T_i)_m < (T_i)_p$; as in Section 11.2.1, 2 of the 4 quantities k_M, L, p_{it} and T_i can now be chosen as desired and the rest are then fixed, except for $a = 1/3$; then only either p_{it} or T_i can be among the quantities to be chosen at will. The preceding condition for the initial temperatures would in many cases (for instance uniform initial temperature at thermal equilibrium corresponding to flight at $M \approx 1$ and at altitudes below about 40 km (130,000 ft)) lead to pre-cooling of the model. If in addition $L_m < L_p$, then $(k_M)_m < (k_M)_p$ because of equality in the third similarity parameter. Whether the air pressure inside the structure can be equal to that of the laboratory during model tests depends on the particular case and follows from Eq. (11.2.16).

11.3 Temperature-dependent thermal properties

Thermal properties of solids may vary considerably with temperature as can be seen from Table 7.2. If large temperature differences occur in the structure, the use of constant mean thermal properties may not be justified. In this section the influence of variable thermal properties on similarity is investigated following Ref. 11.3.

The equation of heat conduction in one dimension is now

$$(\varrho c)_M \frac{\partial T}{\partial t} = \frac{\partial}{\partial x}\left(k_M \frac{\partial T}{\partial x}\right) \tag{11.3.1}$$

If two or three dimensions are involved, the results of the following analysis remain essentially the same.

The thermal properties are approximated here as follows:

$$k_M = k_M^{(0)} T^{\lambda_1} \quad \text{and} \quad (\varrho c)_M = (\varrho c)_M^{(0)} T^{\lambda_2} \tag{11.3.2}$$

with $k_M^{(0)}$, $(\varrho c)_M^{(0)}$, λ_1 and λ_2 as suitable constants and T as an absolute temperature. Because the absolute level of the temperature is now important, we use a non-dimensional temperature as defined by Eq. (11.2.4) with the initial temperature as a suitable reference value.

On introducing Eq. (11.3.2) into (11.3.1) one obtains

$$\Theta^{\lambda_2} \frac{\partial \Theta}{\partial \tau} = \frac{\partial}{\partial \xi}\left(\Theta^{\lambda_1} \frac{\partial \Theta}{\partial \xi}\right) \tag{11.3.3}$$

provided that

$$\tau = \frac{\varkappa_M(T_i)t}{L^2} \quad \text{and} \quad \xi = \frac{x}{L} \tag{11.3.4}$$

where τ differs from Eq. (11.1.5) only by $\varkappa_M$ being taken at the initial temperature, while ξ is the same as used previously. The boundary conditions can be treated in a similar way. Instead of the initial temperature any other suitable reference temperature could have been chosen. In this way one obtains the general case of Section 11.2 with temperature-dependent thermal properties. The results can be summarized as follows:

Similarity law 3:

> If the variations of the thermal properties with temperature are important and if they can be expressed as in Eq. (11.3.2), the similarity laws 2.1 and 2.2 are valid with the following additional conditions: (1) Each of the exponents λ_1 and λ_2 must be the same in similar cases and (2) the thermal properties in the similarity parameters are to be taken at a common reference temperature such as T_i.

Therefore the previous conclusions and applications of Section 11.2 are still valid, if the same materials, or materials with the same values of λ_1 and λ_2, are used and the thermal properties in all expressions are taken at corresponding reference temperatures (for instance T_i). If one or both of the modes: free convection or thermal radiation, is unimportant, corresponding similarity parameters can be dropped and the respective conclusions of Section 11.2 have to be changed. However, even if free convection or thermal radiation are absent, but thermal properties vary with temperature, the temperatures become similar only in the absolute levels. Therefore in that case the non-dimensional temperature must be chosen as in Eq. (11.2.4) and the similarity parameters are λ_1, λ_2, $(h_f L)/k_M$ and T_{aw}/T_i for external heat transfer by forced convection, and $\dfrac{q_w L}{k_M T_i}$, λ_1 and λ_2 for given rate of heat flow at the surface; similarity in the distributions of F_i, F_{aw}, F_h and F_q is, of course, presumed. For the thermal properties of some materials of interest in aeronautics a comparison is made in Ref. 11.3 between the temperature dependences and their approximations by Eq. (11.3.2).

11.4 Finite thermal conductances across joints

If there are riveted, bolted, welded or bonded joints in a structure, the thermal conductances across the joints are finite. The boundary conditions for these interfaces are given in Section 3.7 and they can be written in non-dimensional form as before with the help of Eq. (11.1.4). Owing to the joints the following additional similarity parameters arise

$$\frac{(h_{ct})_{w1} L}{k_M}, \frac{(h_{ct})_{w2} L}{k_M}, \ldots, \frac{(h_{ct})_{wn} L}{k_M} \qquad (11.4.1)$$

where $w1$, $w2$, ..., characterize a number of joints which in general have different values of the interface conductances. Due to their large individual scatter, the thermal conductances in different specimens of the same prototype may differ considerably and hence similarity may thereby be affected. It appears to be difficult to construct joints with given interface conductances. If, therefore, the thermal resistances in joints are important for the temperatures in structures, additional difficulties arise in model testing.

References

11.1 LANGHAAR, H. L., *Dimensional Analysis and Theory of Models*, J. Wiley, New York (1951).

11.2 DUNCAN, W. J., *Physical Similarity and Dimensional Analysis*, E. Arnold, London (1953).

11.3 SOBEY, A. J., Advantages and limitations of models, *J. Roy. Aero. Soc.* **63**, 587, 646–656 (1959).

11.4 CALLIGEROS, J. M. and DUGUNDJI, J., Similarity laws required for experimental aero-thermoelastic studies, Massachusetts Inst. of Technology, Aeroelastic and Structures Research Lab., Techn. Rep. 75–1 (1959).

APPENDIX

A SURVEY OF RECENT DEVELOPMENTS

Additional list of symbols:

a . . . . . . Absorption coefficient in Section 3.6

s_{ra} . . . . . . Transmissivity

ρ_{ra} . . . . . . Reflectivity

Recent activities in the field of heat transfer in structures have been lively and mainly concentrated on problems in connection with space vehicles. Thus hypersonic heat transfer and ablation with real gas temperatures have been investigated and extended to higher temperatures (Mach numbers). As regards heat flow inside structures, activities have yielded many details and extensions useful for technical applications, but not much that is fundamentally new. Most interesting in this field are, perhaps, papers on radiative boundary conditions, temperature-dependent thermal properties and heat flow in semi-transparent bodies. Largest progress as far as this book is concerned has been made in heat transfer by radiation which is important particularly for space vehicles, since in space this is the only mode of heat transfer between vehicles and their environment. Methods of calculation have been refined by replacing finite surfaces by infinitesimal surfaces and by including also specular (mirror-like) reflection. Further, many configurations of interest have been investigated such as radiative fins for space vehicles and minimum weight problems of fins.

A selection of important papers is surveyed or listed in the Appendix as well as—where possible—connected with the material in the main part of the book. In a few cases also older papers are included which are important for recent developments.

Chapter A.2

A.2.3.5 *Addendum to Section* 2.3.5

Biot has extended variational methods to problems of convective heat transfer in boundary layer flow (Ref. A.2.3.23) and found that the concept of a local heat transfer coefficient h is unsuitable for certain cases of variable wall temperatures, if h is defined as the surface heat-flow rate divided by the difference between the adiabatic wall temperature and the *local* wall

304

temperature, $T_{aw} - T_w$. This statement has led to a controversy (Ref. A.2.3.24). According to Section 3.1.3 the heat transfer coefficient h is in itself no uniquely defined physical quantity, but rather a convenient way of finding a specific heat-flow rate per unit of a characteristic temperature difference which one is free to chose. By this choice a particular h is defined and in general there may be different kinds of h. In many cases the choice of the characteristic temperature difference is obvious as for boundary layer flow along a flat plate at constant pressure and constant wall temperature T_w when this difference is equal to $T_{aw} - T_w$ and is constant. In this case h varies because of the local variations of the fluid boundary layer. However, when T_w varies locally to such a degree that $T_{aw} - T_w$ changes sign, then the heat transfer coefficient based on local values of $T_{aw} - T_w$ may become negative and may even become infinite in places other than at sharp leading edges (Ref. A.2.3.23). Even in such cases the local heat transfer coefficient for constant wall temperature can be used, if the characteristic temperature difference is replaced by a value $(T_{aw} - T_w)_{x_0}$ in a certain place x_0 plus an expression which takes into account the wall temperature variations (see, for instance, Eqs. (2.3.10) and (2.3.11)); these expressions can be obtained by Duhamel's principle. Now, h retains its meaning as a measure for the fluid-flow conditions and is thus independent of the wall temperature variations; this procedure gives the exact heat-flow rates, although approximate expressions are often used as integrating kernels of the integrals as for instance in Eqs. (2.3.10) and (2.3.11). Besides, as regards heat transfer in structures, the example quoted in Ref. A.2.3.23 is extreme and the wall temperature variations likely to occur at the surfaces of flight structures are more moderate (see Section 7.6.4 and Ref. 7.6.11).

A.2.4 *Addendum to Section* 2.4

When the speed of space vehicles exceeds those of satellites, new phenomena may influence the heat transfer to the vehicles during entry in a planets (or the Earth's) atmosphere. Firstly, the radiant heat flow from the hot gas (air) in and behind the shock layer in front of the vehicle strikes the vehicle and thus it receives an amount of heat in addition to that by forced convection. Secondly, with increasing speed ionization takes place in the gas (air) and this may influence the convective heat transfer. To treat these and other phenomena, particularly those at low density (for instance in the outer parts of an atmosphere) is beyond the scope of this book and the reader is referred to proceedings of a recent congress (Ref. A.2.4.6) and a comprehensive survey article (Ref. A.2.4.7).

References

A.2.3.23 BIOT, M. A., Fundamentals of boundary-layer heat transfer with stream-wise temperature variations, *J. Aero. Sci.* **29**, 5, 558–567, 582 (1962).

A.2.3.24 TRIBUS, M., Comment on "Fundamentals of boundary-layer heat transfer with streamwise temperature variations."

BIOT, M. A., Authors reply. *J. Aero. Sci.* **29**, 12, 1482–1483 (1962).

RUBESIN, M. W., Further comment on "Fundamentals of boundary-layer heat transfer with streamwise temperature variation".

BIOT, M. A., Reply by Author to RUBESIN, M. W.

DZUNG, L. S., Comment on "Fundamentals of boundary-layer heat transfer with streamwise temperature variations". Reply by author to DZUNG, L. S. *AIAA Journal*, **1**, 8, 1961–1963 (1963).

A.2.4.6 *Hypersonic flow research.* Papers presented at a conference on hypersonics, held at Mass. Inst. Techn. Aug. 1961. Edited by F. R. RIDDELL. Academic Press, New York (1962).

A.2.4.7 CHENG, H. K., Recent advances in hypersonic flow research, *AIAA Journal* **1**, 2, 295–310 (1963).

Chapter A.3

A.3.4 *Addendum to Section* 3.4

Ablation is most important in connection with hypersonic flight; recent developments are summarized in Ref. A.2.4.7.

A.3.6.3 *Addendum to Section* 3.6.3

Further information on thermal radiation characteristics of materials suitable for space vehicles is given in Refs. A.3.6.4 and A.3.6.5.

In Section 3.6.3 it has been mentioned that the radiative emission of real bodies deviates from diffuse distribution (i.e. from Lambert's cosine law). Similarly, in the reflected radiation from surfaces of real solids those directions are preferred which lie close to a specular (mirror-like) reflection (see Refs. A.3.6.6, A.3.6.7 and A.3.6.8).

In Section 3.6 only opaque surfaces have been assumed. However, transparent or semi-transparent materials have become important for ablation shields in missile technique (Ref. A.3.6.17) and have been proposed for rocket nozzles (Ref. A.3.6.9). If ϱ_{ra} is the reflectivity defined as the ratio of reflected to incident radiation and s_{ra} the transmissivity defined as the ratio of transmitted to incident radiation, then one obtains for thermal radiation impinging on the interface between two media:

$$\varrho_{ra} + \alpha + s_{ra} = 1 \qquad\qquad (A.3.6.21)$$

α is the absorptivity defined earlier. For real bodies this equation is only valid for a certain wave length, but for black and grey bodies it is independent of the wave length. *Inside* a semi-transparent body (i.e. one which absorbs radiation) and in the absence of interfaces influencing radiation there is

$$\frac{dq_\lambda}{q_\lambda} = -a_\lambda\, dx \qquad (A.3.6.22)$$

where q_λ is the intensity of radiative heat flow for a beam of wave length λ, a_λ the absorption coefficient and dx the path length of the beam. Eq. (A.3.6.22) may be easily integrated and then one obtains for the transmissivity of a layer of constant thickness δ

$$s_{ra,\lambda} = e^{-a_\lambda \delta} \qquad (A.3.6.23)$$

and for its absorptivity $\alpha_\lambda = 1 - s_{ra,\lambda}$. A semi-transparent body also emits radiation from every volume element and the intensity of this radiative flow is, of course, also reduced by absorption along its path within the body; for further details as well as on heat transfer particularly in glass, see Ref. A.3.6.10. For applications in steady-state and transient problems see Refs. A.5.5 and A.3.6.17, respectively.

A.3.6.4 *Addendum to Section* 3.6.4

In order to avoid doubts in connection with the text in the Sections 3.6.4 and 3.6.5, it is mentioned that $dF_{1-1} = F_{1-1}$ is always zero, while $\overline{F}_{1-1}$ is also zero except for concave surfaces, because in this case differential parts of the same surface element "see each other" and then finite values of $\overline{F}_{1-1}$ are obtained according to Eqs. (3.6.11) and (3.6.12). This has to be observed, when summation over surface elements is made as for instance in Eqs. (3.6.14) and (3.6.17).

Shape factors in addition to those given in Section 3.6.4 can be found in Ref. A.3.6.11; among them are the following: (a) a spherical point source and a plane rectangle, (b) a plane point source and a plane circular disk, (c) a plane point or line source and a circular cylinder of finite length, (d) an infinitely long cylinder and an infinite plane parallel to it, (e) a line source and a plane rectangle, and (f) two parallel plane circular disks. Further shape factors can be found in Ref. A.3.6.12 for a number of non-planar surfaces, such as axisymmetrical sections of cylinders, cones, hemispheres radiating internally to annular and circular sections of their bases.

In a new method for calculating shape factors Sparrow (Ref. A.3.6.12a) replaces the area integrals (see Eq. (3.6.11)) by contour integrals using Stoke's theorem[†].

[†] See for instance: F. B. HILDEBRAND, *Advanced calculus for engineers*, Prentice-Hall, New York (1956).

For space vehicles radiation from fins and mutual radiation between fins and bodies is important; about this see Section A.9.5.3.

A.3.6.5.a *Radiative heat transfer between grey surfaces. Refinements and extensions*

Besides the method—often called the radiosity method—described in Section 3.6.5 for calculating radiative heat transfer in enclosures there exists a generalization of this method and two further methods due to Hottel and Gebhart. These are described and discussed in Ref. A.3.6.6 and the reader is referred to this article. However, the modification and the other methods are essentially only other approaches, leading to equations similar to those of the radiosity method, so that the computational effort for solving the equations is the same in all methods (Ref. A.3.6.6).

The methods for calculating radiative heat transfer in enclosures can be used for any configuration of radiating surfaces as for instance inside a cavity with an opening through which the cavity is in radiative heat exchange with its surroundings, if one imagines the cavity closed by control surfaces which take into account the ingoing and outgoing radiation. The imaginary control surface can be of arbitrary form, provided it closes the openings of the cavity. If the surroundings are an infinite space, the control surface would act as the surface of a black body and hence absorb all radiation coming from inside the enclosure. If the surroundings are a vacuum (i.e. at absolute zero temperature), no radiation would be emitted from the control surface to the inside and if surroundings are at finite absolute temperature, it can in most cases be assumed that diffuse black-body radiation is emitted from the control surface to the inside.

Refinements in calculating radiative heat transfer between surfaces have been made by using differential surface elements instead of finite surface elements; thus integral equations are obtained instead of ordinary equations of the type of Eqs. (3.6.15) to (3.6.17). In most cases diffuse emission and reflection is assumed; for cases with specular reflection, see Ref. A.3.6.24. Instead of the quantities $q_{k\leftarrow}$, $q_{k\rightarrow}$ and $q_{w,k}$ used in Section 3.6.5 there are now three corresponding quantities $q(x)_{\leftarrow}$, $q(x)_{\rightarrow}$ and $q_w(x)$ which are in general continuous functions of the coordinates, but are here given as functions of one space variable only. The sum on the right-hand side of Eq. (3.6.17) is equal to the incident radiation intensity at a fixed point, and it can be replaced by an integral and this yields:

$$q(x)_{\leftarrow} = \int q(\xi)_{\rightarrow}\, dF_{x-\xi} \qquad (\text{A.3.6.24})$$

where the integration variable ξ is to cover the whole range of the coordinate x which is, however, fixed in Eq. (A.3.6.24). By definition, according to Eqs. (3.6.9) and (3.6.10),

$$dF_{x-\xi} = \frac{\partial F(x, \xi)}{\partial \xi}\, d\xi \qquad (A.3.6.25)$$

Solutions of the resulting integral equations can rarely be obtained in closed form, hence numerical or approximate methods have to be employed (see Ref. A.3.6.6). When heat exchange between surfaces occurs by thermal radiation only one obtains from Eqs. (3.6.16) and (A.3.6.24) in the new notation where for the integration the same is valid as for Eq. (A.3.6.24).

$$q(x)_{\to} = [1-\varepsilon(x)]\int q(\xi)_{\to}\, dF_{x-\xi} + \varepsilon(x) C_{\sigma} T(x)^4 \qquad (A.3.6.26)$$

Solutions of this linear integral equation in q are readily possible by successive approximations, if the surface temperature $T(x)$ is known. If this is not the case and an additional equation involving $T(x)$ is necessary, for instance if there is heat conduction within the bounding walls, then the integral equations may become non-linear and the previous method may lead to instabilities (see Ref. A.3.6.6).

Sparrow (Ref. A.3.6.13) compared the results of standard approximate calculation procedures using shape factors between finite surface elements (see Section 3.6.5) and of more accurate methods using everywhere infinitesimal surface elements. For parallel plates and disks, and adjoint plates, one surface being black, the other non-black, agreement in overall heat transfer is good for the non-black surface and tolerable for the black surface, as long as the net overall heat transfer there exceeds 20 per cent of the radiant emission (see also Refs. A.3.6.14, A.3.6.18 and A.3.6.18a).

Variational methods have also been successfully used for solving integral equations occurring in radiative heat transfer (Ref. A.3.6.15).

Radiative heat transfer between non-opaque surfaces has been treated in Ref. A.3.6.16. Transient heating has been investigated in Ref. A.3.6.17 with both heat conduction and thermal radiation occurring *inside* a semi-infinite solid which consists of a semi-transparent material.

A.3.6.5.b *Thermal radiation from and within cavities.*

Grey emisson and reflection has been assumed in the following unless otherwise stated. Heat conduction inside the walls is assumed to be absent and steady-state conditions prevail.

The radiative heat losses are treated in Ref. A.3.6.18 from two plane surfaces at equal and uniform temperature to a non-radiating environment; the two surfaces are in the form of strips of finite width but infinite length; in one case they are joined at one edge, in the other they are parallel to each other and at a finite distance. In both cases the heat losses through the gaps of the configurations are an important aim of the investigations.

In Ref. A.3.6.19 the distribution of the heat-flow rate is calculated at the inner surface of a semi-infinite cylindrical enclosure at constant wall temperature; the mouth of the cylinder is open and the surroundings are non-radiating. Extensions to cylindrical enclosures of finite length with one end open and the other closed are made in Ref. A.3.6.20. In both cases the total rate of radiative heat flow leaving the enclosures at the open end has also been calculated. In Ref. A.3.6.21 the wall temperature distribution has been calculated of the inner surface of a finite cylinder open at both ends and possessing at the wall a specified rate of heat input variable in the axial direction. Black-body radiation in an infinite cylinder whose wall has a rate of heat input that is a function of angular coordinate only, has been investigated in Ref. A.3.6.22; the calculations have been extended to include also circumferential heat conduction within the wall. The apparent absorptivity for ingoing and the apparent emissivity for outgoing radiation was found in Ref. A.3.6.23 for spherical enclosures with circular holes of varying size. It is interesting to note that the shape factor between two surface elements A_1 and A_2 in an spherical enclosure, whether they are infinitesimal or finite, is $F_{1-2} = A_2/4\pi r^2$ with r as the radius of the sphere.

A.3.6.5.c Specular reflection

Because reflection from real bodies deviates considerably from the diffuse case, it is useful to make calculations for purely diffuse and for purely specular reflection, as for instance in Ref. A.3.6.24, in order to find the limits within which the solutions for real bodies lie. In this and other calculations, even in case of specular reflection, the emission is usually assumed diffuse in order to avoid undue complications, although this is only an approximation to real bodies. Consider the heat flow between concentric spheres or cylinders and assume two cases: Firstly, diffuse reflection and diffuse emission which yields Eq. (3.6.20); secondly, specular reflection but diffuse emission, for which case the nominator on the right-hand side of this equation is denoted now as $1/\varepsilon_{\text{eff}}$ and is given by

$$\frac{1}{\varepsilon_{\text{eff}}} = \frac{1}{\varepsilon_1} + \frac{1}{\varepsilon_2} - 1 \qquad (A.3.6.27)$$

For $\varepsilon_1 = \varepsilon_2 \approx 1$ the difference between the two cases is small; for $\varepsilon_1 = \varepsilon_2 \ll 1$ and $A_1/A_2 \to 0$, in the first case $\varepsilon_{\text{eff}} = \varepsilon_1$, but in the second case

$\varepsilon_{\text{eff}} = \varepsilon_1/2$. Hence differences between diffuse and specular reflection become large only for small values of ε. This is confirmed in Ref. A.3.6.24 for two parallel plane surfaces at finite distance and of finite width extending infinitely in a direction normal to their width, further for two plane surfaces of the same form but joined at their edges.

A.3.7 *Addendum to Section* 3.7

Thermal contact resistances are important also for space vehicles and in particular their performance in vacuum (i.e. in space), when gas layers in the cavities between the contact surfaces are absent. Then heat transfer between surfaces occurs only by conduction at the points of contact and by thermal radiation.

A mathematical analysis with the aim of theoretically predicting contact resistances between metallic surfaces has been made by Fenech and Rohsenow (Ref. A.3.7.10). The thermal conductance is calculated for an idealized shape of contact points, the real area of each point in contact, the number of contact points per unit area and the average thickness of the cavities between the contact surfaces; the last quantity is important only if the cavities are filled with a medium. In the published analysis the radiative heat transfer between the contact surfaces is neglected, but it can be taken into account. In order to predict conductances the following measurements are needed: Two recorded profiles of the surface, perpendicular to each other, and a hardness test of the softer of the two materials in contact. Experimental verification of predictions was good for an iron–aluminium contact between machined surfaces over a range of contact pressures from 90 to 2600 p.s.i. and with air, water or mercury in the cavities between the surfaces. An effort to correlate existing experimental data has been made in Ref. A.3.7.11. Conductances between steel surfaces in argon can be found in Ref. 3.7.4. Conductance measurements in vacuum are reported in Ref. A.3.7.12 for copper, silver and gold, and in Ref. A.3.7.13 for aluminium and magnesium. In the last reference an extensive list of papers on contact conductances is given, including also those of interest for nuclear power engineering.

References

A.3.6.4   EDWARDS, D. K. and RODDICK, R. D., Spectral and directional thermal radiation characteristics of surfaces for heat rejection by radiation. Progress in Astronautics and Aeronautics. Vol. 11: *Power systems for space flight*. Academic Press (1963).

A.3.6.5   ASKWYTH, W. H., HAYES, R. J. and MIKK, G., Emittance of materials suitable for use as spacecraft radiator coatings. Progress in Astronautics and Aeronautics. Vol. 11: *Power systems for space flight*. Academic Press (1963).

A.3.6.6   SPARROW, E. M., On the calculation of radiant interchange between surfaces. *Modern developments in heat transfer*. Edited by W. IBELE. Academic Press, New York (1963).

A.3.6.7   ECKERT, E., Messung der Reflexion von Wärmestrahlen an technischen Oberflächen. *Forsch. Ing. Wes.* **7**, 265–270 (1936).

A.3.6.8   MÜNCH, B., Die Richtungsverteilung bei der Reflexion von Wärmestrahlung und ihr Einfluß auf die Wärmeübertragung. *Mitteil. Inst. Thermodynamik und Verbrennungsmotorenbau*, ETH Zürich, Nr. 16 (1955).

A.3.6.9   KIRCHNER, H. P. and VASSALLO, F. A., Radiative transport cools rocket nozzles, *SAE Journal* **69**, 7, 96–98 (1961).

A.3.6.10 GARDON, R., A review of radiant heat transfer in glass, *J. Amer. Ceramic Soc.* **44**, 7, 305–312 (1961).

A.3.6.11 HAMILTON, D. C. and MORGAN, W. R., *Radiant-interchange configuration factors*, NACA TN 2836 (1952).

A.3.6.12 BUSCHMAN JR., A. J. and PITTMAN, C. M., *Configuration factors for exchange of radiant energy between axisymmetrical sections of cylinders, cones and hemispheres and their bases*, NASA TN D-944 (1961).

A.3.6.12a SPARROW, E. M., A new and simpler formulation for radiative angle factors, *Trans. ASME (Journal Heat Transfer)* C **85**, 2, 81–88 (1963).

A.3.6.13 SPARROW, E. M., Heat radiation between simply-arranged surfaces having different temperatures and emissivities, *J. Amer. Inst. Chem. Engnrs* **8**, 1, 12–18 (1962).

A.3.6.14 BOBCO, R. P., Gray surface radiation between a differential area and an infinite plane: Non-uniform local heat flux, *ARS Journal* **32**, 8, 1297–1299 (1962).

A.3.6.15 SPARROW, E. M., Application of variational methods to radiation heat-transfer calculations, *Trans. ASME (Journal Heat Transfer)* C **82**, 4, 375–380 (1960).

A.3.6.16 GEBHARD, B., Surface temperature calculations in radiant surroundings of arbitrary complexity — For gray, diffuse radiation, *Int. J. Heat Mass Transfer* **3**, 4, 341–346 (1961).

A.3.6.17 BOEHRINGER, J. C., and SPINDLER, R. J., Radiant heating of semitransparent materials, *AIAA Journal* **1**, 1, 84–88 (1963).

A.3.6.18 SPARROW, E. M., GREGG, J. L., SZEL, J. V. and MANOS, P., Analysis, results, and interpretation for radiation between some simply-arranged gray surfaces, *Trans. ASME (Journal Heat Transfer)* C **83**, 2, 207–214 (1961).

A.3.6.18a COSTELLO, F. A., A note on the paper "Analysis, results, and interpretation for radiation between some simply-arranged gray surfaces", *Trans. ASME (Journal Heat Transfer)* C **85**, 2, 183–184 (1963).

A.3.6.19 SPARROW, E. M. and ALBERS, L. U., Apparent emissivity and heat transfer in a long cylindrical hole, *Trans. ASME (Journal Heat Transfer)* C **82**, 3, 253–255 (1960).

A.3.6.20 SPARROW, E. M., ALBERS, L. U., and ECKERT, E. R. G., Thermal radiation characteristics of cylindrical enclosures, *Trans. ASME (Jovrnal Heat Transfer)* C **84**, 1, 73–81 (1962).

A.3.6.21 USISKIN, C. M. and SIEGEL, R., Thermal radiation from a cylindrical enclosure with specified wall heat flux, *Trans. ASME (Journal Heat Transfer)* C **82**, 4, 369–374 (1960).

A.3.6.22 FRANK, I. and GRAY, E. I., Temperature distributions in long cylindrical shells, *Trans. ASME (Journal Heat Transfer)* C **84**, 2, 190–191 (1962).

A.3.6.23 SPARROW, E. M. and JONSSON, V. K., Absorption and emission characteristics of diffuse spherical enclosures, *Trans. ASME (Journal Heat Transfer)* C **84**, 2, 188–189 (1962).

A.3.6.24 ECKERT, E. R. G. and SPARROW, E. M., Radiative heat exchange between surfaces with specular reflection, *Int. J. Heat Transfer* **3**, 1, 42–54 (1961).

Additional reference:

A.3.6.25 PERLMUTTER, M. and HOWELL, J. R., A strongly directional emitting and absorbing surface, *Trans. ASME (Journal Heat Transfer)* C **85**, 3, 282–283 (1963).

A.3.7.10 FENECH, H. and ROHSENOW, W. M., Prediction of thermal conductance of metallic surfaces in contact, *Trans. ASME (Journal Heat Transfer)* C **85**, 1, 15–24 (1963).

A.3.7.11 GRAFF, W. J., Thermal conductance across metal joints, *Mach. Design* **32** 19, 166–172 (1960).

A.3.7.12 JACOBS, R. B. and STARR, C., Thermal conductance of metallic contacts *Rev. Scient. Instr.* **10**, 140–141 (1939).

A.3.7.13 FRIED, E. and COSTELLO, F. A., Interface thermal contact resistance problem in space vehicles, *ARS Journal* **32**, 2, 237–243 (1962).

Chapter A.5

A.5.7 *Addendum to Section 5.7*

Consider a semi-infinite solid composed of a large number of layers whose interfaces are parallel to each other and to the free surface of the solid. The thermal contact at the interfaces is perfect. The thermal properties are constant within each layer, but differ from one layer to the other. A solution for steady two-dimensional heat flow in this body with an arbitrary temperature distribution at the free surface is given by Vodička in Ref. A.5.3 with the help of a Fourier transform. The same author gives in Ref. A.5.4 a solution for two-dimensional heat flow in a composite plate whose extensions in space are for a three-dimensional rectangular coordinate system (δ finite): $0 \leqslant x \leqslant \delta$, $0 \leqslant y < \infty$, $-\infty < z < \infty$; the temperatures are given as arbitrary functions of y at $x = 0$ and at $x = \delta$; at $y = 0$ the temperature is zero.

A.5.8 *Heat flow by conduction and radiation*

A problem of this type has been solved in Ref. A.5.5 for heat flow *inside* a slab of semi-transparent material.

References

A.5.3 Vodička, V., Two-dimensional steady temperature fields in a stratiform half-space, *Zeitschr. Angew. Math. und Physik*, **12**, 2, 164–167 (1961).

A.5.4 Vodička, V., Steady temperature field in a semi-infinite composite plate, *Appl. Sci. Res.* A **9**, 2–3, 190–196 (1960).

A.5.5 Viskanta, R. and Grosh, R. J., Heat transfer by simultaneous conduction and radiation in an absorbing medium, *Trans. ASME (Journal Heat Transfer)* C **84**, 1, 63–72 (1962).

Additional reference:

A.5.6 Lu, P.-C., On some analytic solutions of steady heat conduction in composite slabs of various cross sections, *Trans. ASME (Journal Heat Transfer)* C **83**, 4, 512–514 (1961).

Chapter A.7

A.7.3 *Addendum to Section* 7.3

The problem stated in mathematical form in Eq. (7.3.4) has been extended to the case of heat being generated at a steady rate within the shell. Solutions in a closed form are given by Unterberg (Ref. A.7.3.3).

A.7.5.1 *Addendum to Section* 7.5.1

Unless otherwise stated one-dimensional heat flow is assumed here.

For the hot surface of the slab treated in Section 7.5.1 charts have been given extending to large values of the heat transfer coefficient as may occur for instance in rocket nozzles (Ref. A.7.5.8a).

Consider one-dimensional transient heat flow in a slab with constant thermal properties and with the rate of heat flow at one surface given as an arbitrary function of time; the other surface of the slab is adiabatic and initially the temperature in the slab is constant. This problem has been treated by Chen (Ref. A.7.5.9), Thomas (Ref. A.7.5.10) and Ojalvo *et al.* (Ref. A.7.5.11). Solutions have been obtained either by functional transformations or by a method of separation of variables (see also Section 7.2). The analytical expressions of the solutions differ in form depending on the method of solution used, however one form can be transformed to the other by suitable mathematical transformations (see Ref. A.7.5.10). Some minor errors in Ref. A.7.5.10 have been found (Ref. 7.5.11). The solution in the form given by Thomas can be obtained immediately from Eq. (7.5.9) with the help of Duhamel's integral as given by Eq. (7.2.11)[†].

[†] The first term on the right-hand side of Eq. (8) in Ref. A.7.5.10 must have a positive sign.

Chen's solution has been extended to cylindrical heat flow by Phythian (Ref. A.7.5.12); similarly the semi-infinite solid, infinite cylinder and solid sphere with arbitrary rate of surface heat input were treated by Schapker (Ref. A.7.5.13) who also proposed an extension of the method to cover heat transfer by both forced convection and thermal radiation. A solution of the slab problem has also been given by Bergles and Kaye (Ref. A.7.5.14) for the case when the initial temperature distribution is not constant, but can be approximated by an even-order polynomial of fourth degree in distance and when the surface rate of heat flow can be approximated by a power series in the time.

Cylindrical heat flow with convective heat transfer at the inner surface and an adiabatic outer surface has been solved in Ref. A.7.5.15 with the help of finite difference methods.

Thermal radiation at the boundaries implies non-linear boundary conditions and hence the usual analytical methods fail. Solutions have so far been found by two methods: (a) Inside the body analytical solutions are used for a certain surface heat-flow rate which is found from an integral equation obtained with the help of Duhamel's principle (see Section 7.2.) and thus exact solutions can be found, or (b) an integral form of the heat conduction equation or a variational method is used (see Section 8.7.2) and then solutions are only approximate. A semi-infinite body has been treated by Chambré (Ref. A.7.5.16) assuming constant initial temperatures and radiation from the surface with a temperature T_w into an environment with temperature $T_\infty \neq T_w$. Solutions were obtained with the help of method (a) above. By the same method, solutions were also obtained by Abarbanel (Ref. A.7.5.17) for a semi-infinite body; further for a slab and for a spherical shell, both with one surface adiabatic, and for a sphere. In these cases radiation takes place into an environment at zero absolute temperature (vacuum), with the effects of finite environmental temperature being estimated. Solutions for a slab with surface radiation into vacuum were obtained by Fairall et al. (Ref. A. 7.5.18) with the help of a finite difference method.

So far thermal properties have been assumed constant; if they depend on temperature (see also Section 3.1.6), the differential equation of heat conduction becomes non-linear and the usual analytical methods fail; solutions can be obtained either by a method of successive approximations (Ref. A.7.5.19) or by using an integral form of the heat conduction equation (see Section 8.7.2). A solution for the semi-infinite solid with temperature-dependent thermal properties has been obtained by Yang (Ref. A. 7.5.19) using the first, and by Goodman (Ref. A. 7.5.20), Yang and Szewczyk (Ref.

A. 7.5.21) using the second of the above mentioned methods. The same problem has also been treated by variational methods (Ref. A.8.24). Corresponding solutions for the slab with given rate of heat flow at the surface have been found in Ref. A.7.5.22 using an integral form of the heat conduction equation.

A modification of graphite possessing poor heat conduction in one direction and good heat conduction in a direction normal to it, is of interest as a structural material capable of withstanding severe thermal loads as may occur in rocket nozzles and space vehicles. A solid body with different values of the heat conductivity in two directions normal to each other is called orthotropic. In such bodies *two-dimensional* heat flow is of particular interest for applications. Transient two-dimensional heat flow in an orthotropic plate and a sphere has been treated in Refs. A.7.5.23 and A.7.5.24 respectively.

A.7.5.2–4 *Addendum to Sections* 7.5.2–4

Additional charts to those of Section 7.5.3 (Fig. 7.6) have been given in Ref. A.7.5.25 for the temperature at the (heated) surface of the insulating layer.

A semi-infinite solid consisting of two layers with different thermal properties has been treated by Schniewind (Ref. A.7.5.26) with heat transfer of the forced-convection type occurring at the free surface.

Composite regions have been treated in a number of papers. The problem of a two-layer slab solved by Mayer (Ref. 7.5.4) has also been investigated in Ref. A.7.5.27, where the eigenvalues occurring in the solutions cover a wider range of the parameters; in both references the conductivity of the heated layer is lower than in the unheated layer. Eigenvalues for the same problem but for a high-conductivity layer exposed to heating with a low-conductivity layer beneath it, were given by Brogan and Schneider (Ref. A.7.5.28). A composite sphere consisting of a core and one layer, and a slab consisting of three layers are treated in Ref. A.7.5.29; the surface temperature was given and the initial temperature constant. More than two layers have been approximately treated by Wing (Ref. A.7.5.30) allowing for forced and radiative heat transfer at the outer surface. An exact solution of the same problem has been obtained by Reid (Ref. A.7.5.31) with the help of Green's theorem when the initial temperature distribution is arbitrary and at the boundaries the temperatures are functions of the time. In Ref. A.7.5.32 general solutions are given for a two-layer medium, in particular a slab, a cylinder and a sphere. The layers are in poor thermal contact and heat is generated within each; at the surface a generalized linear boundary condition is assumed and the initial temperature distribution is arbitrary. A list of 17 relevant papers is also given.

In problems with the protection of solid propellant motors exposed to atmospheric or environmental temperature variations, sinusoidal temperature variations in a two-layer composite slab have been investigated by Stonecypher (Ref. A.7.5.33) using the method of separation of variables (see Section 7.2). Campbell (Ref. A.7.5.34) gives for the same problem solutions obtained by the method of "heat waves" explained in Section 7.5.5.

A.7.6 *Addendum to Section 7.6*

Transient heating has also been treated by Conti (Ref. A.7.6.12) for thin-skinned bodies with variable heat transfer on the surface (due to boundary-layer flow), but uniform temperature across the section for a flat plate, a wedge, a conical shell, a hemispherical shell and a hemicylindrical shell with laminar and turbulent boundary-layer heat-transfer at the surfaces. The heat conduction equation is replaced by an infinite set of first order differential equations, for which a formal solution is comparatively easy to obtain. See Ref. A.7.6.13 for the case of a slender wedge with a constant heat-flow rate at the surface.

A.7.7 *Addendum to Section 7.7*

Hill's method (see Section 7.7 and Ref. 7.7.2) has been supplemented in Ref. A.7.7.4 by basic solutions converging rapidly for small times.

A.7.8.a *Heat conduction in bodies with melting or sublimation at the surface*

See additional references A.7.8.1–A.7.8.8.

References

A.7.3.3 UNTERBERG, W., Temperature histories of internally heated thin bodies cooled by convection and/or thermal radiation, *Nuclear Science and Engineering* **13**, 295–297 (1962).

A.7.5.8a. BAXTER, A. N., Extension of the transient heating charts, *J. Amer. Rocket Soc.* **30**, 9 904–905 (1960).

A.7.5.9 CHEN, S.-Y., One-dimensional heat conduction with arbitrary heating rate, *J. Aero. Sci.* **28**, 4, 336–337 (1961).

A.7.5.10 THOMAS, P. D., Comment on one-dimensional heat conduction with arbitrary heating rate, *J. Aero. Sci.* **29**, 5, 616–617 (1962).

A.7.5.11 OJALVO, I. U., NEWMAN, M. and FORRAY, M., Another comment on one-dimensional heat conduction with arbitrary heating rate, *J. Aero Sci.*, **29**, 9, 1126–1127 (1962).

A.7.5.12 PHYTHIAN, J. E., Cylindrical heat flow with arbitrary heating rates, *AIAA Journal* **1**, 4, 925–927 (1963).

A.7.5.13 SCHAPKER, R. L., On the use of Duhamel's equation for heat-conduction problems, *J. Aero. Sci.* **29**, 7, 883–884 (1962).

A.7.5.14 BERGLES, A. E. and KAYE, J., Solutions of the heat-conduction equation with time-dependent boundary conditions, *J. Aero. Sci.* **28**, 3, 251–252 (1961).

A.7.5.15 HATCH, J. E., SCHACHT, R. L., ALBERS, L. U. and SAPER, P. G., *Graphical presentation of difference solutions for transient radial heat conduction in hollow cylinders with heat transfer at the inner radius and finite slabs with heat transfer at one boundary*, NASA TR R–56 (1960).

A.7.5.16 CHAMBRÉ, P. L., Non-linear heat transfer problem, *J. Appl. Phys.* **30**, 11, 1683–1688 (1959).

A.7.5.17 ABARBANEL, S. S., Time dependent temperature distribution in radiating solids, *J. Math. Phys.* **39**, 4, 246–257 (1960).

A.7.5.18 FAIRALL, R. S., WELLS, R. A. and BELCHER, R. L., Unsteady-state heat transfer in solids with radiation at one boundary, *Trans. ASME* (*Journal Heat Transfer*) C **84**, 3, 266–267 (1962).

A.7.5.19 YANG, K. T., Transient conduction in a semi-infinite solid with variable thermal conductivity, *J. Appl. Mech.* **25**, 1, 146–147 (1958).

A.7.5.20 GOODMAN, T. R., The heat-balance integral — further considerations and refinements, *Trans. ASME* (*Journal Heat Transfer*) C **83**, 1, 83–86 (1961).

A.7.5.21 YANG, K. T. and SZEWCZYK, A., An approximate treatment of unsteady heat conduction in semi-infinite solids with variable thermal properties, *Trans. ASME* (*Journal Heat Transfer*) C **81**, 3, 251–252 (1959).

A.7.5.22 KOH, J. C. Y., One-dimensional heat conduction with arbitrary heating rate and variable properties, *J. Aero. Sci.* **28**, 12, 989–990 (1961).

A.7.5.23 GIEDT, W. H. and HORNBAKER, D. R., Transient temperature variation in a thermally orthotropic plate, *J. Amer. Rocket Soc.* **32**, 12, 1902–1909 (1962).

A.7.5.24 VENKATRAMAN, B., PATEL, S. A. and POHLE, F. V., A note on the transient temperature distribution in an orthotropic sphere due to aerodynamic heating, *J. Aero. Sci.* **29**, 5, 628–629 (1962).

A.7.5.25 HOLTER, W. H. and GROVER, J. H., Insulation temperature for the transient heating of an insulated infinite metal slab, *ARS Journal* **30**, 9, 907–908 (1960).

A.7.5.26 SCHNIEWIND, J., Ein Wärmeleitproblem in einem zusammengesetzten Körper, *Forsch. Ing. Wes.* **25**, 6, 196–198 (1959).

A.7.5.27 HARRIS, JR., R. S. and DAVIDSON, J. R., *An analysis of exact and approximate equations for the temperature distribution in an insulated thick skin subjected to aerodynamic heating*, NASA TN D–519 (1961).

A.7.5.28 BROGAN, J. J. and SCHNEIDER, P. J., Heat conduction in a series composite wall, *Trans. ASME* (*Journal Heat Transfer*) C **83**, 4, 506–508 (1961).

A.7.5.29 ENGL, W., Instationäre Wärmeleitungsvorgänge in stückweise homogenen Medien, *Zeitschr. Angew. Math. Mech.* **42**, 4/5, 163–173 (1962).

A.7.5.30 WING, L. D., Approximate methods for one-dimensional heat-flow analysis, *J. Aero. Sci.* **29**, 6, 689–693 (1962).

A.7.5.31 REID, W. P., Linear heat flow in a composite slab, *J. Aero. Sci.* **29**, 8, 905–908 (1962).

A.7.5.32 REID, W. P., Heat flow in composite slab, cylinder, and sphere, *J. Franklin Inst.* **274**, 5, 352–357 (1962)

A.7.5.33 STONECYPHER, T. E., Periodic temperature distribution in a two-layer composite slab, *J. Aero. Sci* **27**, 2, 152–153 (1960).

A.7.5.34 CAMPBELL, W. F., Periodic temperature distribution in a two-layer composite slab, *J. Aero. Sci.* **27**, 8, 633–634 (1960).

A.7.6.12 CONTI, R. J., *Approximate temperature distributions and streamwise heat conduction effects in the transient aerodynamic heating of thin-skinned bodies*, NASA TN D-895 (1961).

A.7.6.13 THOMSON, R. G. and SANDERS JR., J. L., *Effect of chordwise heat conduction on the torsional stiffness of a diamond-shaped wing subjected to a constant heat input*, NASA TN D-38 (1959).

A.7.7.4 GUINN, G. R., Aerodynamic heating of plane bodies of low thermal diffusivity, *J. Amer. Rocket Soc.* **31**, 1, 158–160 (1961).

A.7.8.1 CITRON, S. J., Heat conduction in a melting slab, *J. Aero. Sci.* **27**, 3, 219–228 (1960).

A.7.8.2 SANDERS, R. W., Transient heat conduction in a melting finite slab: An exact solution, *J. Amer. Rocket Soc.* **30**, 11, 1030–1031 (1960).

A.7.8.3 CHEN, S.-Y. and ALLEN, S. J., Similarity analysis for transient melting and vaporizing ablation, *J. Amer. Rocket Soc.* **32**, 10, 1536–1543 (1962).

A.7.8.4 GOODMAN, T. R., The heat-balance integral and its application to problems involving a change of phase, *Trans. ASME* **80**, 335–342 (1958).

A.7.8.5 GOODMAN, T. R. and SHEA, J. J., The melting of finite slabs, *Trans. ASME* (*Journal Applied Mechanics*) *E* **27**, 1, 16–24 (1960).

A.7.8.6 BIOT, M. A. and DAUGHADAY, H., Variational analysis of ablation, *J. Aero. Sci.* **29**, 2, 227–229 (1962).

A.7.8.7 LOTKIN, M., The calculation of heat flow in melting solids, *Quart. Appl. Math.* **18**, 1, 79–85 (1960).

A.7.8.8 KADANOFF, L. P., Radiative transport within an ablating body, *Trans. ASME* (*Journal Heat Transfer*) *C* **83**, 2, 215–225 (1961).

Chapter A.8

A.8.2.5 *Addendum to Section* 8.2.5

In Section 8.2.5 it was concluded that convergence (or stability) in finite difference methods was not affected by boundary conditions on finite bodies, provided that the boundary condition was satisfied by continuing the body beyond the boundary. If this is not done—and this happens often—the heat capacity of the half-section of width $\Delta x/2$ extending from point 1 to the midpoint between the points 1 and 2 in Fig. 8.5 is neglected, involving, of course, additional numerical errors. Therefore Dusinberre (Ref. 6.6) proposed to satisfy the boundary conditions by establishing for the above mentioned half-section a separate heat balance with the section thermal capacity taken into account. However, additional and in many cases more severe convergence conditions are incurred thereby. To avoid this disadvantage a method has been proposed in Ref. A.8.19.

A.8.3 *Addendum to Section* 8.3

The stability of the finite difference equations (8.2.2), (8.3.2) and (8.7.1) has been investigated in Ref. A.8.20 where numerical results were also given for a slab of homogeneous material divided into 20 sections; this number of sections appears, however unnecessarily large in view of what has been said in Section 8.2.7. Boundary conditions were satisfied by Dusinberre's method mentioned above and this gives additional restrictions for the largest possible time step. The finite difference equation of Crank and Nicolson, Eq. (8.3.2), has been extended to heat flow problems in cylinders (Ref. A.8.21).

A.8.6 *Addendum to Section* 8.6

The set of ordinary differential equations which are obtained by the method of lumped heat capacities and resistances, can be solved by matrix-eigenvalue methods of a kind successfully used in vibration problems (Ref. A.8.22).

A.8.7.2 *Addendum to Section* 8.7.2

The integral form of the heat conduction equation has been used for solving cases when the surface heat-flow rate depends on the time and the surface temperature; for the temperature profile a polynomial of the third degree (Ref. A. 8.23) was assumed. Further refinements of the method given in Ref. A.7.5.20 include the use of a polynomial of fourth degree and extensions to cases with temperature-dependent thermal properties.

A review of Biot's method was given by Lardner (Ref. A.8.24) as well as extensions of its applications to problems with given rate of heat flow at the surface, non-linear boundary conditions and temperature-dependent thermal properties.

References

A.8.19   BACK, H. L., Numerical approximation of the convective boundary condition, *Trans. ASME* (*Journal Heat Transfer*) C **84**, 1, 89–90 (1962).

A.8.20   GAUMER, G. R., Stability of three finite difference methods of solving for transient temperatures, *ARS Journal* **32**, 10, 1595–1597 (1962).

A.8.21   ALBASINY, E. L., On the numerical solution of a cylindrical heat-conduction problem, *Quart. J. Mech. Appl. Math.* **13**, 3, 374–384 (1960).

A.8.22   GURTIN, M. E., On the use of normal coordinates for the solution of lumped parameter transient heat-transfer problems, *J. Aero. Sci.* **27**, 5, 357–360 (1960).

A.8.23   GOODMAN, T. R., The heating of slabs with arbitrary heat inputs, *J. Aero. Sci.* **26**, 3, 187–188 (1959).

A.8.24   LARDNER, T. J., Biot's variational principle in heat conduction, *AIAA Journal* **1**, 1, 196–206 (1963).

Additional references:

A.8.25   LARDNER, T. J. and POHLE F. V., Application of the heat-balance integral to problems of cylindrical geometry, *Trans. ASME* (*Journal Applied Mechanics*) E **28**, 2, 310–312 (1961).

A.8.26   ELROD, JR., H. G., Improved lumped parameter method for transient heat conduction calculations, *Trans. ASME* (*Journal Heat Transfer*) C **82**, 3, 181–188 (1960).

A.8.27   OLIPHANT, T. A., An implicit, numerical method for solving two-dimensional time-dependent diffusion problems, *Quart. Appl. Math.* **19**, 3, 221–229 (1961).

A.8.28   VARGA, R. S., On higher order stable implicit methods for solving parabolic partial differential equations, *J. Math. Phys.* **40**, 3, 220–231 (1961).

A.8.29   UNTERBERG, W., Simple graphical method for temperature distribution in bodies with linear change in environment temperature, *J. Aero. Sci.* **28**, 1, 78–79 (1961).

Chapter A.9

A.9.5.1 *Radiators for spacecraft*

In space vehicles there is a considerable amount of waste heat (from propulsion units, electronic equipment, passengers and similar) which must be removed from the vehicle. On the other hand in many cases solar radiation has to be collected. In both cases heat transfer occurs only by thermal radiation, since space is devoid of a medium to which heat could be transfered by convection. The importance of radiator design is emphasized by the fact that the radiator for disposal of waste heat may be the largest component in a spacecraft. Because the surface temperature is limited in view of the material available and the coefficient of emission can not be larger than one, the heat dissipated by radiation per unit surface is fixed and given by the law of Stefan and Boltzmann (Eq. 3.6.4). Hence the total heat transfered from a spacecraft can be increased only by an increase in the surface area. This means that the spacecraft or parts of it have to be formed as effective and often compact radiators. Design principles for these are well known for *convective* heat transfer, but they can not be applied to spacecraft, because in space heat transfer occurs only by radiation. While in radiators operating predominantly by convective heat transfer, the cooling is not much reduced by surfaces which are facing each other, if they are not too close to each other, this is no longer true for radiators operating by thermal radiation only. The efficiency of this kind of radiator can be severely reduced by mutual radiation depending on the extent to which these surfaces "see each other". Hence it may often not suffice to treat fins as if they were alone in space, but all mutual radiation between surfaces in the whole spacecraft (body and fins) must be taken into account.

Investigations reported in this section refer to steady radiative heat transfer. Often the environment into which heat radiation takes place is assumed at an absolute temperature of zero (i.e. there is no re-radiation from the environment) or at finite absolute temperature when re-radiation must be taken into account. For a general survey on this problem, see Refs. A.3.6.6 and A.9.22.

A.9.5.2 *Thermal radiation from a single fin*

The temperature distribution in and the heat radiated from fins for spacecraft are determined by heat conduction in shells, bars or spikes, and heat transfer by thermal radiation at the surfaces. Usually constant temperature in the cross-section of the fin can be assumed. If heat transfer by grey-body radiation (see Section 3.6.2) occurs with surroundings at a temperature $T_\infty (= \text{const.})$ and no heat exchange with other bodies or between different parts of the surface of the fin (i.e. there are only plane or convex surfaces), then Eq. (5.2.9) is valid if the second term on the right-hand side of this equation is replaced by $U\varepsilon C_\sigma(T_\infty^4 - T^4)$ where ε is the hemispherical emissivity and C_σ the black-body radiation constant (see Section 3.6.3); otherwise the same notations are used and one obtains

$$\frac{d}{dx}\left(kF\frac{dT}{dx}\right) + U\varepsilon C_\sigma(T_\infty^4 - T^4) = 0 \qquad (A.9.5.1)$$

In general k depends on T; F and U on x; a general solution in closed form is not possible except for a shell of constant cross-section and constant k; then Eq. (A.9.5.1) becomes

$$\frac{d^2 T}{dx^2} + \frac{U\varepsilon C_\sigma}{Fk}(T_\infty^4 - T^4) = 0 \qquad (A.9.5.2)$$

and a solution of implicit form can be obtained with the help of the relation $d^2T/dx^2 = (1/2)d(p^2)/dT$ where $p = dT/dx$; with $(U\varepsilon C_\sigma)/(Fk) = B$ Eq. (A.9.5.2) becomes finally

$$\int_T^{\textbf{\textit{T}}} \frac{dT}{\sqrt{(2B\int[T^4 - T_\infty^4]dT + C_1)}} = x + C_2 \qquad (A.9.5.3)$$

Chosing a suitable lower limit in the integrals, the integration constants C_1 and C_2 follow as usual from the boundary conditions. For practical applications, fins of minimum mass are of importance. Fins of the following forms of cross-section have been treated: Rectangular in Refs. A.9.23 to A.9.26, triangular in A.9.27, with exponential sides† in Ref. A.9.28

---

† Mutual radiation between different places on the concave surface was not taken into account; this would appear permissible for walls that are only slightly concave.

and fins in the form of annuli with constant thickness in Ref. A.9.29. A thorough analytical investigation of fins having minimum mass was made by Wilkins (Ref. A.9.30); simplifications in the mathematical treatment are possible for fins of minimum mass. Additional conditions such as specified minimum thickness or a minimum height of the fin could be taken into account; spikes have also been treated. The fin of optimum form has 61 per cent of the mass of the lightest rectangular fin and 91 per cent of the lightest triangular fin.

A.9.5.3 *Mutual radiation between surfaces of spacecraft*

So far radiation from a single fin alone has been considered. However, mutual radiation occurs in most cases between two or more fins and bettween most of the radiating surfaces in an arrangement of fins and supporting bodies; in addition, inside fins and bodies there is also heat flow by conduction. For these complicated and general cases,—even allowing for fins of varying cross-sections—the basic integro-differential equations are given in Ref. A.9.31 for the following arrangements of fins with supporting bodies: (a) Parallel fins on and directed normal to a plane body, (b) longitudinal fins on a cylinder and (c) annular fins on a cylinder with their midplanes normal to the cylinder axis. For simplicity fins of constant cross-section were assumed in the following papers: In Ref. A.9.32 basic solutions were obtained for two plane rectangular fins, joined at one edge with various joint angles[†]. This basic case has been applied among others to the above case (b) and to fins arranged in a zig-zag pattern (similar to a corrugated roof) and mounted on a plane surface. In Ref. A.9.33 a fin was investigated in the form of a flat plate of finite width connected at the edges to two cylindrical base-surfaces; as usual, heat conduction was allowed within the fin, but on the base surfaces the temperature was assumed constant. A fin arrangement as under (c) above has been treated in Ref. A.9.34; in this case only black-body radiation was considered.

References

A.9.22   CALLINAN, J. P. and BERGGREN, W. P., Some radiator design criteria for space vehicles, *Trans. ASME (Journal Heat Transfer)* **C 81**, 3, 237–244 (1959).

A.9.23   BARTAS, J. G. and SELLERS, W. H., Radiation fin effectiveness, *Trans. ASME (Journal Heat Transfer)* **C 82**, 1, 73–75 (1960).

A.9.24   LIEBLEIN, S., *Analysis of temperature distribution and radiant heat transfer along a rectangular fin of constant thickness*, NASA TN D-196 (1959).

---

† This problem differs from a similar one in Ref. 8.3.6.18 in that heat conduction inside the solid fin is allowed for and hence wall temperatures vary along the surface.

A.9.25   LIU, C.-Y., On minimum-weight rectangular radiating fins, *J. Aero. Sci.* **27**, 11, 871–872 (1960).

A.9.26   LIU, C.-Y., On optimum rectangular cooling fins, *Quart. Appl. Math.* **19**, 1, 72–75 (1961).

A.9.27   NILSON, E. N. and CURRY, R., The minimum-weight straight fin of triangular profile radiating to space, *J. Aero. Sci.* **27**, 2, 146–147 (1960).

A.9.28   GRANET, I. and McILROY, W., Optimum radiant straight fin with exponential sides, *ARS Journal* **31**, 1, 80–82 (1961).

A.9.29   CHAMBERS, R. L. and SOMERS, E. V., Radiation fin efficiency for one-dimensional heat flow in a circular fin, *Trans. ASME (Journal Heat Transfer)* **C 81**, 4, 327–329 (1959).

A.9.30   WILKINS JR., J. E., Minimum mass thin fins for space radiators, *Proc. 1960 Heat Transfer and Fluid Mechanics Institute*, 229–243 (1960).

A.9.31   ECKERT, E. R. G., IRVINE JR., T. F. and SPARROW, E. M., Analytic formulation for radiating fins with mutual irradiation, *ARS Journal* **30**, 7, 644–646 (1960).

A.9.32   SPARROW, E. M., ECKERT, E. R. G. and IRVINE JR., T. F., The effectiveness of radiation fins with mutual irradiation, *J. Aero. Sci.* **28**, 10, 763–772, 778 (1961).

A.9.33   SPARROW, E. M. and ECKERT, E. R. G., Radiant interaction between fin and base surfaces, *Trans. ASME (Journal Heat Transfer)* **C 84**, 1, 12–18 (1962).

A.9.34   SPARROW, E. M., MILLER, G. B. and JONSSON, V. K., Radiating effectiveness of annular-finned space radiators, including mutual irradiation between radiator elements, *J. Aero. Sci.* **29**, 11, 1291–1299 (1962).

Additional references:

A.9.35   STOCKMAN, N. O. and KRAMER, J. L., *Effect of variable thermal properties on one-dimensional heat transfer in radiating fins*, NASA TN D-1878 (1963).

A.9.36   REYNOLDS, W. C., A design-oriented optimization of simple tapered radiating fins, *Trans. ASME (Journal Heat Transfer)* **C 85**, 3, 193–202 (1963).

Chapter A.10

A.10.1 *Addendum to Section* 10.1

For the case of two-dimensional heat-flow formulae are given in Ref. A.10.8 for conductivities between points in a field whose lumped elements are of arbitrary shape. The results can be applied to steady and transient heat flow. For a general survey on analogues, see Ref. A.10.9.

A.10.3 *Addendum to Section* 10.3

In Refs. A.10.10 and A.10.11 examples are given of direct discrete electrical analogues for transient heat conduction; in the equipment of Ref. A.10.10 transient electrical voltages change comparatively slowly, while in that of Ref. A.10.11 and of Ref. A.10.15 they change comparatively rapidly and are displayed as a standing pattern on a cathode ray tubo. In Ref. A.10.12 an analogue of the same kind and of the "slow" type useful for work in connection with heat flow in structures due to aerodynamic heating is described; the equipment is simple and contains function generators for simulating variable adiabatic wall temperatures and variable heat transfer coefficients. In Refs. A.10.13 and A.10.14 combined geometric and network analogues are described with continuous conductances and discontinuous capacities. A description of electrical analogues of the discrete type for cylindrical and spherical heat flow can be found in Ref. A.10.15.

References

A.10.8   GAIR, F. C., Unifying design principle for the resistance network analogue, *Brit. J. Appl. Phys.* **10**, 4, 166–172 (1959).

A.10.9   HELDENFELS, R. R., Models and analogs, *AGARDograph* **28**, 323–354 (1958).

A.10.10   GUILE, A. E. and CARNE, E. B., An analysis of an analogue solution applied to the heat conduction problem in a cartridge fuse, *Trans. Amer. Inst. Electr. Engnrs* Part I, **72**, 861–868 (1953).

A.10.11   ROBERTSON, A. F. and GROSS, D., An electrical-analog method for transient heat-flow analysis, *J. Res. Nat. Bur. Stand.* **61**, 2, 105–115 (1958).

A.10.12   ROBINSON, H. G. R., An analogue computer for convective heating problems, *Aero. Res. Council, Current Paper* No. 374 (1957).

A.10.13   PASCHKIS, V., Combined geometric and network analog computer for transient heat flow, *Trans. ASME (Journal Heat Transfer)* C **81**, 2, 144–150 (1959).

A.10.14   CLARK, A. V., A simplified method for the study of two-dimensional transient heat flow using resistance paper, *ASME Preprint* 57–S–9 (1957).

A.10.15   LAWSON, D. I. and McGUIRE, J. H., The solution of transient heat-flow problems by analogous electrical network, Pt. I and II, *Engineer, London* **196**, 5090, 217–219, 249–252 (1953).

Additional reference:

A.10.16   DEAN, L. E., The solution of two-dimensional steady state heat-transfer problems by the use of electrically conductive paper, *ARS Preprint*, 246–55 (1955).

Chapter A.11

For additional references see Ref. A.10.9 and A.11.5.

Reference

A.11.5   DUGUNDJI, J. and CALLIGEROS, J. M., Similarity laws for aerothermoelastic testing, *J. Aero. Sci.* **29**, 8, 935–950 (1962).

AUTHOR INDEX

(Italic figures correspond to the pages where the Author's name occurs in a reference list.)

Abarbanel, S. S., 167, *181*, 315, *318*
Adams, M. C., 29, *48*
Albasiny, E. L., 320, *320*
Albers, L. U., 310, *312*, 315, *318*
Allen, D. N. de G., 113, 125, *127*, 224, *239*
Allen, S. J., 317, *319*
Ambrosio, A., 275, *281*
Ashkenas, H., 19, *47*
Askwyth, W. H., 306, *312*

Bachmann, H., 145, *180*
Back, H. L., 319, *320*
Barber, A. D., 270, *281*
Bartas, J. G., 322, *323*
Bartz, D. R., 25, *47*
Barzelay, M. E., 85–88, *89*, *90*
Baxter, A. N., 314, *317*
Beckmann, W., 74, *89*
Beckwith, I. E., 16, 20, 21, 22, 24, *47*
Belcher, R. L., 315, *318*
Berggren, W. P., 322, *323*
Bergles, A. E., 315, *318*
Berman, I., *255*
Betz, A., 127, *127*
Biot, M. A., 226, *239*, 304, 305, *306*, 317, *319*
Bobco, R. P., 309, *312*
Boehringer, J. C., 306, 307, 309, *312*
Boison, I. C., 21, *47*
Boley, B. A., 270, *281*
Braslow, A. L., 40, *49*
Brinich, P. F., 34, *48*
Brogan, J. J., 316, *318*
Brooks Jr., W. A., 255, *280*
Brull, M. A., 64, *89*
Brunot, A. W., 85, 87, *89*
Bryson, A. E., 163, 164, 165, *181*

Buckland, F. F., 85, 87, *89*
Budiansky, B., 164, 165, *181*
Burbank, P. B., 36, *48*
Buschman Jr., A. J., 307, *312*
Bussel, B., 275, *281*

Calligeros, I. M., 288, *303*, 325
Callinan, J. P., 322, *323*
Campbell, W. F., 152, *180*, *181*, 317, *319*
Carne, E. B., 324, *325*
Carrier, G. F., 164, 165, *181*
Carslaw, H. S., 50, 63, 66, *88*, 93, 104, 128, 129, 130, 131, 136, 139, 140, 141, 142, 144, 145, 156, 160, 162, *180*, 243, 244, 256, 258, 260, 261, 263, 264, 268
Chambers, R. L., 323, *324*
Chambré, P. L., 315, *318*
Chapman, D., 26, *47*
Charters, A. C., 40, *49*
Chen, S.-Y., 258, 267, 270, *280*, 314, 317, *317*, *319*
Cheng, H. K., 305, *306*
Citron, S. J., 317, *319*
Clark, A. V., 325, *325*
Clutter, D. W., 39, 40, *49*
Cohen, N. B., 29, *48*
Conti, R. J., 317, *319*
Costello, F. A., 309, 311, *312*, *313*
Coulbert, C. D., 86, *90*
Crabtree, L. F., 29, *48*
Crank, J., 60, *89*, 207, *239*, 320
Curry, R., 322, *324*
Curtiss, H. A., 21, *47*

Daughaday, H., 317, *319*
Davidson, J. R., 316, *318*
Dean, L. E., *325*

Dhawan, S., 40, *49*
Dolton, T. A., 224, 225, *239*
Dorrance, W. H., 27, *48*
Drake Jr., R. M., 14, 75, 78, 80, 81, *88*
Driest, E. R. van, 17, 18, 29, 40, *47*, *49*
Dugundji, J., 288, *303*, *325*
Duncan, W. J., 288, *303*
Dunkle, R. V., 79, *89*, 274
Dunning, R. W., 39, *48*
Dusinberre, G. M., 125, *127*, 184, 319, 320
Dzung, L. S., 305, *306*

Eckert, E. R. G., 14, 75, 78, 80, 81, *88*, 306, 308, 310, 311, *312*, *313*, 323, *324*
Edwards, D. K., 306, *311*
Edwards, R. H., 163, 164, *181*
Elrod Jr., H. G., *321*
Emmons, H. W., 125, *127*, 164, *181*
Engl, W., 316, *318*
Englert, G. W., 23, *47*
Eyres, N. R., 59, *89*

Fairall, R. S., 315, *318*
Fannelöp, T., 37, *48*
Fay, J. A., 21, 28, 29, *47*
Feldman, S., 15, *47*
Fenech, H., 311, *313*
Fishenden, M., 76, *89*
Forray, M., 314, *317*
Forsythe, G. E., 185, *239*
Frank, I., 62, 270, *281*, 310, *313*
Frankel, S. P., 126, *127*
Freed, N. H., *239*
French, F. W., *281*
Fried, E., 311, *313*
Fritz, R. J., 152, *181*

Gair, F. C., 324, *325*
Gardon, R., 307, *312*
Gatewood, B. E., 261, 273, *280*, *281*
Gaumer, G. R., 320, *320*
Gebhart, B., 308, 309, *312*
Giedt, W. H., 316, *318*
Gier, J. T., 79, *89*, 274
Goldberg, M. A., 267, *280*

Goldsmith, A., 144, *180*
Goodman, T. R., 67, 69, *89*, 315, 317, *318*, *319*, 320, *320*
Gordon, C. K., 275, *281*
Graaf, J. G. A. de, 73, 74, *89*
Graff, W. J., 311, *313*
Granet, I., 322, *324*
Gray, E. I., 310, *313*
Green Jr., L., 26, *48*
Gregg, J. L., 309, *312*, 323
Griffith, G. E., 270, 271, *281*
Gröbner, W., 161, *181*
Grosh, R. J., 307, 313, *314*
Gross, D., 324, *325*
Grover, J. H., 150, 151, *180*, 316, *318*
Gruenewald, K. H., 21, 22, *47*
Guile, A. E., 324, *325*
Guinn, G. R., 317, *319*
Gurney, H. P., 145, *180*
Gurtin, M. E., 320, *320*

Hamilton, D. C., 307, *312*
Hanawalt, A. J., 166, *181*, 305
Haneman, W. S., 218, *239*
Hansen, C. F., 29, *48*
Harris Jr., R. S., 316, *318*
Hartree, D. R., 59, *89*, 137, *180*, 218, *239*
Hatch, J. E., 315, *318*
Hayes, R. J., 306, *312*
Hayes, W. D., 27, 41, 42, *48*
Heaps, N. S., 159, *181*
Heisler, M. P., 145, *180*
Held, E. F. M. van der, 73, 74, *89*
Heldenfels, R. R., 324, *325*
Hele-Shaw, H. S., 283, *287*
Hildebrand, F. B., *307*
Hill, P. R., 172, *181*, 317
Hilsenrath, J., 15, *47*
Hirschhorn, H. J., 144, *180*
Hodge, B. L., 36, *48*
Hoff, N. J., 240, 242, 253, 261, 264, 271, 272, 273, *280*
Hofreiter, N., 161, *181*
Hollo, G., 85, 87, *89*
Holloway, G. F., 85–88, *89*, 90
Holter, W. H., 150, 151, *180*, 316, *318*
Hornbaker, D. R., 316, *318*

Horton, E. A.,   40, *49*
Hottel,   308
Howe, J. T.,   26, *48*
Howe, R. M.,   218, *239*
Howell, J. R.,   *313*
Hyman, M. A.,   185, 186, 194, *239*

Ingham, J.,   59, *89*
Irvine Jr., T. F.,   323, *324*
Ishimoto, T.,   275, *281*

Jackson, R.,   59, *89*
Jacobs, R. B.,   311, *313*
Jaeger, J. C.,   50, 63, 66, *88*, 93, 104,
   128, 129, 130, 131, 136, 139, 140, 141,
   142, 144, 145, 156, 160, 162, *180*, 243,
   244, 256, 258, 260, 261, 263, 264, 268
Jakob, M.,   75, 84, *88*
Johnson, C. H. J.,   159, *181*
Jones, R. A.,   151, 152, *180*
Jonsson, V. K.,   310, *313*, 323, *324*

Kadanoff, L. P.,   317, *319*
Kamke, E.,   *218*
Kaplan, S.,   185, 186, 194, *239*
Karplus, W. J.,   286, *287*
Kaye, J.,   235, 236, *239*, 271, 315, *318*
Kemp, N. H.,   21, 28, 29, *47*
Kirchner, H. P.,   306, *312*
Knox, E. C.,   40, *49*
Knuth, E. L.,   285, 287
Koh, J. C. Y.,   316, *318*
Kopal, Z.,   *20*
Korkegi, R. H.,   40, *49*
Korobkin, I.,   21, 22, *47*
Kouwenhoven, W. B.,   87, *89*, 311
Kramer, J. L.,   *324*
Kumm, E. L.,   285, *287*

Laasonen, P.,   222, 224, *239*
Landau, H. G.,   67, *89*, 179, 180
Langhaar, H. L.,   288, *303*
Lardner, T. J.,   *281*, 316, 320, *320*, 321
Larson, H. K.,   46, *49*

Lawson, D. I.,   324, 325, *325*
Lees, L.,   23, 24, 30, *47*, 67, *89*
Leppert, G.,   211, *239*
Lieblein, S.,   322, *323*
Liebmann, G.,   224, *239*, 286
Liebmann, H.,   124, *127*
Liepmann, H. W.,   40, *49*
Lighthill, M. J.,   26, *48*, 163
Linn, C. C.,   37, *48*
Liu, C.,   86, *90*
Liu, C.-Y.,   322, *324*
Lotkin, M.,   317, *319*
Lu, P.-C.,   *314*
Lurie, J.,   145, *180*
Lutz, O.,   127, *127*

MacInnes, W. F.,   275, *281*
Manos, P.,   309, *312*, 323
Mayer, E.,   148, 149, 151, *180*, 316
McAdams, W. H.,   75, 76, 80, *88*
McGuire, J. H.,   324, 325, *325*
McIlroy, W.,   322, *324*
Mersman, W. A.,   26, *48*
Michel, R.,   37, *48*
Mickley, H. S.,   26, *48*
Mikk, G.,   306, *312*
Miller, G. B.,   323, *324*
Miltonberger, G. H.,   270, 271, *281*
Moeckel, W. E.,   34, *48*
Monaghan, R. J.,   15, 17, 18, 19, 29, *47*, *48*
Moore, A. D.,   283, 284, *287*
Moore, F. K.,   9, *46*
Morgan, W. R.,   307, *312*
Morkovin, M. V.,   40, *49*
Mull, W.,   73, *89*
Münch, B.,   306, *312*
Murray, W. D.,   79, *89*

Nall, K. L.,   26, *48*
Newman, M.,   314, *317*
Nicolson, P.,   207, *239*, 320
Nilson, E. N.,   322, *324*

O'Brien, G. G.,   185, 186, 194, *239*
Ojalvo, I. U.,   314, *317*

Oliphant, T. A., *321*
Oliver, H., 250, 251, 264, 271, 273, *280*
Oppenheim, A. K., 83, *89*

Pappas, C. C., 26, *48*
Parker, H. M., 158, *181*
Parkes, E. W., 250, 251, 261, 271, *280*
Paschkis, V., 325, *325*
Patel, S. A., 316, *318*
Perlmutter, M., *313*
Phythian, J. E., 315, *318*
Pittman, C. M., 307, *312*
Pohle, F. V., 250, 251, 255, 264, 271, 273, *280*, *281*, 316, *318*, *321*
Potter, J. H., 87, *89*, 311
Probstein, R. F., 27, 29, 37, 41, 42, *48*

Quinville, J. A., 275, *281*

Rallis, C. J., *239*
Rayleigh, L., 73, *89*
Reid, W. P., 316, *318*
Reiher, H., 73, *89*
Reshotko, E., 16, 20, 21, 22, 23, 24, *47*
Reynolds, W. C., 224, 225, *239*, *324*
Richtmyer, R. D., 110, 183, 185, 208, 222, 223, 224, *239*
Riddell, F. R., 19, 21, 28, 29, *47*, 305, *306*
Roberts, L., 67, *89*
Robertson, A. F., 324, *325*
Robinson, H. G. R., 324, *325*
Roddick, R. D., 306, *311*
Rohsenow, W. M., 311, *313*
Rose, P. H., 29, *48*
Roshko, A., 40, *49*
Ross, R. C., 26, *48*
Rubesin, M. W., 26, *47*, *48*, 305, *306*

Saelman, B., 138, *180*
Sanders, R. W., 317, *319*
Sanders Jr., J. L., 317, *319*
Sands, N., 34, *48*
Saper, P. G., 315, *318*
Sarjant, R. J., 59, *89*

Saunders, O. A., 76, *89*
Schaaf, S. F., 42, *49*
Schacht, R. L., 315, *318*
Schapker, R. L., 315, *318*
Schlichting, H., 19, 20, 24, *46*
Schmidt, C. M., 166, *181*, 305
Schmidt, E., 95, 184, *239*
Schneider, P. J., 126, *127*, 316, *318*
Schniewind, J., 316, *318*
Schuh, H., 86, 87, 88, *90*, 120, 122, *127*, 165, 166, *181*, 204, 212, 214, 222, 227, 228, 229, *239*, 251, 261, *280*, *281*
Sellers, W. H., 322, *323*
Severn, R. T., 224, *239*
Shea, J. J., 317, *319*
Short, B. J., 18, *47*
Siegel, R., 310, *313*
Singham, J. R., 79, *89*
Slote, L., 79, *89*
Smith, A. M. O., 39, 40, *49*
Snyder, N. W., 79, *89*, 274
Sobey, A. J., 288, 301, *303*
Somers, E. W., 323, *324*
Sommer, C. S., 18, *47*
Soroka, W. W., *287*
Southwell, R. V., 113, 125, *127*
Sparrow, E. M., 306, 307, 308, 309, 310, 311, *312*, *313*, 322, 323, *324*
Spindler, R. J., 306, 307, 309, *312*
Squyers, A. L., 26, *48*
Starr, C., 311, *313*
Stockman, N. O., *324*
Stonecypher, T. E., 317, *319*
Sutton, G. W., 67, *89*
Szel, J. V., 309, *312*, 323
Szewczyk, A., 315, *318*

Tearnen, J. C., 174, *181*
Thomas, P. D., 314, *317*
Thomson, R. G., 317, *319*
Tideman, M., 158, 161, 162, 164, *181*
Tong, K. N., 85, 87, *89*
Tribus, M., 305, *306*
Trimpi, R. L., 151, 152, *180*
Truitt, R. W., *46*
Tsien, H. S., 43, *49*
Tucker, M., 24, *47*

Ulmann, E. F., 39, *48*
Unterberg, W., 314, *317*, *321*
Usiskin, C. M., 310, *313*

Varga, R. S., *321*
Vassallo, F. A., 306, *312*
Venkatraman, B., 316, *318*
Vinson, J. R., 64, *89*
Viskanta, R., 307, 313, *314*
Vodička, V., *104*, 313, *314*

Wagstaff, J. B., 59, *89*

Wasow, W. R., 185, *239*
Waterman, T. E., 144, *180*
Weiner, J. H., 270, *281*
Wells, R. A., 315, *318*
Wilkins Jr., J. E., 323, *324*
Wing, L. D., 316, *318*
Wolf, F., *127*
Womersley, J. R., 218, *239*
Woods, B. H., 29, *48*

Yang, K.-T., 315, *318*
Young, D., 126, *127*

SUBJECT INDEX

Ablation, 6–8, 66–72, 176–180, 285, 306, 317–318
Absorptivity, 43, 78, 79, 306, 307
Accuracy of finite difference method, 120–122, 182, 198–204, 212, 214, 221
Adiabatic wall temperature, 3, 12, 14–16
Aerodynamic heating, 4, 9–46
  moderate, 4
  severe, 4, 23, 28, 159, 252, 265, 277, 293, 300, 314
Analogues, 91, 282, 324, 325
  direct, 282–285
  electrical, 92, 282, 283, 285, 286, 324, 325
    "fast type", 324
    "slow type", 324
  equipment for aerodynamic heating problems, 324, 325
  for steady heat flow, 283, 324
  for transient heat flow, 284, 324, 325
  indirect, 282, 286, 287
  mechanical, 92, 282–284
  mixed: continuous and discrete, 325
  of continuous type, 282, 283
  of discrete type, 282–287, 324, 325
Analytical solutions of heat flow equation,
  at large times, 144, 145, 147, 148, 243, 250, 251, 255, 256, 258, 264, 268
  at small times, 145, 147, 151, 152–156, 244, 246, 247–249, 253, 254, 263, 268
  for steady state, 97–104
    one-dimensional case, 97–104
    two-dimensional case, 104
  for transient state, 128–167, 240–271, 276, 277, 280
  obtained by,
    Laplace transformation, 129, 130, 141, 151, 246, 247, 253, 268, 280
    method of separation of variables, 128, 144, 148, 243, 258, 264, 268
    sources and sinks, 131, 160
Angle of incidence, influence on convective heat transfer, 31–33, 36
Auxiliary points in finite difference methods, 195–198, 200, 202, 205, 209, 216
  influence on solutions of explicit difference equation, 197, 198, 221

Behaviour of finite difference solutions, 182, 187–193, 197, 198, 205–207, 211, 213, 219, 220, 223
Biot modulus, 61, 144, 146, 151, 200–204, 268, 290–292, 298
Black body radiation, 77
Bluntness of a body, influence on convective heat transfer, 31, 34–36
Boundary conditions for internal heat flow, 52–56
  in analogues, 284, 287
  in analytical methods, 129, 131, 136, 148, 152–156, 167, 177
  in finite difference methods, 195–197, 204–206, 219, 319
  non-linear, 54–56, 94, 102, 103, 122, 123, 136, 169, 204, 205, 295–301, 315
  time-dependent, 53, 131, 136, 167, 262, 265–267, 317
Boundary layer in fluid flow, 3, 9–13, 16, 17, 23, 26, 29, 31, 36, 41
  hypersonic, 9, 13, 27–30
  interaction with shock waves, 41
  laminar, 11, 15, 18, 20, 22–24, 26, 28–30, 33, 36, 41, 46
  steady state, 9
  subsonic, 13
  supersonic, 9, 13

Boundary layer in fluid flow (*continued*)
　transient state, 9
　turbulent, 11, 15, 18, 26, 29, 33, 36, 46

Composite bodies and structures,
　methods of solving heat flow equations
　　in,
　　analytical, 152–156, 253–254, 258
　　using lumped heat capacities and
　　　resistances, 215–223, 284, 285
　　steady heat flow, 97, 98
　　transient heat flow, 93, 95, 147–156,
　　　215–223, 227–231, 241–280, 313, 317
　　two-dimensional heat flow in, 222, 223
Composite slabs or shells, 97, 147–156,
　313, 317
Composite structures (*see under*, Compo-
　site bodies and structures)
Computational work in finite difference
　methods, amount of,
　for steady-state heat flow, 111, 112,
　　116, 120
　for transient heat flow, 92, 93, 95, 182
　　explicit method (Schmidt–Binder), 199
　　implicit method (Crank–Nicolson),
　　　208
Conductance, thermal, 222, 284
　across interfaces, 56, 85, 267, 303, 311
　of joints, 86–88, 303
Conductivity, thermal, 15, 20, 50, 59,
　93, 104, 302
Contact resistance, thermal, (*see under*:
　Conductance, thermal)
Continuum flow, limits for, 42, 43
Convective heat transfer (*see under*, Heat
　transfer)
Cylindrical and spherical bodies:
　heat conduction in, 58, 59
　heat transfer on surface of,
　　forced convection, 20–23
　　free convection, 74–76
Cylindrical and spherical layers,
　heat conduction in, 100, 205–207

Diffusivity, thermal, 57
Dissociated air, convective heat transfer
　in, 27–29

Duhamel's method in transient heat flow,
　128, 131, 136, 167, 172, 174, 194
Dynamic viscosity, 15

Effective heat transfer coefficient in ther-
　mal radiation, 54
Emissivity, thermal, 4, 43, 78, 79
Enclosures, radiative heat flow in, 82–84,
　308
Enthalpy, 4, 14
　in flow with dissociation, 28
Equilibrium temperature, 4, 43–45, 97
Error function and function erfc (*x*), 140
Error in finite difference solutions, 94,
　182, 183, 199, 204, 223, 228, 232,
　236–238
Evaporation on ablating body, 7, 68, 70,
　143
Explicit finite difference equation in tran-
　sient heat flow (Schmidt–Binder),
　183–205
　boundary conditions for, 195–198, 204,
　　205
　for cylindrical and spherical bodies,
　　205–207
　for thin shells, 211, 213–215, 227–229
　solutions of, 186–188, 200, 202, 227,
　　228, 248, 277
　　accuracy, 198–204, 212, 214, 215
　　amount of computational work for,
　　　198–199
　　stability, 185
Exponent in law for friction coefficient,
　for laminar boundary layers, 19, 20, 157
　for turbulent boundary layers, 19, 20,
　　157

Finite difference equations for steady-state
　heat flow, 105–127
　boundary conditions in, 106, 109, 110,
　　115, 126
　in one-dimensional case, 106–112
　in two-dimensional case, 123–127
Finite difference equations for transient
　heat flow,
　accuracy, 182, 198–204, 212, 214, 221,
　　223

Finite difference equations for transient heat flow (*continued*)
behaviour, 182, 186–193, 197, 206, 207, 211, 213, 219–221, 223
boundary conditions in, 193–197, 204, 205, 219, 319
convergence, 94, 182, 183
explicit, 183–187, 192, 193, 199, 200, 205–207, 211–215
implicit, 207–211, 224, 320
in one-dimensional case, 183–222, 223, 224, 227–234
in two-dimensional case, 222, 223, 235–238
regularity of, 182, 186–189
stability of, 94, 182, 183, 185
Finite difference methods (*see under*, Finite difference equations)
Fins with thermal radiation at surface, 321–323
Flat plate, ideal, 10
heat transfer on, 17–20, 31, 33
at an angle of incidence, 31–33
at zero angle of attack, 17–20
Forced convection (*see under*, Heat transfer)
Free convection (*see under*, Heat transfer)

Graphical method, 123, 126, 127
Grashof number, 72
Grey-body radiation, 78, 308–310

Heat capacities, 95, 217, 284
Heat conduction equations in solids, 50
boundary conditions for, 52–56, 59, 102, 103, 129, 136, 137, 148, 152, 169, 171, 172, 177, 314, 315
for linear heat flow, 57, 97, 107, 148, 156, 241
for radial heat flow, 58, 100
for spherical heat flow, 58, 100
methods of solution for,
analytical, 93, 98–104, 128–131, 136, 137, 152–156
finite-difference, 94, 105–114, 182–184, 195–198, 205–208, 217–222, 223–226, 319, 320

semi-analytical, 94, 167–176, 317
using integral forms of equation, 224–226, 315, 320
variational, 226, 319, 320
shells of revolution, 62–63, 64–66
shells, spherical, 64
steady state, 92, 97, 99–101, 105, 107–109, 112, 123, 124
transient state, 50, 57–61, 63–66, 92, 93, 128, 137, 148, 156, 159, 177, 178, 241, 257, 276
with variable properties of materials, 59, 104, 315, 320
Heat reservoirs, 222
Heat transfer,
forced convection, 16–33, 51, 289, 304
at hypersonic speeds with dissociation, 27–30
free convection, 51, 54, 72–77, 94, 102, 273, 274, 295–301
in boundary layers,
with laminar flow, 17–26, 28–30, 33, 45, 157–165, 317
with turbulent flow, 17–26, 29, 33, 46, 157–162, 317
with variable wall temperature, 25, 26
radiative, 4, 43–45, 54, 77–84, 102, 273, 274, 295–299, 306–311, 315
Heat transfer coefficient (*see also*, Heat transfer)
definition, 3, 53, 54
effective, in radiative heat transfer, 54–56
Heat waves in transient heat flow, 94, 152–156, 253–256
Hydrocal, 284

Images in transient heat flow, 128, 131, 152–156, 253–256
Implicit finite difference equation, 207–211, 224
extensions to cylindrical flow, 320
methods of solving, 208
solutions, stability of, 208
Instantaneous plane heat source, 131, 186
Insulating layers, 149–151

Interaction of boundary layers with external flow, 41
Interfaces, thermal conductance of, 56, 84, 85, 87, 267, 303, 311
Irradiation, 2, 51

Joint, thermal conductance of, 86–88, 303

Kinematic viscosity, 17

Lambert's law, 77, 79, 306
Laplace transformation, 128–130, 246, 247, 253, 268, 280
  tables of Laplace transforms, 130
Lewis number, 27–29
Linearized expression for radiative heat transfer, 54
Liquid layer on ablating body, 67, 69–71
Lumped circuits, in heat flow problems, 94, 95, 215–222, 270, 284, 285, 320

Mach number, 3, 4, 9, 10, 13, 16, 18, 21, 22–24, 27, 32–35, 37–42, 235, 238, 271
Materials, thermal properties of, tables, 132–135
  transparent and semi-transparent, 306
Molecular mean free path, 42
Mutual radiation between fins and bodies, 321, 323

von Neumann's method for investigating stability of finite difference solutions, 185
Nusselt number, 20, 72–76

Orthotropic bodies, two-dimensional heat flow in, 316

Parameter p in finite difference equations, for steady heat flow, 108

for transient heat flow,
  in lumped circuits, 219
  in shells, 211
  inside solids, 184, 206
Penetration depth, 142, 225, 277
Prandtl number, 15, 17, 20, 72–76
Pressure gradient, influence on heat transfer, 23–25
Prototype in similarity laws, 292, 295, 299, 301

Radiation coefficient, 54, 103
Radiation constant of a black body (Boltzmann constant), 78
Radiative heat transfer, 4, 77–84, 305–311
  inside semi-transparent bodies, 307, 313
  methods of calculation, 80–84, 308–311
  minimum-mass fins for radiators, 323
  non-opaque surfaces, 306, 307, 309
  opaque surfaces, 77–84
Radiator for spacecraft, 321–323
Ratio of specific heats, 14
Rayleigh number, 72, 73
Recovery factor, 15, 16
Reference temperature in external heat transfer, 53, 54
Reflection,
  diffuse, 82, 83
  specular, 306, 310, 311
Reflectivity, 304, 306
Regions with different thermal properties, 147–152
Relaxation method,
  for steady heat flow, 112–114
  for transient heat flow, 224
Repeated integrals of the error function, $i^n \operatorname{erfc}(x)$, 142
Resistance,
  electrical, 282, 283, 285–287
  thermal, 62, 95, 98–102, 216, 285
Reynolds number, 9, 17, 18, 20, 34, 37

Sandwich wall, 229–232
Semi-analytical methods in transient heat flow, 167–176
Semi-infinite bodies, 139–142, 309

Semi-transparent material, heat flow in, 307, 309

Separation of variables, solutions obtained by, 128

Severe rates of aerodynamic heating, 4

Shape factor in radiative heat transfer, 80, 81, 307

Shell,
heat flow in, 60, 61, 99, 101, 107, 156–161, 317
conditions for uniform temperature in cross-section, 60, 61
with discontinuity in thickness, 276–280
with uniform temperature, 137–139, 314
spherical, heat flow in, 64

Shells of revolution,
heat flow in,
three-dimensional case, 64–66
two-dimensional case, 63

Similarity laws for heat flow in structures, 291, 294, 298, 300, 302, 325
external and internal heat transfer, 295–301
external heat transfer only, 289–295
for similar flight plans, 291, 295, 298, 300, 301
with joints, 303
with variable material properties, 301–303

Simulated laboratory testing of structures, 292, 295, 299, 301

Skins reinforced by stiffeners, temperatures in, 240–271
influence of contact resistance in joints, 267–271
influence of flight plans, 261–267
numerical examples, 227, 271–275
with convective heat transfer on skin surface, 240–251, 256–259
with internal heat transfer, 259–261
with rate of heat flow given at skin surface, 252–256
with uniform temperature in skin, 242–246

Slab, transient heat flow in, 144–147, 314

Solid fin, 231–234

Solid wing, 235–238

Sources and sinks in transient heat flow, 128, 131

Space vehicles, 304, 306

Spherical layers, heat flow in, 64

Stability of finite difference methods, 182, 183, 185

Stagnation point or line, heat transfer in, 16, 20–23, 30

Structures,
composite, 229, 240, 256, 267, 276
Hoff's particular case, 240–256

Thermal conductance,
across interfaces, 56, 84, 85, 87, 311
in gases, 85, 311
in vacuum, 311
across joints in metal sheets, 86–88

Thermal conductivity, 50, 97, 98

Thermal diffusivity, 57

Thermal emissivity, 78

Thermal environment, 2

Thermal radiation, 6, 77–79, 94, 102, 103
heat transfer by, 4, 6, 43, 54, 80–84
between black surfaces, 80–82
between grey surfaces, 308, 309
between solids, 84
in enclosures with grey walls, 82–84, 308–310
shape factors, 80, 81, 307, 309

Thermal resistance, 98, 99

Thermal shield, 6, 143

Thermal shock, 139, 143

Thin shell, heat conduction in, 106–110, 120–122, 156–167, 211–215, 276–280
explicit finite difference equations for, 211–215
accuracy of solutions, 212, 214
stability of solutions, 211–213
with uniform temperature, 137–139
with variable heat transfer along the surface, 156–165, 317

Total enthalpy, 15

Total temperature, 14

Transition between laminar and turbulent boundary layers, 11, 34, 36–40

Transpiration cooling, 26

Variational methods in,
 ablation of solids, 319
 heat conduction in solids, 226, 320
 heat transfer by forced convection, 304
 thermal radiation, 309

Wall temperature variations, 163–167
 influence on heat transfer, 25, 26, 304,
  305

Wave length in thermal radiation, 78
Wing reinforced by stiffeners (*see also*,
  Skins reinforced by stiffeners)
 asymmetrical heat flow in, 256–259

Yaw angle, influence on heat transfer of,
  16, 19, 20, 21

OTHER TITLES IN THE SERIES IN AERONAUTICS AND ASTRONAUTICS

DIVISION I. SOLID AND STRUCTURAL MECHANICS

Vol. 1 SAVIN — Stress Concentration around Holes
Vol. 2 GOL'DENVEIZER — Theory of Elastic Thin Shells
Vol. 3 NOWACKI — Thermoelasticity
Vol. 4 COX — The Buckling of Plates and Shells
Vol. 5 MORLEY — Skew Plates and Structures
Vol. 6 MANSFIELD — The Bending and Stretching of Plates

DIVISION II. AERODYNAMICS

Vol. 1 SCORER — Natural Aerodynamics
Vol. 2 LANDAHL — Unsteady Transonic Flow
Vol. 3 GUDERLEY — The Theory of Transonic Flow

DIVISION III. PROPULSION SYSTEMS INCLUDING FUELS

Vol. 1 PENNER — Chemistry Problems in Jet Propulsion
Vol. 2 DUCRAME, GERSTEIN and LEFEBVRE (Eds.) — Progress in Combustion Science and Technology Vol. 1.
Vol. 3 RAGOZIN — Jet Propulsion Fuels
Vol. 4 KHOLSHCHEVNIKOV — Some Problems in the Theory of Assessment of Turbo-jet Engines
Vol. 5 ZUYEV and SKUBACHEVSKII — Combustion Chambers for Jet Propulsion Engines

DIVISION IV. AVIONICS

Vol. 1 FLINDT — Aircraft Instruments and Automatic Control

DIVISION V. AVIATION AND SPACE MEDICINE

Vol. 1 WILLIAMS — Human Engineering and Aviation Medicine

DIVISION VI. FLIGHT TESTING

Vol. 1 BABISTER — Aircraft Stability and Control

DIVISION VII. ASTRONAUTICS

Vol. 1 ALPERIN, STERN and WOOSTER (Eds.) — Vistas in Astronautics I
Vol. 2 ALPERIN and GREGORY — Vistas in Astronautics II
Vol. 3 DRAPER, WRIGLEY and HOVORKA — Inertial Guidance
Vol. 4 NIKOLAYEV — Thermodynamic Assessment of Rocket Engines

DIVISION VIII. MATERIALS, SCIENCE AND ENGINEERING

Vol. 1 HARRIS — Metallic Fatigue

DIVISION IX. SYMPOSIA

Vol. 1 KARMAN (Chairman Editorial Committee) — Advances in Aeronautical Sciences (Volumes 1 & 2)

Vol. 2 ALPERIN and SUTTON (Eds.) — Advanced Propulsion Systems

Vol. 3 DEVIENNE (Ed.) — Rarefied Gas Dynamics

Vol. 4 HOFF and VINCENTI (Eds.) — Aeronautics and Astronautics — Durand Centennial Conference

Vol. 5 PLANTEMA and SCHIJVE (Eds.) — Full Scale Fatique Testing of Aircraft Structures

Vol. 6 BROGLIO (Ed.) — Current Research in Astronautical Sciences

Vol. 7 & 8. Advances in Aeronautical Sciences (Volumes 3 & 4)

Vol. 9 PERRY — Flight Test Instrumentation Vol. I

Vol. 10 BUCHANAN BARBOUR and WHITTINGHAM — Human Problems of Supersonic and Hypersonic Flight

Vol. 11 CASCI (Ed.) — Advances in Astronautical Propulsion (Proc. Milan Conf.).

Vol. 12 BARROIS and RIPLEY (Eds.) — Fatigue of Aircraft Structures (Proc. Paris Symposium)

Vol. 13 DEARDS — Recent Developments in Network Theory

Vol. 14 PERRY — Flight Test Instrumentation Vol. II

Vol. 15 FERRARI — High Temperatures in Aeronautics

Vol. 16 SAMSON — Development of the Blue Streak Satellite Launcher

Vol. 17 CASCI — Fuels and New Propellants